The
FROZEN
RECORD

Examining the Ice Core History of the
Greenland and Antarctic Ice Sheets

ICR TECHNICAL MONOGRAPH

MICHAEL J. OARD

INSTITUTE FOR CREATION RESEARCH
SANTEE, CALIFORNIA
www.icr.org

First Printing: June 2005

Library of Congress Control Number: 2005926548

ISBN 0-932766-82-X

Managing Editor: Deborah S. Brooks
Assistant Editors: Greta M. Rohrer and Mary Smith
Production & Interior Design: Lee E. Pierce
Cover Design: Janell Robertson, Farewell Communications, Green Forest, Arkansas

Customer Service: (800) 628-7640
www.icr.org

Printed in the United States of America

This book is dedicated to my son-in-law and oldest daughter, Mark and Tara Wolfe, and their three daughters, Madison, Hailey, and Tia. Mark commonly helps me with illustrations and amalgamated the illustrations and text for one of my other books.

CONTENTS

ILLUSTRATIONS

Figures

Tables

FOREWORD

This remarkable monograph is in considerable measure the result of several months of intensive study by Michael Oard while he was here at ICR on a special adjunct faculty research assignment. He had already authored an excellent monograph published by ICR entitled An Ice Age Caused by the Genesis Flood, written while he was still working as a meteorological scientist with the National Weather Service. He has also written numerous other articles, monographs and books on various themes supporting the Creation/Flood Model of earth history, and we knew and honored him largely on the basis of these important writings.

This time, however, we got to know him personally as well, and it was a great experience. Mike is a soft-spoken, modest, courteous and devout Christian gentleman. His knowledge of the meteorological, hydrological and geological aspects of Earth history is wide-ranging and insightful, and he has treated this present excursus into glaciology with remarkable depth and breadth. This new monograph makes an outstanding case for the earth's one Ice Age as indeed a result of the worldwide Noahic Flood just a few thousand years ago.

Mike Oard is well qualified by education and long experience, as well as extensive reading and critical analysis, to write on such a subject. We can only hope that evolutionary geologists and glaciologists will be willing to read his monograph and give it thoughtful consideration. He has concentrated especially and in great detail on the earth's history as deduced from ice cores in its great ice sheets in Greenland and Antarctica, arguing that they show conclusively the reality of the great flood, with its following glacial period, just a few thousand years ago.

It is my privilege to recommend this new monograph by Michael J. Oard both to creationist scientists and to open-minded evolutionists. He has become a respected personal friend as well as a true scientist and convinced creationist.

Henry M. Morris, PhD.
President Emeritus
Institute for Creation Research

PREFACE

Many post-Flood phenomena and dating methods have been pooled together to paint a picture of repeating ice ages for a period of around 2.5 million years in geological time. These phenomena include deep-sea cores, pollen cores, varves, tree rings, tropical island coral terraces, and ice cores drilled on the Greenland and Antarctic Ice Sheets. Dating methods include carbon-14, uranium series disequilibrium, amino-acid racemization, electron-spin resonance, tephrachronology, and cosmogenetic nuclides. Of all the methods used in determining the earth's age, the most detailed and supposedly the most accurate record is the one from ice cores.

The enormous Greenland and Antarctic Ice Sheets have intrigued man for many centuries. These continental scale masses of ice cover 15.6 million km^2 and are deeper than 3,000 meters in places. Glaciologists proclaim that these ice sheets represent hundreds of thousands to millions of years of slow accumulation of snow. Their arguments seem plausible given the current precipitation rate and the size of these ice sheets. The Christian that holds God's Word as sacred and inspired, and that believes God is able to communicate His thoughts accurately, realizes that the genealogy passages and many other verses in the Bible support a young earth of thousands of years old. If this is true, then how can we account for the Greenland and Antarctic Ice Sheets?

Scientists have drilled about a dozen ice cores in the Greenland and Antarctic Ice Sheets, as well as smaller ice caps, for over four decades. After the ice is brought up in hollow corers, the scientists measure numerous variables in the ice. They claim to have physically counted 110,000 annual layers or more in the GISP2 ice core obtained from the summit of Greenland. The argument is powerful that the earth is older than 6 to 10 thousands years.

Glaciologists also claim that ice cores are a window into future climate (Alley and Bender, 1998; Alley, 2004). They have discovered rapid changes in temperature in the ice cores and suggest that bone-chilling cold spells could be triggered by the increase in greenhouse gases. These abrupt changes have spawned a paradigm shift in climatology. The threat of rapid climate change is even making it into the popular imagination (Kolbert, 2002).

Naturalists and professing Christians who believe the earth to be millions to billions of years old have used the dates from ice cores as "solid" evidence against the literal interpretation of the Bible. For instance, Warren H. Johns (1993, p. 129) used the ice-core-obtained date of about 11,600 years BP [before present] for the end of the ice age to support the Irish-German tree ring chronology that extends to about that age in the uniformitarian timescale. Furthermore, the Greenland and Antarctic ice sheets, especially their old age, are claimed to be ultimate proof that Noah's Flood was not global (Seely, 2003).

Are the Greenland and Antarctic Ice Sheets showcases for uniformitarian geology and glaciology? Do the ice cores surely prove an old earth? As Christians, we need to apply I Thessalonians 5:21: "Prove all things; hold fast that which is good" (King James Version). Many Christian intellectuals and lay people fail to follow this verse when they simply believe the interpretations of uniformitarian geology and evolutionary biology. While holding fast to God's sacred Scripture, we need to examine such claims—in depth, and carefully.

This monograph examines the Greenland and Antarctic Ice Sheets and their ice cores in depth. It focuses in on both specific and general aspects by scrutinizing whether 110,000 annual layers exist in the GISP2 core and by analyzing the claim that ice cores on Antarctica have reached down to ice that is from 400,000 to over 700,000 years old. The issue of why many data sets and chronological measurements seem to fit together and support the uniformitarian story of slow gradual processes over millions of years is also addressed. Finally, the monograph presents an alternative model and interpretation of the data, which is then contrasted with the uniformitarian old age model. Data that is more supportive of the Creation-Flood ice core model will be presented, as well.

ACKNOWLEDGEMENTS

Dr. John Morris and the Institute for Creation Research (ICR) are to be commended for providing financial support for the writing of this monograph. I especially thank Dr. Larry Vardiman from ICR for providing feedback, encouragement, and technical support throughout the preparation of this monograph, including some of the illustrations. I appreciate Dr. Henry Morris, past president of ICR, for taking the time to write the foreword. I am grateful for all the help from Ruth Richards of ICR with the English in the manuscript. Most of the illustrations were redrawn by Ron Hight and Laurel Hemmings, to whom I want to thank for all their time. I am grateful for Dan Lietha of Answers in Genesis for redrawing figure 3.2 and Andrew Snelling for providing the photo in figure 3.4. Lastly, I thank the three anonymous reviewers who provided valuable comments.

Chapter 1

The Greenland and Antarctic Ice Sheets

A s one looks at a map of the earth, one cannot but be struck by the large landmasses of the earth that are almost totally covered by ice. These are the Greenland and Antarctic Ice Sheets. Glaciologists who specialize in the study of glaciers and ice sheets tell us that these ice sheets are the product of many millions of years of climate. They drill out ice cores from these ice sheets and claim they have proved the ice sheets to be ancient. Is this true?

This ice is so extensive and thick that the question naturally arises as to how all this ice can accumulate in such a short time based on the Scriptural timescale. This timescale is derived from the straightforward genealogies of Genesis 5, 10, and 11. Genesis 1–11 reads like straightforward history, similar to Genesis 12–50 and other historical books of the Bible. It does not make sense to claim that Genesis 1–11 are poetic, mythical, or that Christians need to force evolution and millions of years into these chapters (Sarfati, 2004). It has always mystified me why anyone would deny the clear teaching of the Bible in favor of the speculations of sinful men about the unobservable, unscientific prehistoric past.

In this chapter I will describe some of the basic properties of the Greenland and Antarctic Ice Sheets before analyzing the claims of the Evolutionary-Uniformitarian model in later chapters.

Size of the Ice Sheets

T here is an enormous amount of ice locked up in the Greenland and Antarctic Ice Sheets. These ice masses cover about 10% of the land area of the earth. There has been a fair amount of variability in the estimates of the amount of ice locked up in the ice sheets. Table 1.1 shows the latest volume estimates along with other statistics of the ice sheets. These estimates should be more accurate than earlier estimates, because the ice depth is better known due to ice-penetrating radar that shows the bottom of the ice sheet quite well. Moreover, previous gaps in measurements have mostly been filled.

The latest measurements for the Greenland Ice Sheet are an ice volume of 2.93 million km^3 that covers an area of 1.8 million km^2 (Bamber, Layberry, and Gogineni, 2001). This volume represents an average thickness of 1,600 meters and a maximum depth estimated to be 3,367 meters. Land is exposed around most of the edge of the ice sheet. The ice at the top of the ice sheet flows little, but the flow increases towards the periphery (Bamber et al., 2000). Several large ice streams initiate in the interior and spread out to the periphery. These ice streams include the rapidly moving Jakobshavns Isbrae that moves up to 7,000 m/yr near its terminus (Iken et al., 1993) and the most recently discovered ice stream in northeast Greenland, the largest of all, that is nearly straight for about 700 kilometers and moves at a maximum velocity of 500 m/yr near its terminus (Joughin et al., 2001). The velocity of the northeast ice stream is probably due mainly to basal melting (Layberry and Bamber, 2001). Figure 1.1 shows a map of the Greenland Ice Sheet with elevations above sea level (ASL) and the locations of the main ice cores drilled into the ice sheet. Table 1.2 displays the major climatic and topographic information of the Greenland ice cores. The NorthGRIP (Greenland Ice Core Project) core finally hit bedrock on July 17, 2003, after seven years of drilling that included a failed attempt, stuck drill corers, and very slow drilling for about the last 100 meters (Dahl-Jensen et al., 2002; Grossman, 2003; Oard, 2003c; North Greenland Ice Core Project Members, 2004).

Ice Sheet	Area (10^6km^2)	Volume (10^6km^3)	Avg. Depth (meters)	Max Depth (meters)	Avg. Precip. (cm/yr H$_2$O)	Time to Build
Greenland	1.8	2.9	1,600	3,367	32	5,000 yrs
Antarctic	13.9	26.4	1,900	4,200	18.6	10,215 yrs

Table 1.1 Area, volume, average depth, maximum estimated depth, average annual precipitation in water equivalent amount, and the time to build up the ice sheets at present precipitation if no melting is assumed.

Ice Core	Date Drilled	Surface Elevation (meters)	Ice Thickness (meters)	Core Depth (meters)	Avg. Temp. (^{0}C)	Accum-mulation (cm/yr H$_2$O)
Camp Century	1963–1966	1,885	1,390	1,390	−24	38
Milcent	1973	2,450	2,350	398	−23	50
Crete	1974	3,172	3,200	405	−30	32
Dye 3	1981	2,486	2,037	2,037	− 20	56
Renland	1988	2,340	324	324	− 18	50
GRIP	1990–1992	3,230	3,029	3,029	− 32	23
GISP2	1989–1993	3,208	3,053	3,053	− 31	24
NorthGRIP	1999–2003	2,921	3,080	3,080	− 32	20

Table 1.2 Major climatic and topographic properties of major Greenland ice cores.

2

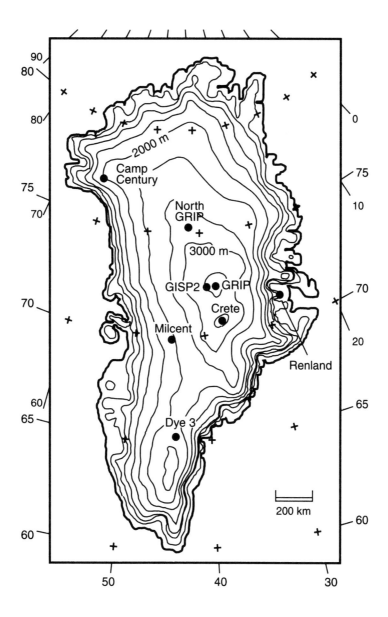

Figure 1.1   Map of Greenland showing ice thickness above sea level with major ice core locations.

The Antarctic Ice Sheet, which is divided into the West and East Antarctic Ice Sheets by the Transantarctic Mountains, is eight times the area of the Greenland Ice Sheet. The area of the Antarctic Ice Sheet, including ice shelves and the Antarctic Peninsula, is 13.9 million km² and contains a volume of 26.4 million km³ of ice (Bamber and Huybrechts, 1996; Vaughan et al., 1999b; Huybrechts et al., 2000). This volume represents an average ice depth of 1,903 meters with a maximum depth of around 4,200 meters. These figures, shown in table 1.1, are the latest estimates using further data on ice thickness. They are 12% less than previous figures derived over a decade ago. One of the reasons for less ice volume is because it has been found that Dronning Maud Land between 0 and 90°E longitude is much more mountainous with about 600 meters less ice than previously thought (Steinhage et al., 1999). There are very few areas of exposed land at the edge of Antarctica. Vast ice shelves occur around the edge of the continent, the most famous of which is the Ross Ice Shelf. Five ice streams, one or two that move rapidly, spread onto the Ross Ice Shelf from the West Antarctic Ice Sheet. Although the top of the ice sheet flows little, new research has found that a dendritic pattern of major flow extends further inland than previously thought (Huybrechts et al., 2000). Figure 1.2 shows the elevation of the Antarctic Ice Sheet with the major ice cores. Table 1.3 presents data on the major ice core locations.

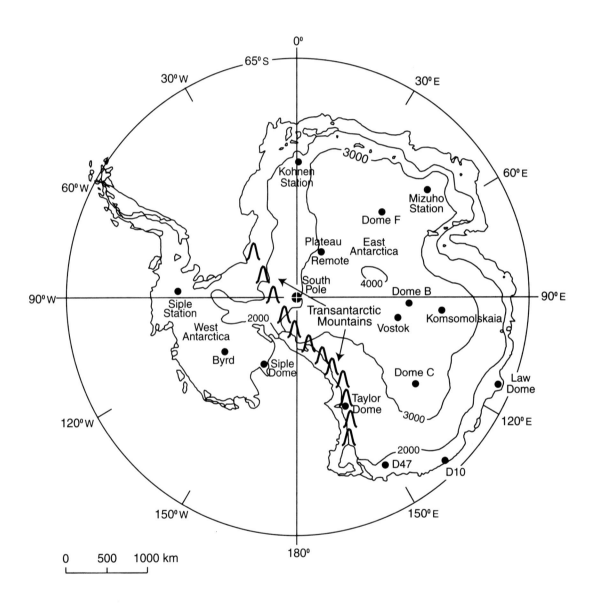

Figure 1.2   Map of Antarctica showing ice thickness above sea level with major ice core locations.

Ice Core	Date Drilled	Surface Elevation (meters)	Ice Thickness (meters)	Core Depth (meters)	Avg. Temp. (^{0}C)	Accum-mulation (cm/yr H_2O)
Byrd	1968	1,530	2,164	2,164	−28	12
D10	1974	235	310	303	−14	15
Dome C(old)	1977–1978	3,240	3,400	950	−54	3.8
Komsomol-skaya	1983	3,498	3,550	850	−53	50
Mizuho Station	1984	2,230	~2,000	700	−23	10
Dome B	1988	3,600	3,460	780	−58	3.1
D47	1988–1989	1,550	1,700	870	−25	30
Law Dome	1991–1993	1,370	1,220	1,196	−22	70
Taylor Dome	1994	2,365	1,811	554	−43	6
Dome F	1995–1996	3,810	3,090	2,503	−58	6
Vostok	1998	3,490	3,700	3,623	−55	2.3
Siple Dome	1996–1999	621	1,010	1,003	−22	~8
*Dome C(new)	2001–2003	3,233	3,300	3,200	−54	3.4
Kohnen Station	Future Drilling Location					

*New Dome C is located 55km south of Old Dome C

Table 1.3   Major climatic and topographic properties of major Antarctic ice cores.

There is evidence that the Antarctic Ice Sheet was substantially thicker along the coastal periphery and has since melted to its present depth. This is based not only on glacial striations, erratic boulders, and other glacial indicators on nunataks but also on evidence that the ice sheet extended further offshore. A nunatak is an isolated peak of bedrock that projects above the surface of a glacier (Bates and Jackson, 1984, p. 351). The evidence is substantial that ice on the Antarctic Peninsula and Dronning Maud Land of East Antarctica was around 1,000 meters deeper (Holmlund and Näslund, 1994; Bentley and Anderson, 1998; Canals, Urgeles, and Calafat, 2000; Canals et al., 2003). After a very large chunk of the ice recently broke off the Larsen Ice Shelf along the northern Antarctic Peninsula, scientists probing the bottom were surprised to find a deep trough with hanging side valleys (Domack et al., 2001). This trough is likely a fjord caused by an ice stream around 1,000 meters thick that flowed from off the Antarctic Peninsula. Apparently, the ice continues to thin in areas along the margin of the Antarctic Ice Sheet, such as around Mizuho Station (Naruse, 1979; Matsuoka et al., 2003, pp. 2–3).

If all the ice from Greenland and Antarctica were suddenly placed on the United States with an area of 9.4 million km^2, the average depth of ice would be 3.1 kilometers. If all the Antarctic Ice Sheet melted, taking into account downward isostatic compensation of the added water into the ocean, sea level would rise 61 meters (Huybrechts et al., 2000). Seven meters of this sea level rise would come from the smaller West Antarctic Ice Sheet (Cuffey and Marshall, 2000). If the Greenland Ice Sheet also melted, another seven meters would be added to sea level (Cuffey and Marshall, 2000). The melting of both ice sheets would raise sea level 68 meters. Other glaciers of the world, if melted, would add little to the sea level rise.

Climate on the Ice Sheets

These large ice sheets are generally believed to be in equilibrium, in other words, there appears to be a balance between the amount of snow that falls on the ice each year and the ice lost by melting and calving of icebergs into the sea. The amount of snow that falls on the ice sheets is difficult to determine, and there is much variability in accumulation rate over recent decades and centuries (Bolzan and Strobel, 1994; Friedmann et al., 1995; McConnell et al., 2000; Hanna, Huybrechts, and Mote, 2002). Recent compilations of annual snow accumulation for the Greenland and Antarctic Ice Sheets are shown in figures 1.3 and 1.4, respectively. Greenland receives an average of about 32 cm of water equivalent amount of snow each year with a wide variation and about 23% uncertainty (Thomas and PARCA Investigators, 2001, p. 33,692; Bales et al., 2001). The southeast margin receives the most precipitation by far with up to 250 cm/yr (Ohmura and Reeh, 1991, p. 145), but only about 150 centimeters is solid precipitation, as seen in figure 1.3.

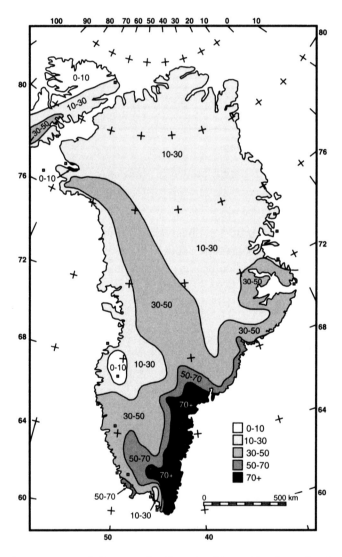

Figure 1.3   Annual snow accumulation map for Greenland in centimeters of water equivalent amounts per year (from Ohmura and Reeh, 1991, p. 147).

6

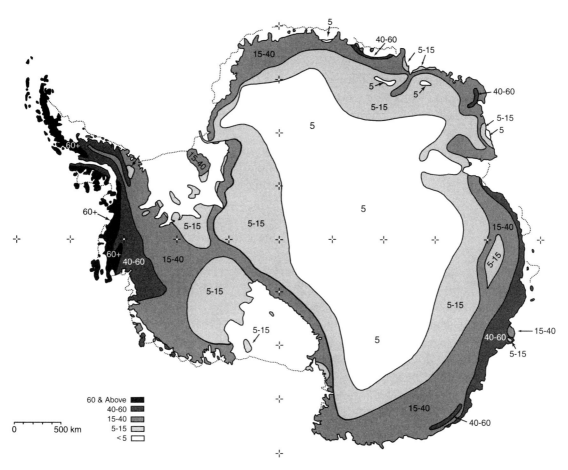

Figure 1.4   Annual snow accumulation map for Antarctica in centimeters of water equivalent amounts per year (from Bromwich, 1988, p. 152).

During World War II, an interesting story began on July 15, 1942, when six P-38 Lightning and two B-17 Flying Fortress aircraft were forced to land on the southeast Greenland Ice Sheet (Bloomberg, 1989; Monmaney, 1994; Petrow, 1992). All the men survived and were later rescued. After the war practically all P-38 aircraft were destroyed by the military, so the aircraft became rare and valuable. A wealthy entrepreneur, Pat Epps, had the audacity to attempt to retrieve one or more of the aircraft from the ice sheet and later fly one. The exploratory team at first thought the job of retrieving the aircraft would be easy and expected the aircraft to be covered with only 2 to 12 meters of snow. However, after several failed attempts to even locate the craft, they finally used sophisticated equipment in order to find them. After 12 years of failure, frustration, and over a million dollars of expenditures, the team led by Epps located the aircraft 1.6 km from their original location. By the time they melted a hole to retrieve one of the P-38's, the ice was 79 meters thick! The aircraft was brought up piece-by-piece through a narrow ice shaft and re-assembled in Middlesboro, southeast Kentucky. What could explain the unexpected ice thickness? The planes' location! The planes had landed on the snowiest part of the Greenland Ice Sheet at low altitude and only 28 kilometers from the open water of the ocean. Figure 1.3 shows that over 70 cm/yr of ice accumulates in this area. These solid precipitation rates provide an inkling of the possible snowfall rates at the time the ice sheet was just beginning to build up.

Examining figure 1.4, most of the snow on the Antarctic Ice Sheet accumulates at the periphery. The high central plateau receives less than 5 cm of water equivalent amount of snow each year. Thus, the top of the Antarctic Ice Sheet is a virtual *polar desert* with a substantial part of the precipitation falling as ice crystals during clear skies (Schwerdtfeger, 1969; Bromwich, 1988). It seems like this ice sheet would need millions of years to grow to its current height. How then did the Antarctic Ice Sheet build up in the short timescale from Scripture? This question will be dealt with in chapter 3.

To get a ballpark idea of the length of time needed to build such a huge ice sheet, the current volume can be divided by the average yearly snowfall of 18.6 cm of ice equivalent (Huybrechts et al., 2000, p. 56). At this rate and assuming no melting, it would take only about 10,000 years to build the Antarctic Ice Sheet (table 1.1)—not an inordinate amount of time for the short timescale of Scripture. At the average precipitation rate of 32 cm/yr today and assuming no melting, the present Greenland Ice Sheet would build up in about 5,000 years, which is about the time since the Flood.

The average temperature on top of the Greenland Ice Sheet ranges from −20°C at Dye 3 in the south to −32°C at the highest elevation at Summit (table 1.2). Renland is near the edge of the ice sheet, so it is not included in this range of temperatures. These temperatures are warm enough that over 50% of the Greenland Ice Sheet has some summer melting, in particular in the south and lower elevations (Thomas and PARCA Investigators, 2001, p. 33,692).

Temperatures are significantly colder on Antarctica, as one might expect from the higher elevations and more polar location. Vostok averages −55°C (Yiou, Vimeux, and Jouzel, 2001, p. 31,875), which is representative for the plateau; in contrast, Law Dome averages −22°C, and D10 near the coast averages −14°C (table 1.3). Little summer melting occurs on Antarctica, even at coastal stations.

Tremendous katabatic winds are common on the Antarctic Ice Sheet (Parish and Bromwich, 1991; Parish and Wendler, 1991). These winds are created when surface cooling produces air of greater density that then blows down the slope of an ice sheet. The very top of the ice sheet has little wind, which is one reason that ice cores are commonly drilled at these locations. Descending from the top of the ice sheet, the wind increases; and by the time the coast is reached, hurricane force winds occur in some locations. The wind at Cape Denison, Terre Adélie Land, with its average speed of 20 m/sec, is among the strongest surface winds ever recorded. Port Martin, near Cape Denison, reaches hurricane force winds (32 m/sec) an average of 122 days a year. A number of Antarctic explorers have lost their lives due to Antarctic coastal blizzards caused by katabatic winds. There are deviations from this wind regime caused by converging and diverging relief, so that some coastal stations have relatively light winds. Greenland also has katabatic winds, but these winds are significantly less than on the Antarctic Ice Sheet.

Bedrock before and after Glaciation

The character of the bedrock underneath the ice sheets has been determined by ice-penetrating radar. Greenland's topography consists of a N-S central trough mostly surrounded by mountains (figure 1.5). The below-sea-level elevation of this trough is attributed to the earth's crust responding to a load by isostatically sinking. Such isostatic subsidence was demonstrated when Lake Mead filled, depressing the crust 20 centimeters (Dott and Batten, 1976, p. 117). Isostatic uplift of the crust occurs when a load is taken off. When the water in pluvial Lake Bonneville evaporated, the highest shoreline bowed upward 70 meters in the middle, which was the deepest part of the lake (King, 1965, p. 850). It is assumed that the amount of subsidence is proportional to the density of the added weight versus the density of the crust and upper mantle, which is usually assumed to be about 2.7 gm/cm^3 for the crust and 3.3 gm/cm^3 for the upper mantle. Since ice has a density of a little less than 1 gm/cm^3, it is calculated that the Greenland Ice Sheet has pushed the crust down by as much as 1,000 meters (Letréguilly, Huybrechts, and Reeh, 1991; Bamber, Layberry, and Gogineni, 2001, p. 33,776). If all the ice were melted, isostatic rebound would eventually raise the land significantly, as shown in figure 1.6. These isostatically-raised elevations would represent the height of the bedrock before glaciation. Generally, Greenland before glaciation was composed of a long, north-south ridge running down the middle that is remarkably flat (Bamber, Layberry, and Gogineni, 2001, p. 33,776).

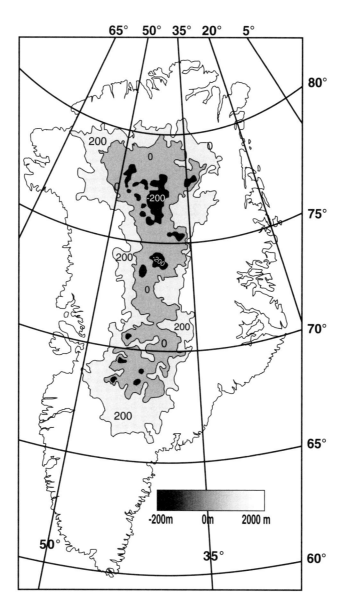

Figure 1.5   Bedrock elevations below the Greenland Ice Sheet (from Bamber, Layberry, and
           Gogineni, 2001).

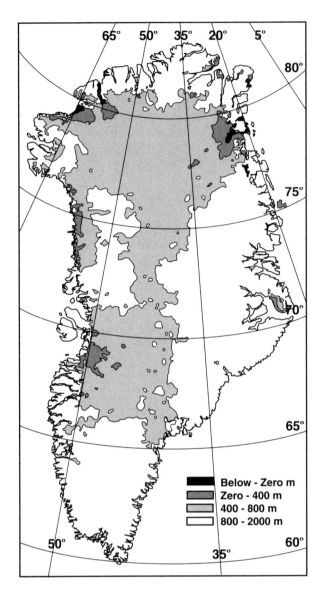

Figure 1.6   Bedrock below the Greenland Ice Sheet raised to account for isostatic depression caused by the ice. These elevations would represent the surface of Greenland just before glaciation (from Bamber, Layberry, and Gogineni, 2001).

For Antarctica, analogous maps of the bedrock below the ice and the height of bedrock if all the ice were removed are shown in figures 1.7 and 1.8 (Drewry, 1983; Bamber and Huybrechts, 1996). There are slight inconsistencies when comparing figures 1.7 and 1.8. Figure 1.8 is supposed to be an isostatically raised version of figure 1.7. The inconsistencies are because figure 1.8 is based on older data. As can be seen from figure 1.7, West Antarctica is composed of mountain ranges surrounded by deep troughs or basins lying well below sea level. All this is filled with ice, except for several mountain ranges that stick up out of the ice forming nunataks. The 4,000-meter-high Transantarctic Mountains with valley glaciers separate West from East Antarctica.

10

Much of East Antarctica is above sea level, but significant proportions, especially just east of the Transantarctic Mountains, are below sea level. If the weight of the ice were taken off the continent allowing isostatic rebound (figure 1.8), even more of East Antarctica would be above sea level. This would be the height of Antarctica when the ice sheet first started.

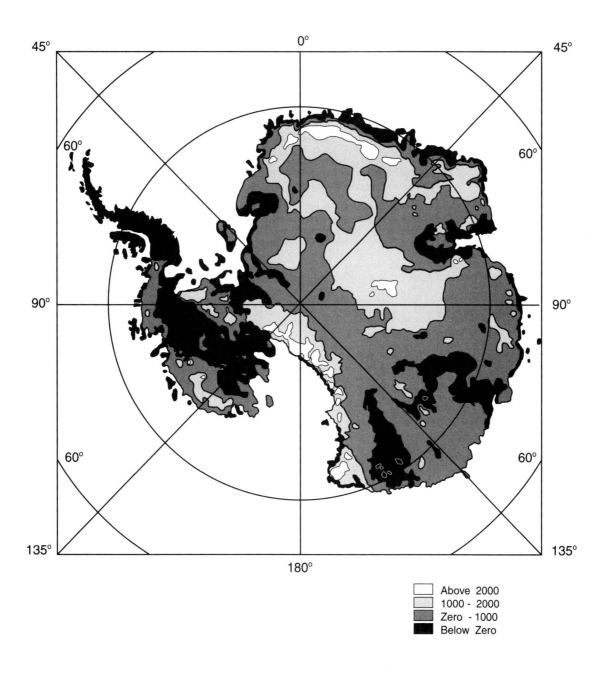

Figure 1.7   Bedrock elevations below the Antarctic Ice Sheet (from Bamber and Huybrechts, 1996, p. 371).

11

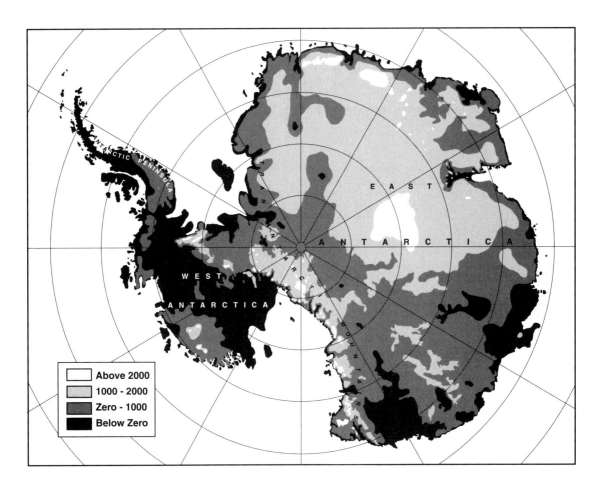

Figure 1.8   Bedrock below the Antarctic Ice Sheet raised to account for isostatic depression caused by the ice. These elevations would represent the surface of Antarctica just before glaciation (from Drewry, 1983, folio 6).

Internal Properties of the Ice Sheets

The internal properties of the ice sheets have been discovered from examining all the ice cores drilled to bedrock or deep within the Greenland and Antarctic Ice Sheets.

The top of the ice sheet consists of compacted snow called *firn*. Deeper in the ice sheet, snow changes to ice either by summer meltwater percolating downward and refreezing or by the pressure of the overlying snow compacting the firn until ice is formed. There is little, if any, summer melting today at the top of the ice sheets; so currently firn snow changes to ice mainly by pressure of the snow above. The firn-ice transition is usually around 50 to 100 meters depth in the ice sheets. For the GISP2 core on Greenland, the firn-ice transition is at 75 to 77 meters (Gow et al., 1997, p. 26,560); in contrast, in the Dome F core on Antarctic it is at 106 m (Watanabe et al., 1999, p. 178). The deeper transition zone in Antarctica probably reflects the colder temperatures of the snow and ice.

It has been discovered that the temperature of the ice sheets remains more or less constant from the top of the ice sheet to well down into the ice sheet. About midway down in the ice sheet, the temperature warms with depth down to bedrock. Figure 1.9 shows the temperature profile for the GRIP core. Most of the bottom ice on Greenland, like that of GISP2 and GRIP, was believed to be well below freezing (Huybrechts, 1996), but it came as a surprise to discover that the bottom of the NorthGRIP core in central Greenland was at the pressure melting point with liquid water (Grossman, 2003). Much of the bottom ice below the Antarctic Ice Sheet is at the pressure melting point.

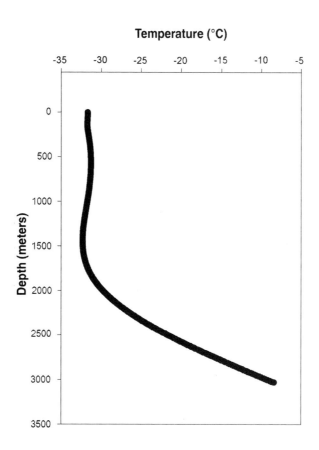

Figure 1.9 Temperature profile for the GRIP core.

The ice in the top 1,400 meters or so contains a high concentration of bubbles. The bubbles are abundant in the top of this interval with a concentration of about 200 bubbles per square centimeter (Gow et al., 1997, p. 26,560). This represents the air trapped in the firn at the firn-ice transition. Ten percent of the volume of the ice at this transition is compressed air, which is why the ice has a density of 0.83 grams/cm^2 at the transitions. This compares to water with a density of 1.00 gm/cm^3 and bubble-free, pure ice with a density of about 0.92 or 0.93 g/cm^3. The bubbles are observed to decrease in size downward in the ice cores until they seem to disappear at about 1,200 to 1,400 meters. Actually, the air bubbles form an air hydrate or clathrate, a crystalline molecular complex formed from the mixture of water and atmospheric gases at high pressure (Miller, 1969; Shoji and Langway, 1982; Uchida et al., 1994, p. 143). Upon decompression of the ice cores, the bubbles reappear.

Another ice sheet property is a brittle layer found about one-third to one-half the depth down. In the GISP2 core, small fractures are seen between 450 to 650 meters, but the well-fractured brittle layer is between about 650 and 1,400 meters (Gow et al., 1997, p. 26,560). This is also the zone of greatest core loss. The recovered 3-meter long core segments from this depth are handled with care as even the slightest mechanical shock induces more cracking and splintering. Such brittleness is attributed to (1) relief of confinement pressure that exceeds the tensile strength of the ice and (2) depressurization of highly pressurized air bubbles in the ice. Since bubbles disappear into the ice matrix below 1,400 meters, the ice becomes less brittle and more ductile below this depth, resulting in a significant improvement in the quality of the core. It is difficult to measure many properties of the ice in this brittle layer; but it was found that if the core sections were left alone for several months to allow relaxation of the ice, the core sections could be better analyzed.

The top portion of the ice is very clean of impurities, especially the Antarctic Ice Sheet. Then at a certain depth, which varies from core to core depending upon the snowfall rate, dust and both soluble and insoluble impurities increase dramatically. This increase occurs quite deep in the Greenland cores, but high up in the deep Antarctic cores. As we will see in later chapters the cleaner ice represents the post–Ice Age period and the dusty ice the glacial period. Dust concentrations increase by one hundred times in the NorthGRIP core, Greenland, during the Last Glacial Maximum (LGM) compared to the ice above (Ruth et al., 2003). The soluble impurities include both bases and acids. The Antarctic ice is mostly acidic throughout, while the Greenland ice is acidic at the top and mostly basic in the dusty part of the lower portion of the ice. The reason for this basic ice is because the greater concentration of dust during the Ice Age overwhelms the acids. The impurities, or *chemical species* as they are called, are rich sources of information about past atmospheric conditions (Dansgaard et al., 1982, p. 1,273). Many of these species show differences in concentration between winter and summer at the top of the ice sheet and in the atmosphere. Hence, these chemicals can be used for annual layer measurements. The annual layer method using dust will be discussed in chapter 6, while the annual layer method based on soluble chemicals is the subject of chapter 7.

The ice sheets have been found to possess systematic structure with depth that is fairly similar from core to core on each ice sheet. For Greenland cores, the ice crystals of the ice first increase in size from the top of the core downward, become of nearly constant size, decrease in size at the transition to glacial time, and finally increase significantly near the bottom of the core (figure 1.10). The crystal size oscillates a fair amount during the glacial part of the core (Alley and Woods, 1996). In the GRIP core (figure 1.10) this texture is caused by normal grain growth down to 700 meters. The constant crystal size between 700 and 1,600 meters is likely the result of a balance between crystal growth and fracturing, called *polygonization*, due to increasing strain (Thorsteinsson, Kipfstuhl, and Miller, 1997). The small crystal size at the top of the glacial ice is believed to have been mainly caused by increased impurities, and the oscillating crystal size in the glacial ice is likely inversely related to the variable impurity content (Alley and Woods, 1996). It is especially the insoluble impurities that are inversely correlated to ice crystal size (Paterson, 1991; Thorsteinsson et al., 1995). The large increase in crystal size below 2,930 meters is thought to be due to rapid grain growth (annealing recrystallization) caused by warmer ice. The Antarctic ice cores have a similar pattern of ice crystal growth with depth as the Greenland ice cores do, except the decrease in crystal size above the glacial-post-glacial transition is not as dramatic and the crystal size increases more downward in the glacial ice (Gow and Williamson, 1976; Duval and Lorius, 1980; Lipenkov et al., 1989; Azuma et al., 1999).

Each ice crystal has a three dimensional shape, just like a rock in a stream. There is a long dimension, the a-axis; an intermediate dimension, the b-axis; and the shortest dimension, the c-

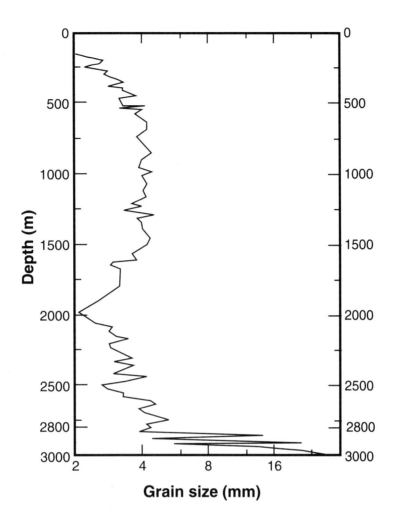

Figure 1.10   GRIP profile of ice crystal size with depth.

axis. The normal to the c-axis of a crystal defines the crystal orientation or the fabric of the ice. It has been discovered from ice cores that the ice at the very top has a random crystal orientation. However, the c-axis orientation becomes more vertical with depth and reaches a maximum vertical orientation fairly deep down in the ice sheet. A vertical c-axis orientation means that the elongated portion of the crystal is horizontal, which is believed to cause faster horizontal slippage (Thorsteinsson et al., 1999). The c-axis orientation becomes less vertical again near the very bottom. There does not seem to be a strengthening of the c-axis fabric at the boundary between glacial and post-glacial ice (Anandakrishnan et al., 1994; Azuma et al., 1999). It is believed that vertical compression is responsible for the development of the vertical c-axis development with depth (Thorsteinsson, Kipfstuhl, and Miller, 1997). Although much has been learned about the cause of such ice fabric, including the texture, there is still some uncertainty; and the modeling of these features has had only partial success (Ktitarev, Gödert, and Hutter, 2002).

Such a preferred crystal orientation is thought to cause the ice to deform or strain faster with depth; this is especially characteristic of the Ice Age ice which can be strained two to four times faster than in post-glacial ice (Paterson, 1991, p. 75; Thorsteinsson et al., 1999). This ice with a

15

higher strain rate is called *soft* ice. Others believe, however, that the high microparticle content causes the soft ice and faster strain rate (Fisher and Koerner, 1986).

The bottom of the ice sheets have been shown to be very complicated. This area is commonly deformed with dirt bands. In the 2,164-meter Byrd core (from an area that lies well below sea level), the bottom 4.83 meters of ice contained much stratified debris that included particles as large as cobbles (Gow, Epstein, and Sheehy, 1979). Water was also encountered at the ice-rock interface, and the ice is believed to have formed by the freezing of basal water. This type of ice, called *superimposed* ice, is bubble free.

The intent of the drillers of the new deep Vostok core was to reach bedrock. However, they stopped at 3,623 meters because Lake Vostok lay just below at about 3,750 meters, and they did not want to pollute the lake with drilling fluid. Researchers have discovered at least 68 lakes that lie under three to four kilometers of ice in East Antarctica (Vincent, 1999). Lake Vostok is the largest by far with a depth of 600 meters, a length of 230 kilometers, and a width of 50 kilometers. Most of the other lakes are much smaller with diameters of a few kilometers (Ridley, Cudlip, and Laxon, 1993). It was discovered that in the Vostok core the last 84 meters of drilled ice and 137 meters of undrilled ice is probably "lake ice" formed by freezing of the lake water (superimposed ice) capping Lake Vostok (Jouzel et al., 1999). (Lately, Jouzel may be backing off on his hypothesis of superimposed ice in the lower portion of the Vostok core [Pokar, 2003, p. 21].) Glaciologists did not expect lakes at the bottom of the ice sheet because the pressure gradient beneath the ice should have driven out subglacial water (Oswald and Robin, 1973, p. 253).

The siltiness of the very bottom six to seven meters of ice in the GRIP core is attributed to the ice forming in a swamp before glaciation (Souchez et al., 1994, 1995; Tison et al., 1994; Souchez, Lemmens, and Chappellaz, 1995; Souchez, 1997). The reasons for this deduction are because of bubble-free interlayered clear ice, low oxygen concentration, very high values of carbon dioxide and methane, and high oxygen isotope ratios implying warm temperatures. The low oxygen and high carbon dioxide and methane suggest a swampy environment before the Greenland Ice Sheet developed. When the ice sheet began to build, the bottom mixed with the ice produced when the swamp froze. It is believed that this bottom ice is 2.4 million years old (Souchez, 1997). This basal silty ice is also given as evidence against the hypothesis that the ice sheet melted in the last interglacial, as some researchers have postulated (Koerner, 1989, 1997).

An interesting dispute arose concerning the interpretation of layers of ice near the bottom of the GRIP and GISP2 cores. The GRIP core reached bottom first, and the European glaciologists interpreted the quite variable $\delta^{18}O$ of the ice between 2,780 and 2,880 meters as caused by large temperature changes in the last interglacial period, called in Europe the *Eemian* and in North America the *Sangamon* (Johnsen et al., 1992a, 1995b, 1997; Greenland Ice-Core Project (GRIP) Members, 1993; Dansgaard et al., 1993). After the GISP2 core reached bedrock, the American glaciologists interpreted the abrupt oscillations in this interval as caused by flow disturbances (Peel, 1995; Alley et al., 1995). In fact, folds and other deformations were discovered hundreds of meters above bedrock in the GISP2 core (Alley et al., 1997b). This surprised the researchers because such deformation is not supposed to occur in the ice below the center of an ice sheet. Because of the controversy over the interpretation of the bottom ice from GRIP and GISP2, the Europeans drilled NorthGRIP to bedrock 203 miles (325 kilometers) north northwest of GRIP (see figure 1.1). Researchers also believe that they have been able to tease out the previous interglacial and glacial period from the bottom 10% of the GRIP core by comparing the $\delta^{18}O$ of atmospheric O_2 and CH_4 with the Vostok core (Landais et al., 2003). I will revisit the meaning of the large $\delta^{18}O$ oscillations deep in the Greenland cores in chapter 10.

Chapter 2

PAST CLIMATE FROM ICE CORES

Scientists especially would like to know the climate of the prehistoric past. Knowing the past climate would aid them not only to understand past events but also to be able to predict future climate changes. Temperature and precipitation are the most important measures of climate. Ice cores in theory can provide an estimate of the past temperatures and precipitation. This chapter will focus mainly on the temperature derived from the ice cores.

The property of the ice core that provides a downcore estimate for the past temperature is the stable isotope ratio of the atoms in the water molecule. Since there are two different atoms (each with several isotopes) in the water molecule, there are two stable isotope measures for the surface temperature: the oxygen isotope ratio and the deuterium isotope ratio. Since isotopes can be measured easily by a mass spectrometer, it seems a straightforward exercise to determine at least the temperature of the past from ice cores.

In reality, it is not that easy to infer the past temperature, because the stable isotope ratios also depend upon many other variables besides surface temperature. The relationship of the ratios with temperature is highly statistical and sometimes contains errors. The other variables related to the stable isotope ratio are listed and explained in appendix 1. Under some conditions, these other variables become important.

Stable Isotope Ratios

Oxygen exists in three isotopes—^{18}O, ^{17}O, and ^{16}O—depending upon the number of neutrons in the nucleus of the atom. Oxygen-17 occurs in the smallest concentration and is not used in stable isotope analysis; it is only the ratio of ^{18}O to ^{16}O that is measured. Hydrogen is found in three isotopes: ordinary hydrogen, H, having just a proton with no neutrons in the nucleus; deuterium, D, having one neutron in the nucleus; and tritium having two neutrons in the nucleus. Since there is much less tritium than deuterium, only the deuterium isotope ratio, the ratio of deuterium to ordinary hydrogen, is measured.

Since the water that ends up as ice in the ice sheets is evaporated from the ocean, the isotope ratios were first measured for seawater. The abundances of the isotopes in seawater is presented in table 2.1 in parts per million (Epstein, 1959; Dansgaard, 1961, 1964; Craig and Gordon, 1965; Dansgaard et al., 1973). Since the amount of HDO^{16} and H_2O^{18} is so low compared to H_2O^{16}, the isotope ratios are standardized by comparing to a set standard and multiplied by one thousand. The oxygen isotope ratio is standardized by the following equation:

$$\delta^{18}O = [(^{18}O/^{16}O)_{sample} - (^{18}O/^{16}O)_{vsmow}]/ (^{18}O/^{16}O)_{vsmow} \times 1000‰ \qquad (2.1)$$

17

where $({}^{18}O/{}^{16}O)_{sample}$ is the oxygen isotope ratio of the sample, $({}^{18}O/{}^{16}O)_{vsmow}$ is the oxygen isotope ratio of the standard, and the values are in thousandths or per mil, ‰. The reference standard for oxygen isotopes is standard mean ocean water (SMOW) that has a value near zero. SMOW did not have a unique definition and was poorly characterized until it was standardized in what is called *VSMOW* (Vienna standard mean ocean water) (Coplen, Kendall, and Hopple, 1983; Coplen, 1995).

Isotopes of Water	Concentration (ppm)
H_2O^{16}	997,680
HDO^{16}	320
H_2O^{18}	2,000

Table 2.1   The abundance of the stable isotopes of the water molecule in the ocean in parts per million that are used in ice core analysis. D in the chemical formula for water stands for deuterium.

In table 2.1, the deuterium to hydrogen ratio, or the deuterium isotope ratio, in the water is given by a similar equation.

$$\delta D = [(D/H)_{sample} - (D/H)_{vsmow}]/(D/H)_{vsmow} \times 1000‰ \qquad (2.2)$$

The deuterium isotope ratio will be discussed little in this monograph, since it is generally proportional to the oxygen isotope ratio by the following formula:

$$\delta^{18}O = 8\delta D + d \qquad (2.3)$$

where "d" is called the *deuterium excess*, which averages 10‰. However, the deuterium excess can vary around its average value depending upon a number of factors that can have important significance for the moisture source. Some of the figures later in this chapter will be plotted in relation to δD instead of $\delta^{18}O$.

The oxygen isotope ratio has been applied to many systems that contain oxygen, including ice, the carbonate in the shells of microorganisms from the ocean bottom, mollusk fossils, corals, claimed "paleosols" (believed to be buried ancient soils), and ice core air bubbles (Kock, Zachos, and Dettman, 1995; Bender et al., 1985; Sowers et al., 1991). Ice cores are considered the superior record of the past because the measurements represent a continuous time series with no hiatuses and a resolution often within a year (Dansgaard et al., 1971).

The water molecule undergoes many phase changes from when it first evaporates from the ocean to when it ends up as ice in the ice sheets. Because one isotope has a heavier molecular weight than the other, phase changes favor one isotope over another. Evaporation favors more of the lighter isotopes in the water molecule, while condensation favors more of the heavier isotopes.

The difference in the molecular weight of the isotopes in table 2.1 causes a little different vapor pressure. The vapor pressure of the light isotope is greater than that of the heavier isotope. It is the ratio of the vapor pressure of H_2O^{18} and HDO compared to H_2O^{16} that causes the oxygen or deuterium isotope ratio differences during phase changes. These differences are called *fractionation*, and the vapor pressure ratios are called the *fractionation factors*. Thus, these fractionation factors determine the proportion of the heavy isotope to the light isotope. In the case of evaporation from the ocean, the first phase change, the vapor has less ^{18}O than the surface water. Since the standard $\delta^{18}O$ is zero, the resulting $\delta^{18}O$ of the vapor is negative while the surface ocean water is a little more positive.

When water vapor condenses, the fractionation factors favor more of the heavier isotope in the raindrop or snowflake, leaving the precipitate more positive and the remaining vapor in the cloud more negative. Figure 2.1 shows the isotopic cycle of water vapor from the ocean, with a $\delta^{18}O$ of zero, to the top of the Antarctic Ice Sheet, where values below −50‰ are measured. The water vapor has been fractionated during evaporation at low and midlatitudes with a greater proportion of the lighter isotope remaining in the vapor. The oxygen isotope ratio of the vapor is about −10‰ (the up arrows) in the atmosphere at low and midlatitudes. If this water vapor condenses and falls out as rain right away, the drops are fractionated and returned to the ocean value of zero (represented by the down arrows). As more and more precipitation falls out of an air mass, usually as the vapor is transported poleward from where it originated in the ocean, the remaining vapor becomes more negative than −10‰. This will in turn cause the condensed water to be more negative as well, although not as negative as the vapor. For instance, if the water vapor in the atmosphere of the middle latitudes has a $\delta^{18}O$ of −20‰, rain that condenses from this vapor will have a $\delta^{18}O$ of around −10‰. This schematic is a simplification, since mixing of different water masses will complicate matters.

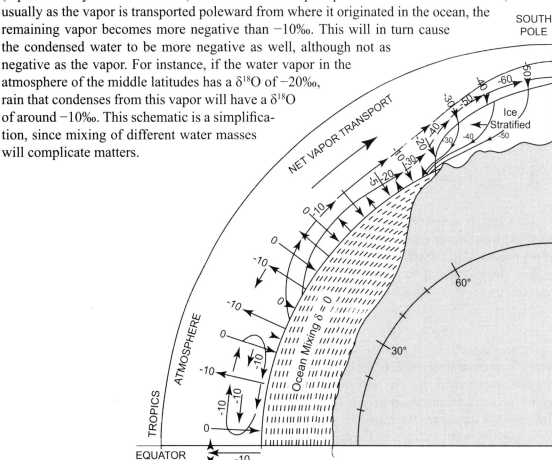

Figure 2.1   The changes in $\delta^{18}O$ during multiple phase changes starting from evaporation from the ocean to deposition on the Antarctic Ice Sheet (after Robin, 1977, p. 150).

By the time the vapor reaches the polar regions, cooler temperatures and further condensation cycles along the way cause the remaining water vapor, as well as the condensate, to become progressively more negative. Figure 2.2 shows the change in oxygen isotope ratio of both the vapor and the liquid/solid phase as the original amount of water vapor is depleted. For instance, after 50% of the vapor has been removed by previous condensation and precipitation cycles, the oxygen isotope ratio of the remaining vapor is around −13‰. The next condensation cycle will result in the liquid or solid in the cloud being about −5‰. From figure 2.2, it can be seen that the oxygen isotope ratio becomes quite low as the original vapor is depleted more and more below 50%. This is the situation the vapor is in by the time the air reaches the polar regions and the top of the Antarctic Ice Sheet.

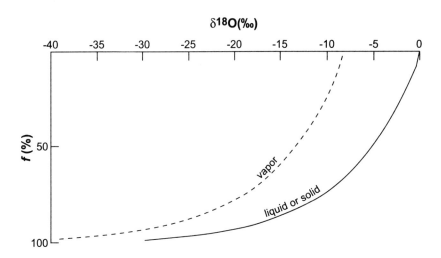

Figure 2.2   The oxygen isotope ratios of vapor (dashed line) and the liquid or solid phase (solid line) in proportion to the percentage (f) of the amount of original vapor depleted. The vapor first evaporates from the ocean with $\delta^{18}O$ about −10‰.

Glaciologists measure the oxygen or deuterium isotope ratios down an ice core. Then they relate the ratio to past temperature based on an empirical relationship worked out for many areas of the present world. Based on observations of average annual surface temperature and the mean oxygen isotope ratio of the precipitation, Dansgaard and colleagues came up with the following relationship for the oxygen isotope ratio:

$$\delta^{18}O = 0.69T_a - 13.6‰ \tag{2.4}$$

where T_a is the annual mean air temperature at the surface. Figure 2.3 shows the average annual oxygen isotope ratios for the Northern Hemisphere. Figure 2.4 displays a plot of mean annual air temperature versus mean annual oxygen isotope ratio for many stations around the world. Equation 2.4 represents the least squares linear relationship for all the data. Equation 2.5 is the corresponding relationship with the deuterium isotope ratio:

$$\delta D = 5.6T_a - 100‰ \tag{2.5}$$

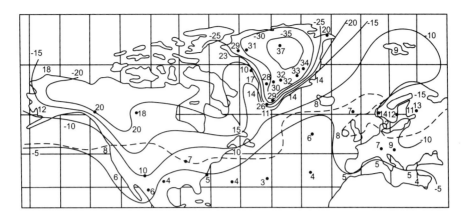

Figure 2.3 The mean annual oxygen isotope ratio of rain and snow for the Northern Hemisphere. Values are actually negative value, as shown by contours (from Bradley, 1985, p. 131).

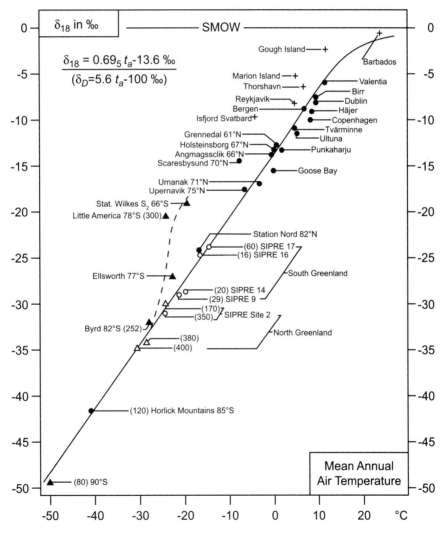

Figure 2.4 The mean annual oxygen isotope ratio plotted against the mean annual surface air temperature for many stations around the world (from Dansgaard, 1964).

Climatic Interpretation of the Oxygen Isotope Ratio

Based on equations 2.4 and 2.5, we can now examine the meaning of the oxygen isotope ratios measured in the ice down many of the ice cores drilled from the Antarctic and Greenland Ice Sheets. From these ratios, it is believed that we can infer past temperatures.

The precipitation rate is generally proportional to temperature, and therefore would be proportional to the oxygen or deuterium isotope ratio, at least in the modern climate. So, glaciologists simply assume that low oxygen isotope ratios mean less annual precipitation and vice versa for high oxygen isotope ratios. Some investigators go so far as to claim that the lower $\delta^{18}O$ during ice ages resulted in a snow accumulation rate of 25% of the modern value and a thinner ice sheet of a few hundred meters at most (Cuffey and Clow, 1997).

Figure 2.5 is the oxygen isotope ratio of the first core drilled to bedrock, the Camp Century core drilled on the northwest Greenland Ice Sheet. Figures 2.6 to 2.8 show three of the more recent Greenland ice cores drilled to bedrock (see figure 1.1 for locations and table 1.2 for information on these cores). One can see that all four of these ice cores show similar features. They can be divided up into three general layers. The top layer is characterized by nearly constant average oxygen isotope ratio. The variability around the average in this layer varies in figures 2.5 to 2.8 because of different averaging techniques applied to the plots. This layer is composed of firn snow at the top that increases in density downward until the firn-ice transition occurs between 50 and 100 meters deep. Below that point, it is compressed as ice. This layer, which includes practically all of the Renland core and the upper half the GISP2 core, is assigned to the Holocene, the past 10,000 years in the Evolutionary-Uniformitarian model, in which temperatures have remained generally the same. In the Creation-Flood model, this layer corresponds to the post–Ice Age period. (The two models will be discussed further in chapter 3.)

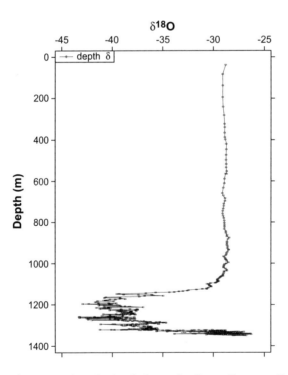

Figure 2.5   The oxygen isotope ratio to bedrock down the Camp Century, Greenland, ice core. Just the average oxygen isotope ratio shown for the top layer.

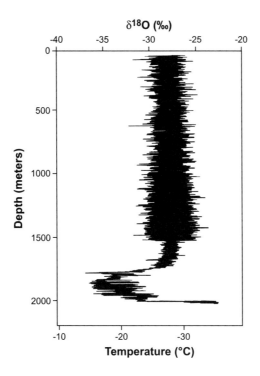

Figure 2.6   The oxygen isotope ratio to bedrock down the Dye 3, Greenland, ice core. Notice the coarser change of scale below 1500 meters that results is less amplitude to the oxygen isotope ratios in the deeper layer.

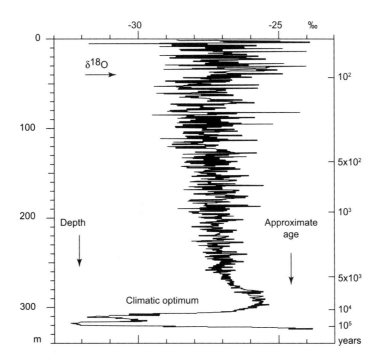

Figure 2.7   The oxygen isotope ratio to bedrock for the Renland, east central Greenland, ice core. This ice core was drilled on a high ice dome near the east coast (after Johnsen et al., 1992b).

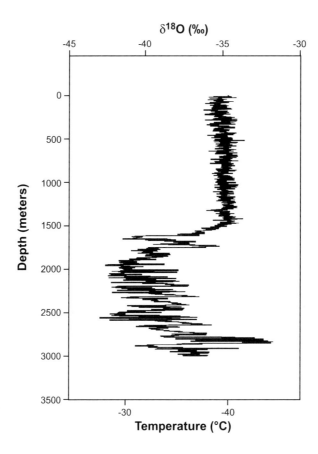

Figure 2.8   The oxygen isotope ratio to bedrock for the GISP2 core at the summit of the Greenland Ice Sheet. The GRIP core, drilled 28 kilometers east, is very similar to the GISP2 core.

The second layer in the cores corresponds to the Ice Age portion of the core in the Creation-Flood model and the last ice age in the Evolutionary-Uniformitarian model. In this layer, the oxygen isotope ratio becomes dramatically more negative with oscillations between relatively low and high values. Based on equation 2.4, this second layer represents temperatures about 5 to 10°C cooler than now. Glaciologists also believe that precipitation was much less during the glacial period due to cooler temperatures (Alley and Bender, 1998). The relatively low oxygen isotope values in the oscillations are defined as *stadials* while the high values are called *interstadials*, which are cold and milder periods, respectively, during the Ice Age. Glaciologists have come to view these oscillations as abrupt climate changes that take place in a few decades and last a few thousand years. The meaning of these oscillations will be discussed further in chapter 10.

In the third general layer, the bottom section of the core, the oxygen isotope ratio becomes more positive toward the bottom. This layer is thin, except for the GISP2 core, in which it is about 200 meters thick with large oscillations. Based on equation 2.4, this layer would be relatively warm, the positive oscillations being even warmer than the temperatures derived from the top layer, which represents the current climate. This layer is considered to represent the previous interglacial period in the Evolutionary-Uniformitarian model. Within the Creation-Flood model, layer three represents the beginning of the Ice Age when ocean temperatures were originally quite warm but cooled with time.

24

Figure 2.9 shows the second core ever drilled to bedrock, the Byrd core on the West Antarctic Ice Sheet. Figures 2.10 to 2.12 display three deep cores from East Antarctica (see figure 1.2 for locations and table 1.3 for information on these cores). These cores show similarities and differences with the Greenland cores. The Byrd core looks very much like the Greenland cores, with the presence of a slowly decreasing oxygen isotope ratio with depth in layer one (above 1,000 meters). Layer two is the colder Ice Age layer between 1,000 and 2,100 meters while the warmer third layer lies below 2,100 meters. The isotope ratio in layer three is lower than in layer one in contrast to the Greenland cores. The Law Dome core (figure 2.12) drilled to bedrock looks very similar to the Renland core, which is not too surprising since both are cores drilled near the coast.

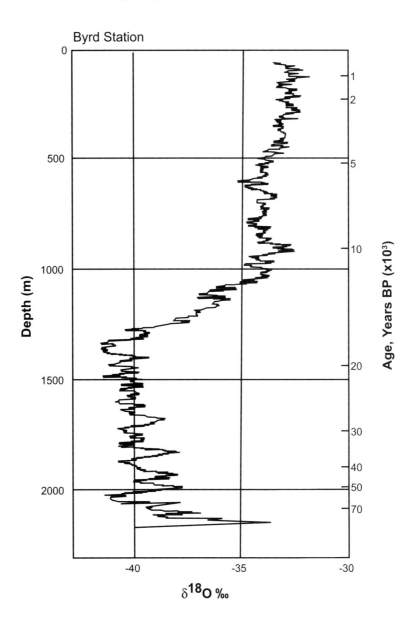

Figure 2.9   The oxygen isotope ratio to bedrock for the Byrd core on the West Antarctic Ice Sheet (from Robin, 1983c).

25

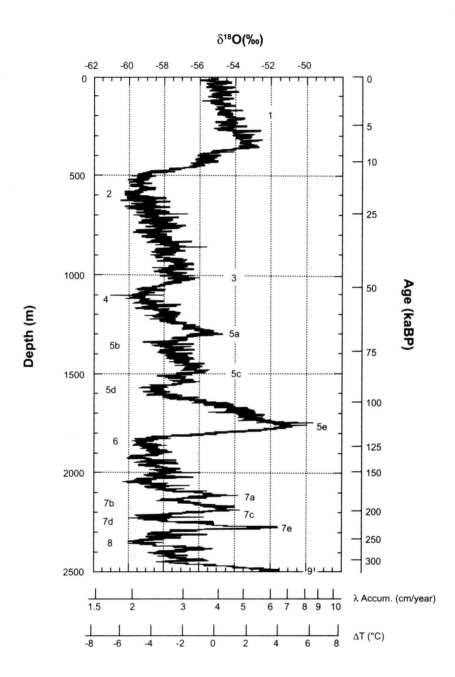

Figure 2.10 The oxygen isotope ratio in the Dome F deep core from East Antarctica (from Watanabe et al., 1999). The numbers 1 to 9 to the right and left of the graph are assumed marine isotope stages that are supposed to represent glacial (even numbers) and interglacial (odd numbers) events. The suggested accumulation in water equivalent amounts and temperature changes for oxygen isotope values are provided at the bottom of the figure.

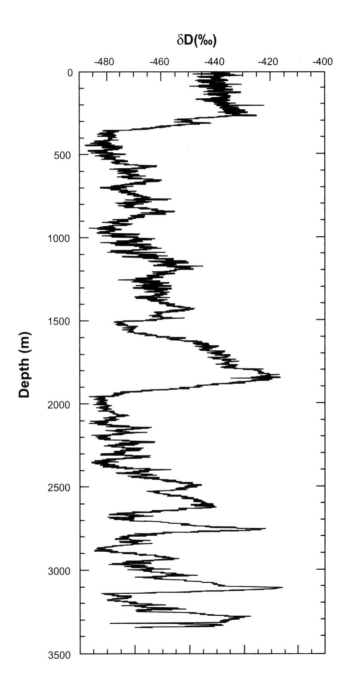

Figure 2.11 The deuterium isotope ratio in the Vostok deep core from East Antarctica (from Petit et al., 1999).

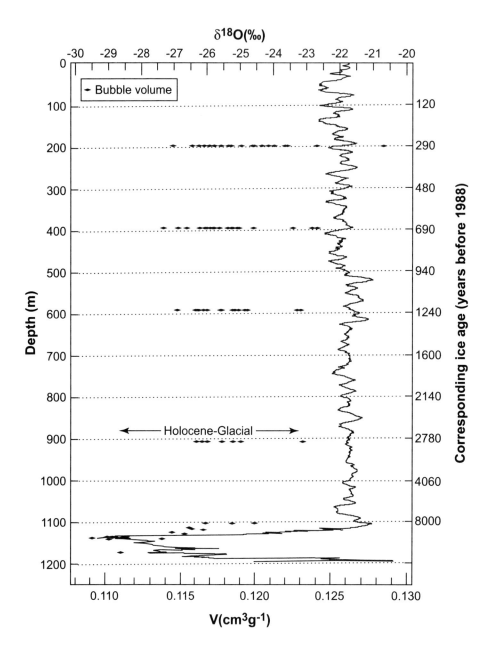

Figure 2.12 The oxygen isotope ratio and bubble volume for the Law Dome core drilled to bedrock near the coast of East Antarctica (from Delmotte et al., 1999).

The real difference between Antarctic and Greenland cores becomes apparent in the Dome F and Vostok cores, figures 2.10 and 2.11, respectively. Though neither one of these Antarctic cores was drilled to bedrock, they were drilled very deep. Notice in figure 2.11 that the deuterium isotope ratio is measured in the Vostok core, while the oxygen isotope ratio is measured in the Dome F core in figure 2.10. Marine isotope stages 1 to 9 are added to the Dome F core. These two cores are very similar. Layer one is only about 300 to 400 meters thick. This goes along with the present very low temperature and snowfall (see figure 1.4) and indicates little change since the Ice Age.

The stable isotope ratios do decrease a bit going upward and could be interpreted as a cooling trend during the Holocene, possibly as the interior of the ice sheet increased its height.

Layer two in the Dome F and Vostok cores consists of generally more negative stable isotope ratios, corresponding to the Ice Age. Oscillations exist, as in the Greenland ice cores, but these oscillations are of much higher amplitude in the Antarctic cores. In fact, the stable isotope ratios sometimes exceed those from the Holocene part of the cores. These less negative stable isotope ratios in the Antarctic cores have been interpreted as interglacials instead of interstadials. The more negative stable isotope ratios have been interpreted as glacial periods in these deep Antarctic cores. One can see three of the large amplitude positive oscillations in Dome F and four positive oscillations in the Vostok core. Since ice ages are believed to cycle every 100,000 years within the Evolutionary-Uniformitarian model, the bottom interglacial in the Vostok core has been automatically dated to around 400,000 years old. In January 2003, the new Dome C ice core drilled by the European Project for Ice Coring in Antarctica (EPICA) reached the 3,200-meter level, and glaciologists claimed to date the ice back to 740,000 (Pokar, 2003; McManus, 2004; EPICA Community Members, 2004). The new Dome C core supposedly drilled through seven of these large oscillations.

Isotope-Temperature Relationship Not Accurate during the Ice Age

Recently, glaciologists have made a troubling discovery. They found that equations 2.4 and 2.5 do not hold for the glacial part of the Greenland ice cores. They calculated ice age temperatures, starting from the current temperature in the GRIP and GISP2 boreholes and worked backwards by considering the change in temperature with time. The variables used are geothermal heat added from the ground upwards into the core, the sinking of cold surface snow, and heat conduction from the surface (MacAyeal, 1995). The ice age temperatures ended up at least twice as cold as given in equations 2.4 and 2.5 (Johnsen et al., 1995a; Cuffey et al., 1995; Kerr, 1996; Jouzel et al., 1997; Cuffey and Clow, 1997; Jouzel, 1999). Therefore, the ice age is now believed to have been 20 to 25°C colder than present, instead of about 10°C colder as assumed before (Hvidberg, 2000)! So, the isotope-temperature relationship in equations 2.4 and 2.5 do not accurately represent the past according to the Evolutionary-Uniformitarian scientists. This inaccuracy could be due to one or more of the other variables, besides surface temperature, that affect the oxygen isotope ratio (see appendix 1). Researchers are actively attempting to figure out the influence of the other variables on ice age temperatures. Cuffey and Marshall (2000, p. 591) speculate that the larger temperature change is caused by changes in the seasonal timing of precipitation (Charles et al., 1995) and cooler tropical temperatures (Boyle, 1997). On the other hand, the claim of much colder ice age temperatures could be due to the stretched out Evolutionary-Uniformitarian timescale and the assumed little change in altitude of the Greenland Ice Sheet.

Furthermore, the bottom of the ice cores is now considered to have been 5 to 10°C warmer than the current climate, corresponding to the higher oxygen isotope ratios (Souchez et al., 1994; Cuffey and Marshall, 2000). As a result, some glaciologists believe much of the interglacial ice on Greenland melted, contributing to a 4 to 5.5 meter rise in sea level (Koerner, 1989, 1997; Cuffey and Marshall, 2000). However, the total gas content data (discussed in chapter 8) indicate the ice sheet did not melt but remained about the same height during the previous interglacial, if there really was a previous interglacial and assuming that the total gas content is an accurate altimeter.

So, either there are problems relating equations 2.4 and 2.5 to the ice cores and deriving past temperatures, or the inferences from the gas content of the ice may be off, or both. Equations 2.4

and 2.5 have been widely applied assuming that the spatial relationship observed today holds for the Ice Age. In general this assumption is qualitatively good, but there are likely exceptions that will become important for determining the climate of the Ice Age.

Chapter 3

THE TWO MODELS OF EARTH HISTORY

There are two ways of viewing the origin and development of the Greenland and Antarctic Ice Sheets. These views are a consequence of two different ice age models that are derived from two different paradigms or worldviews of earth history. One model is an outgrowth of the Evolutionary-Uniformitarian paradigm, and the second model is derived from the Creation-Flood paradigm.

The Evolutionary-Uniformitarian Model of Ice Ages

The Evolutionary-Uniformitarian paradigm has been developed over many years by mainstream scientists. This paradigm attempts to explain the origin of everything by natural processes without recourse to a supernatural Creator. It postulates that the universe and earth are billions of years old, having developed by natural processes. The sedimentary rocks and fossils are believed to have been laid down by slow processes over a few billion years—based on the uniformitarian principle developed in the early 1800s and almost universally accepted today with some modification to allow for a few catastrophes. Mainstream scientists believe that they see evolutionary development over time—from molecules to man—in the rocks and fossils.

From this paradigm, a model for the ice age was developed of which a theory of the origin of the Greenland and Antarctic Ice Sheets is an outgrowth. In the Evolutionary-Uniformitarian worldview, the period of time for the origin and development of the ice sheets is the mid- and late Cenozoic era. This period corresponds to a general cooling of the oceans (figure 3.1) that is caused by a cooling of the atmosphere. Ice developed on Antarctica first in the mid-Cenozoic and on Greenland early in the late Cenozoic. The time frame for the ice age proper is called the *Pleistocene* or *Quaternary*, which corresponds to the very late Cenozoic, about the last 2 million years. This is the time when the other ice sheets (which have since melted) formed over Europe and North America. Actually, the ice age is now believed to have developed a little before the Pleistocene within the late Pliocene, about 2.5 million years ago within the uniformitarian timescale.

The Evolutionary-Uniformitarian model postulates five major periods of glaciation in earth history (figure 3.2). It is only the "last" major ice age during the mid- and late Cenozoic that will concern us in this in-depth study.

The exact time for the origin of the Antarctic Ice Sheet has been rather controversial (Wise et al., 1991; Ehrmann et al., 1992). At least one scientist in the 1960s believed there was no good evidence of a Tertiary origin for the ice sheet; it must have developed in the Pleistocene

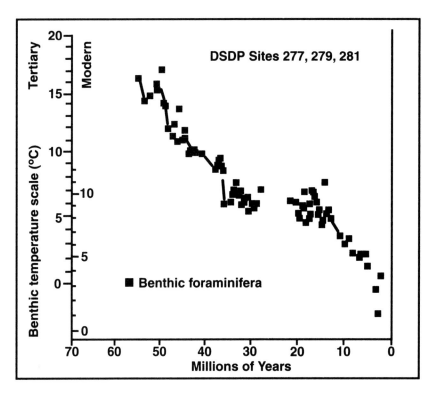

Figure 3.1 Temperature change in sea-floor sediments based on oxygen isotopes for benthic foramin-ifera in the uniformitarian timescale from Deep Sea Drilling Project sites 277, 279, and 281 (after Shackleton and Kennett, 1974).

Geologic Timescale

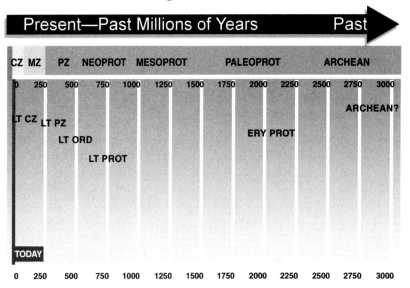

Figure 3.2 Five major ice age periods in earth history according to the Evolutionary-Uniformitarian model (from Crowell, 1999, redrawn by Dan Lietha). The Archean "ice age" is still considered speculative. The Pleistocene ice age is referred to as the late Cenozoic (LT CZ) because Antarctica supposedly developed in the mid- and late Cenozoic.

(Rutford, Craddock, and Bastien, 1968). However, the East Antarctic Ice Sheet is now believed to have developed early in the mid-Cenozoic after the Eocene warm period, in the late Eocene or early Oligocene epoch, about 34 to 42 million years ago in the uniformitarian timescale (Kennett, 1982, pp. 721–729; Oglesby, 1989; Crowell, 1999; DeConto and Pollard, 2003; Barrett, 2003). These dates are based on deep-sea cores showing matrix-supported gravels, called *diamict*, on the Antarctic continental shelf and on ice-rafted debris carried away from Antarctica and recovered in deep water (Ehrmann et al., 1992; Crowell, 1999, p. 6). This debris indicates that at least mountain glaciers that reached the coast existed on Antarctica by the early Oligocene. Models suggest that the East Antarctic Ice Sheet grew abruptly to 40% or more of its current volume at the Eocene-Oligocene boundary and expanded further in the mid-Miocene (Barker et al., 1999). It is believed to have remained stable with only minor fluctuations for the past 15 million years (Anderson, 1986).

The West Antarctic Ice Sheet is believed to have developed later than the East Antarctic Ice Sheet. Barker et al. (1999, p. 262) write that it did not develop until around the mid- to late Miocene, about 10 million years ago. Hvidberg (2000, p. 551), on the other hand, states that the ice sheet did not form until several million years ago. So there is a discrepancy in the timing of the development of the West Antarctic Ice Sheet.

Regardless, the development of the East Antarctic Ice Sheet is considered the prime event that brought an end to the Eocene warm period. According to theory, the ice sheet may have developed because of a fundamental change in ocean circulation, such as the development of the Antarctic Circumpolar Current after the plate tectonic separation of South America and Australia from Antarctica. A more west to east current after this event is supposed to have transported 15–20% less heat to Antarctica (DeConto and Pollard, 2003). New research concludes that such a change in geography is less important than a decrease of carbon dioxide from four times to about three times the preindustrial level (DeConto and Pollard, 2003; Barrett, 2003). Regardless, some researchers believe that the Antarctic Ice Sheet should have developed even sooner during previous warm periods, since Antarctica has laid over the South Pole since the Mesozoic. Kennett (1982, p. 724) asks:

> Why did the first significant sea-ice apparently form at high latitudes 38 m.y. ago and why did the first glacial conditions appear so much later than the time when Antarctica first moved into a south polar position during the Mesozoic?

Actually a few uniformitarian scientists postulate that significant ice must have developed on Antarctica in the Cretaceous and continued through the Cenozoic (Oglesby, 1989, p. 137).

An interesting dispute related to the Evolutionary-Uniformitarian history of the Antarctic Ice Sheet developed in the 1980s and early 1990s. Some scientists postulated that the East Antarctic Ice Sheet mostly melted several million years ago (Webb et al., 1983, 1984; Harwood, 1983, 1985; Anderson, 1986; Barrett et al., 1992; Sugden, 1992; Verbers and Damm, 1994). This rather outrageous deduction was based on three discoveries, all dated between 2 and 5 million years old: (1) a large concentration of fossilized wood with roots, plants, pollen, and spores in cliffs 1,800 meters ASL only 5° from the South Pole; (2) fossilized marine protozoa and diatoms along the Transantarctic Mountains; and (3) a fossilized dolphin on Prydz Bay. To account for such observations, the Transantarctic Mountains would have to have been uplifted 3,000 meters within the last 5 million years. Such a drastic climate change and recent uplift of the Transantarctic Mountains was difficult for most scientists to swallow, especially when climate models indicate that it would take a climatic warming of 25°C to melt the ice sheet (Huybrechts, 1994). The evidence for this Pliocene deglaciation has been disputed. The diatoms high up on the Transantarctic Mountains have been attributed to wind transport, a likely possibility, since diatoms are also found in ice cores from the South Pole, Siple Dome, and Taylor Dome (Kellogg and Kellogg, 1996; Burckle and Potter, 1996). Furthermore, Wilch et al. (1993) claim that there has been little uplift of the Transantarctic Mountains based on radiometric dating of basalt flows in the dry Taylor Valley. Most scientists lean away from the idea of Pliocene melting, but the controversy has not been settled (Barrett, 2003; Hambrey et al., 2003).

The Greenland Ice Sheet, on the other hand, is generally believed to have developed about 2.5 million years ago at the same time the other ice sheets of the Northern Hemisphere developed for the first time in the ice age. Souchez (1997, p. 26,317) considers the bottom 6 meters of ice in the central part of the ice sheet as local ice from just before the original buildup 2.4 million years ago. However, other researchers believe that little is known of when the ice sheet developed, and it may be significantly older (Larsen et al., 1994). Ice-rafted debris, glacial till, and glaciomarine diamict dated at 7 m.y. old was discovered off the southeast coast of Greenland (Larsen et al., 1994; Crowell, 1999, p. 6). This implies that since the late Miocene Greenland had at least mountain glaciers that reached sea level. On the other hand, Koerner (1989, 1997) believes the ice sheet mostly melted during the previous interglacial about 120,000 years ago within the Evolutionary-Uniformitarian dating system. Most glaciologists reject this idea because we are in an interglacial today, and the ice sheet is in steady state. Besides, what would cause such warmth greater than today?

Many geologists and glaciologists over the years have admitted that the cause of the ice age is unknown. One of the latest is David Alt (2001, p. 180) in a book about the massive Lake Missoula flood at the peak of the ice age: "Although theories abound, no one really knows what causes ice ages." The main reason for such difficulty in explaining the ice age is that summer temperatures need to cool many tens of degrees with much greater snowfall (Oard, 1990). For instance, in the north central United States where summer temperatures average over 20°C, temperatures must cool to around −10°C. This is such a drastic cooling that it is difficult (impossible?) to postulate such a cooling mechanism, and that is why there have been dozens of ice age theories. And even if some cooling mechanism were found, such cooling causes the air to hold less moisture for precipitation, which is the basis for the idea that there is much less snowfall on the ice sheets during an ice age. This frustrates the second needed condition for an ice age—abundant precipitation. Furthermore, the climate for an ice age must persist for tens of thousands of years.

Despite the lack of a cause for the ice age, geologists believe they have found the mechanism for the glacial/interglacial oscillations that they believe occurred during the Pleistocene. During each interglacial, the ice completely melts, except for in Greenland and Antarctica. We are supposed to be living in an interglacial, called the *Holocene,* that is fast ending. Ice ages are supposed to have cycled regularly every 100,000 years for the past 800,000 years, and every 40,000 years between 2.5 million and 800,000 years ago. This hypothesis results in a lot of ice ages—the four-ice-age theory widely believed and supported by most data for sixty years was tossed out in the 1970s. Scientists now believe there were as many as thirty regularly repeating ice ages (Kennett, 1982, p. 747). The glacial/interglacial cycles are believed to have been caused by periodic changes in the earth's orbit. This is called the *astronomical theory* of the ice ages, or the *Milankovitch theory*, after the scientist who developed it early in the twentieth century. This theory supposedly has been proved by matching the Milankovitch radiation cycle, caused by the changes in the earth's orbital geometry, at about 60°N latitude with climate sensitive variables down deep-sea cores (Hays, Imbrie, and Shackleton, 1976). I will have more to say about the Milankovitch theory of ice ages in chapter 9.

The Creation-Flood Model of the Ice Age

The Creation-Flood model is a very different paradigm of earth history. We believe that the verses of Genesis 1–11 are accurate history, since these verses blend in with the history of Genesis 12 up to the time of Jesus that generally can be verified by archeology, in spite of the fact that most archeologists do not believe in the Bible. Moreover, there is no hint that these verses should be interpreted allegorically. Jesus referred to the events in Genesis 1–11 as accurate history. Besides, does not God have the power to motivate and direct the Bible writers to accurately record what He wanted written in the Bible (2 Timothy 3:16–17)? So the Bible can be read in a straightforward manner, and we can believe what the Bible says about earth history, namely that there was a creation in six literal days, a fall of man into sin, a curse placed on the universe, a global flood, and man spreading all over the earth with different languages after the Tower of Babel incident. Furthermore, adding up the geneologies in Genesis 5, 10, and 11 indicates that the earth and universe are young—6,000 years old or a little more.

The Evolutionary-Uniformitarian model of the ice age has been in existence for over 150 years. Although the cause of the ice age is unknown, the model seems well established, and many pieces of data and dates appear at a distance to fit nicely with one another. However, although millions of hours, billions of dollars, and countless research articles have been devoted to the model, up close, the model has major problems. There are also major subsidiary mysteries associated with their model, such as the origin of pluvial lakes in currently semi-arid regions, origin of persistent non-glaciated areas poleward of the edge of glaciation, the mix of warm- and cold-climate plants and animals during the ice age, the lack of glaciation in the lowlands of Siberia and Alaska, the existence and death of the woolly mammoths in Siberia and Alaska, and the mass extinction of large mammals and birds at the end of the ice age (Oard, 1990; 2004b). Does the Creation-Flood paradigm have a model for the ice age? Is this model able to better explain the data?

Based on the Creation-Flood paradigm of earth history, the evidences for ice ages need to be explained. The five major ice ages over geological time postulated by the uniformitarian scientists (figure 3.2) can be divided up into the pre-Cenozoic ice ages and the mid- and late Cenozoic ice age (using uniformitarian terminology), which will simply be referred to as the late Cenozoic ice age.

1) Pre-Cenozoic Ice Ages

The pre-Cenozoic or pre-Pleistocene ice ages were not ice ages at all; the evidence from the rocks used to deduce these "ice ages" has been misinterpreted (Oard, 1997a). The rocks that suggest pre-Cenozoic ice ages are found within thick masses of sedimentary rocks, even dated as old as 2.2 billion years within the Evolutionary-Uniformitarian timescale. These sedimentary rocks were laid down during the Genesis Flood. The "ice age" layers are composed of stones inside a lithified fine-grained matrix (figure 3.3). When such a layer is derived from a glacier it is called *till*. When the layer is consolidated, it is called a *tillite*. Sometimes seeming ice age features, such as striated pavements (scratches on bedrock surfaces) (figure 3.4) and striated rocks (scratched cobbles or boulders) are also found. There is no doubt that these layers show a superficial resemblance to true glacial deposits.

However, there is strong evidence that the secular geologists have misinterpreted these peculiar rocks, as even a few uniformitarian geologists have pointed out in regard to the late Precambrian tillites (Schermerhorn, 1974). There are many features of these tillites that are contrary to the ice age interpretation (Oard, 1997a). An alternative mechanism can account for these till-like deposits. This mechanism is mass movement, or in other words, *gigantic landslides*. Two main types of

Figure 3.3   "Tillite" from the late Precambrian "ice age" near Pocatello, Idaho.

Figure 3.4   Striated pavement from Precambrian "ice age" Hallett Cove, just south of Adelaide, Australia (photo by Andrew Snelling).

landslides are debris flows and turbidity currents, but there are also other types of mass flows. A debris flow is a moving mass of rock fragments of all sizes within a finer-grained matrix. A turbidity current is similar, but generally with fewer rocks and more water within the moving mass. The underwater flow of sediment is supported by fluid turbulence. When debris flows and turbidity currents stop moving, they are called *debrites* and *turbidites*, respectively.

Debrites and turbidites can mimic real ice age features. A debrite (figure 3.5) can mimic ice age deposits called *till*, which contains rocks of various sizes mixed within a fine-grained matrix. Striations result when rock scrapes against rock or bedrock during a mass flow. I have examined a debris flow found on top of the Gravelly Mountains of Southwest Montana. The flow resulted in isolated striated rocks and a well-defined striated pavement (figure 3.6) that has since been broken up by subsequent slumping. These features were not made by glaciation, although at one time the deposit was interpreted as an ancient Eocene glacial deposit. Fine-layered turbidites containing transported stones can look just like another glacial feature, silt/clay rhythmites with rocks dropped from icebergs floating in a lake.

Since these pre-Cenozoic "tillites" are part of the great accumulation of sedimentary rocks laid down by the Genesis Flood, mass flow during the Flood is the explanation. The Flood was a time of rapid sedimentation. It is reasonable that some of this sediment would become unstable after deposition and begin sliding because of tectonics or giant earthquakes during the Flood. The mass would eventually stop on a flat bottom or a gentle slope. These mass movements would be on a large scale, which can account for the huge size of some of these supposed ice age deposits. Since the Genesis Flood can account for these unique rocks in this way, the many millions of years suggested by pre-Cenozoic "ice ages" disappear. This indicates that the *addition of another variable or a new mechanism can change the entire chronological picture*. What some scientists view as a hopeless contradiction to the timescale of Scripture turns into support for a short time-scale during the Flood. The Flood often provides a solution to these apparent time contradictions presented by the Evolutionary-Uniformitarian paradigm.

Figure 3.5   Volcanic debrite, a lahar, in the Ellensburg Formation, 16 kilometers west of Ellensburg, Washington. The lahar flowed out of the Cascade Mountains of Western Washington.

Figure 3.6   Debrite with a striated boulder sitting on top of a striated pavement on top of the Gravelly Range Mountains of Southwest Montana.

2) The Late Cenozoic Ice Age

The late Cenozoic ice age includes the glaciation of Antarctica and Greenland and the development of the Northern Hemisphere ice sheets in the late Pliocene and Pleistocene within the uniformitarian timescale. This ice age is characterized by unconsolidated debris that is composed of variable-sized stones and mixed in a fine-grained matrix. This debris, called *glacial till*, lies on the surface of many areas at mid- and high latitudes. Landslides cannot account for this debris over such a huge distance of low relief. Striated pavements upon which the ice sheets slide (figure 3.7), as well as striated boulders in moraines (figure 3.8), are relatively common. Erratic boulders often transported in icebergs on lakes or meltwater-gorged rivers, lie within and just south of the area once occupied by the continental ice sheets. The Belleview erratic in the Willamette Valley (figure 3.9) is an example of a large boulder that was transported well south of the ice sheet by an iceberg during the Lake Missoula flood (Oard, 2004a). Many mountain areas of the midlatitudes and tropics possess glacial features at much lower elevations than the present day snow lines. Distinctive horseshoe-shaped moraines are found at the entrances to mountain valleys all over the western United States (figure 3.10). Such geometric shapes could not form during the Flood, so this Ice Age was real and *followed* the Flood. Furthermore, many of the glacial features appear to be fresh with little sign of weathering, suggesting that the Ice Age happened recently.

Some of these supposed ice age deposits likely represent mass movements. On ridges just to the east of Glacier National Park, U.S.A., and adjacent Waterton Lakes National Park, Canada, as many as seven ice ages as old as 2.5 million years are supposedly recorded by paleosols, stone fabrics, and paleomagnetism (Karlstrom, 2000; Karlstrom and Barendregt, 2001). These deposits, called the *Kennedy drift*, cap ridges that are erosion surfaces and display little evidence for glaciation, except for striated rocks (Klevberg and Oard, 2005). Striated rocks commonly occur in mass movement (Schermerhorn, 1974; Oard, 1997a, pp. 41–47). The claim that the deposits contain paleosols in the Kennedy drift is based on questionable assumptions. A field study indicates that

38

Figure 3.7   Striated pavement in the Sun River Canyon of the Rocky Mountains west of Great Falls, Montana.

Figure 3.8   Striated boulder from a terminal moraine on the high plains west of the Sun River Canyon in the Rocky Mountains, Montana.

39

Figure 3.9   Belleview erratic from Willamette Valley, Oregon. This large boulder is composed of a slightly metamorphosed shale, called *argillite*, which could not have rolled hundreds of miles from its nearest source in northern Idaho or western Montana.

Figure 3.10   Horseshoe-shaped lateral and terminal moraine extending out onto a small plain with overdeepened Wallowa Lake filling the depression between moraines, northern Wallowa Mountains, northeast Oregon. Notice how sharp crested the moraines are, which indicates their youth.

the alleged paleosols and till are more readily interpreted as a mass flow deposit from off Glacier and Waterton National Parks during the late Flood period (Klevberg, Oard, and Bandy, 2003; Klevberg, Bandy, and Oard, 2005).

Although uniformitarian scientists have not been able to discover the cause of the ice age, nor have they found adequate solutions to its subsidiary mysteries, creationists have a viable mechanism. The Ice Age represents a transition climate from the Flood catastrophe to the present climate (Oard, 1990; Oard, 2004b). The Flood involved unprecedented, widespread volcanic and tectonic activity. After the continents and mountains rose out of the floodwaters and/or the water subsided, a shroud of volcanic dust and aerosols remained in the atmosphere, obscuring part of the sun. This would cause the land to cool dramatically. The dust and aerosols would replenish themselves for hundreds of years following the Flood due to continued volcanism as the earth moved toward equilibrium. There is a great amount of evidence for extensive volcanism within Ice Age sediments (Charlesworth, 1957, p. 601). There are 700 volcanic acidity signatures in the Ice Age portion of the GISP2 core that indicate volcanism greater than historical eruptions (Zielinski et al., 1996). There are more than 500 major acidity peaks in the 2,503-meter long Dome F core (Fujita et al, 2002a). These volcanic spikes represent a huge amount of volcanism when telescoped into the short Creation-Flood Ice Age timescale (Oard, 1997c), which will be discussed below. This justifies the assumption of enormous post-Flood volcanism to cool the land in summer during the Ice Age (Oard, 1990).

Moisture for snow would come from an ocean that had been warmed by volcanism, meteorite impacts, lava flows, the friction of tectonics, and possibly water from the crust during the eruption of the "fountains of the great deep." The warm water would have been well mixed during the turbulence of the Flood and would have extended from pole to pole and from the surface of the ocean to the ocean floor. A well-known principle that affects the formation of clouds and precipitation is: the warmer the water, the greater the evaporation. Such a warm ocean would allow huge amounts of moisture to evaporate at mid- and high latitudes, which would be picked up by storms and dumped as rain and snow on the nearby continents.

This powerful evaporation would continue for hundreds of years until the oceans cooled. Once the oceans cooled, the Ice Age would end because of reduced moisture. To derive the time for the post-Flood Ice Age, I used heat balance equations to derive the cooling time for the ocean and atmosphere. I estimated heat inputs and outputs and was able to arrive at a ballpark figure. Since the balance equations for the ocean and atmosphere would be speculative and applied to a cooler, wetter Ice Age climate, I used minimum and maximum values for the variables. From this I calculated a maximum and minimum time required to reach glacial maximum. Based on the cooling time for the ocean, the amount of time necessary to reach glacial maximum turned out to be a minimum of 174 years and a maximum of 1,765 years. Using values in the midrange of the variables, I calculated about 500 years to reach glacial maximum (Oard, 1990).

Regardless of which values are used for the variables in the heat balance equations, the ice sheets would have developed in a relatively short time compared to uniformitarian estimates. The ice sheets would have generally developed in place, except for those areas too close to the warm ocean, which would have glaciated later in the Ice Age. Based on the estimated proportion of moisture available to fall on the ice sheets, I obtained a minimum glacier depth of 515 meters and a maximum depth of 905 meters for the Northern Hemisphere. The best estimate is an average depth of 700 meters. For Antarctica the minimum and maximum depths are 725 meters and 1,675 meters respectively, with the best estimate of 1,200 meters. (Based on the data in table 1.1 and information on the Antarctic Ice Sheet, the high estimate of 1,675 meters is probably the most accurate.) The ice sheet would be thicker or thinner than average in various areas, depending upon the distance from the main moisture source, which is the warm ocean, and the distance from the main storm tracks.

These thickness values are lower than uniformitarian estimates by around 50%. However, the thicknesses of past ice sheets are really only guesses, despite the confidence of some glacial geologists. Geologists have generally *assumed* that past ice sheets would have been as thick as the current Antarctic Ice Sheet. Bloom (1971, p. 367) writes:

> Unfortunately, few facts about its thickness are known. . . . In the absence of direct measurements about the thickness of the Laurentide ice sheet [in central and eastern Canada], we must turn to analogy [Antarctica] and theory.

It is now confirmed that, contrary to earlier expectations, the Laurentide Ice Sheet was significantly thinner along most of its southern (Mathews, 1974; Clayton, Teller, and Attig, 1985; Beget, 1986; Hooyer and Iverson, 2002) and most of its northwest periphery (Beget, 1987). Furthermore, the interior of the ice sheet was likely multidomed and thinner (Shilts, Cunningham, and Kaszycki, 1979; Shilts, 1980). A thinner ice sheet lends support to the post-Flood/rapid Ice Age model, which postulates a significantly thinner ice sheet than that postulated by uniformitarian scientists.

Using the equation for the energy balance over a snow or ice cover, I discovered the ice sheets in the Northern Hemisphere would melt in about 100 years near the periphery and in about 200 years in the interior of the ice sheets (Oard, 1990, pp. 109–133). This melt rate compares favorably with the current melt rates in the ablation areas of Icelandic, Alaskan, and Norwegian glaciers (Sugden and John, 1976, p. 39). So the Ice Age ice sheets melted catastrophically.

There is even room to account for John Shaw and colleagues' subglacial flood hypothesis (Shaw, 1996, 2002; Oard, 2004a, pp. 59–67) in the creationist model. Rapid melting and possibly even a thinner ice sheet towards the center of the Laurentide or Cordilleran Ice Sheets could result in the ponding of a large lake well behind the periphery. After a huge volume of water collected for many years, the lake could have burst from underneath the ice sheet periphery as enormous subglacial floods.

Within the Flood model there could only be one Ice Age. Most of the evidence for multiple ice ages during the late Cenozoic stems from multiple assumptions (Oard, 1990, pp. 135–166). It is especially because of the acceptance of the astronomical theory of the ice age that many glacial/ interglacial oscillations are postulated. There are a number of serious problems with this theory (Oard, 1990, pp. 15–18), which will be discussed more in chapter 9.

So, if the total duration of the Ice Age was about 700 years, there is a great disparity with the Evolutionary-Uniformitarian model's assertion that, over the past million years, each ice age lasted an average of 100,000 years. The minimal erosion caused by ice sheets and the preservation of erosion surfaces in glaciated areas is further straightforward evidence for a rapid, post-Flood Ice Age (Lidmar-Bergström, Olsson, and Olvmo, 1997). Evidence indicates that only one Ice Age elapsed, not many.

The Ice Age is only one example of the many processes thought to take too much time for the Scriptural timescale. These processes can happen rapidly using *different* assumptions, such as the Genesis Flood. Many other challenges to the Creation-Flood model have reasonable solutions when the Flood is considered.

Not only is there a creationist model for the Ice Age, but this Ice Age can also explain a number of subsidiary mysteries (Oard, 1990). Pluvial lakes in currently semi-arid areas can be explained by the Flood initially filling the enclosed basins with water and the Ice Age maintaining the lakes. The persistent non-glaciated areas, such as the driftless area in southwest Wisconsin (figure 3.11), would be the result of one thin ice sheet that surged around this area. Many thick ice sheets, as in the Evolutionary-Uniformitarian model, could not fail to cover this area at least once. The mix of warm- and cold-climate plants and animals is explained by warm winters and cool summers, as well as areas of heavy precipitation that would be characteristic of the Creation-Flood Ice Age model. This climate would be a result of the volcanic ash and aerosols trapped in the stratosphere causing summer cooling, and the warm mid- and high-latitude oceans, causing warmer winters. The ocean temperatures also explain Ice Age mysteries in Siberia and Alaska: (1) the lowlands were never glaciated and (2) the existence of millions of woolly mammoths and other animals in the lowlands. As the Ice Age ended, the climate would become much drier and the winters much colder. Such a climate would cause drought and massive dust storms. It is believed that these features caused the latter Ice Age extinctions of many large mammals and birds. Gigantic dust storms are invoked to explain not only the burial and preservation of the woolly mammoths in the permafrost of Siberia and Alaska, but also to account for a number of unique features in the small number of carcasses found in those regions (Oard, 2000; Oard, 2004b).

Figure 3.11   Pinnacles of St. Peter sandstone that would not have survived glaciation from the driftless area in southwest Wisconsin.

Model Predictions for the Greenland and Antarctic Ice Sheets

Within the Evolutionary-Uniformitarian model, the Greenland and Antarctic Ice Sheets had been more or less in equilibrium for at least a few million years. Equilibrium means that the ice sheets generally maintained the same thickness throughout the various glacial and interglacial periods in the model. Glaciologists used to believe that the annual layer thickness, the yearly amount of precipitation turned to ice, remained the same throughout this time, but this assumption had been relaxed to allow for less precipitation during glacial periods. The annual layer thickness was the average amount of snow that fell in a year, but in ice equivalents. Based on the fact that cooler air is drier, Alley and Bender (1998, p. 83) believed that the coldest parts of the ice age had four to five times less precipitation. Such low annual accumulation would cause the Greenland and Antarctic Ice Sheets to thin a little—only a few hundred meters at most. This change in altitude was insignificant in regard to the equilibrium assumption. However, such low ice age precipitation would be a problem in developing the ice sheets over North America and Eurasia.

Based on equilibrium, glaciologists believe that over the years each annual layer deposited at the top of the ice sheet is buried deeper and deeper. As the annual layer sinks vertically downward in the ice sheet, the edges of the ice sheet flow outward (figure 3.12). Thus, each annual layer thins vertically and stretches horizontally more and more with time (figure 3.13). The annual layers thin with depth so much that by the time they approach the bottom of the ice sheet they are paper thin. The thinning of annual layers in the Evolutionary-Uniformitarian model is shown by the bottom curve in figure 3.14.

Such thin annual layers near the bottom of the core represent much more time than the top of the core. For instance, the plot of the oxygen isotope ratio with depth for the Camp Century core, shown in figure 2.6, would look like the plot shown in figure 3.15 in an oxygen isotope ratio versus time plot. The top 85% of the core represents about 10,000 years, while the bottom 15% of the core represents over 100,000 years within the Evolutionary-Uniformitarian timescale. The calculated age of an ice layer with depth is shown in figure 3.16. Theoretically the very bottom of the ice could be millions of years old under such annual layer thinning.

The Creation-Flood model postulates that there were no ice sheets immediately after the Flood. Any pre-Flood ice sheets would have been destroyed by the Flood. The ice sheets built rapidly

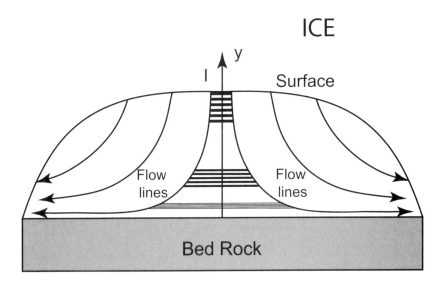

Figure 3.12   The Evolutionary-Uniformitarian long-age ice flow model. Note that the annual layers, shown schematically as horizontal lines down the center of the ice sheet, thin considerably as the ice moved deeper in the ice sheet.

44

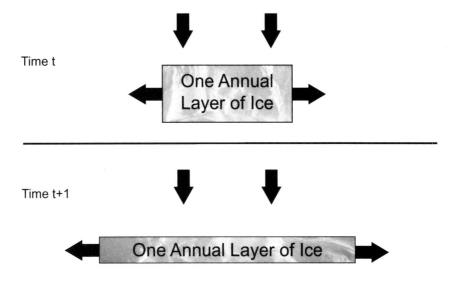

Figure 3.13   Annual layers of ice are compressed vertically due to pressure from the ice above. Horizontal lengthening compensates for the vertical shortening.

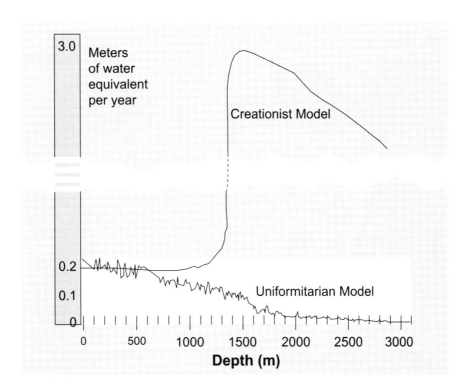

Figure 3.14   The thickness of annual ice layers down the GRIP ice core on central Greenland, calculated according to the Evolutionary-Uniformitarian (De Angelis et al., 1997, p. 26,683) and Creation-Flood (Oard, 2001) models.

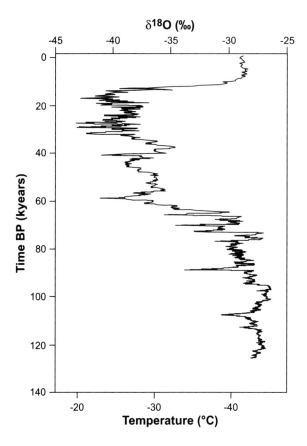

Figure 3.15 The oxygen isotope ratio versus time in the Evolutionary-Uniformitarian model for the Camp Century core (after Vardiman, 1993, p. 5).

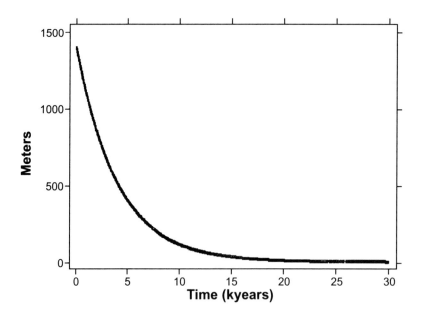

Figure 3.16 Calculated age of an ice layer versus depth in the Evolutionary-Uniformitarian model (after Vardiman, 1993, p. 38).

during the post-Flood Ice Age and then tapered off to the amount of precipitation observed today (Oard, 1990; Vardiman, 1993, 2001, pp. 41–68). Since the oxygen isotope ratio at the bottom of the Camp Century core, as well as other Greenland cores (Souchez, 1997, p. 26,317), indicates warmer temperatures, it is possible that snow did not accumulate right away on Greenland. Being surrounded by quite warm water at the beginning of the Ice Age, glaciation of Antarctica and Greenland likely started in the mountains right after the Flood. It would take some time for the ice sheets to develop over the lowlands. Some climate simulations of the Greenland Ice Sheet have shown that if the ice sheet were removed, it may not reform in the present climate (Crowley and Baum, 1995; Letréguilly, Huybrechts, and Reeh, 1991, p. 149). (This also brings up the question of how the Greenland Ice Sheet formed [Crowley and Baum, 1995].) Other simulations indicate the opposite, but show that a warming of only 6°C is enough to melt the current ice sheet. So, if the climate were a little warmer, such as at the very beginning of the Flood, the ice sheet probably would not develop right away. It is doubtful a similar argument could be made for East Antarctica because of its larger size and higher mountains (Huybrechts, 1994), but the formation of the West Antarctic Ice Sheet would be delayed because of its topography of mountains surrounded by warm ocean water. However, early in the Ice Age, mountain glaciers would be expected on Greenland and West Antarctica. As temperatures cooled during the Ice Age, both the Greenland and West Antarctic Ice Sheets would have developed rapidly.

The buildup of the ice sheet at Camp Century would have generally followed the curve shown in figure 3.17. The resulting plot of the oxygen isotope versus time, considering compression for 4,500 years, would look like figure 3.18—much different than the corresponding plot in the Evolutionary-Uniformitarian model shown in figure 3.15. The calculated age of an ice layer with depth is shown in figure 3.19. Each annual layer in the Creation-Flood model, just like in the Evolutionary-Uniformitarian model, would become compressed with depth, but the amount of compression in the Creation-Flood model would be much less. Moreover, in the Creation-Flood model, the annual layer thickness is much greater over the lower half or so of the Greenland cores when compared with the other model.

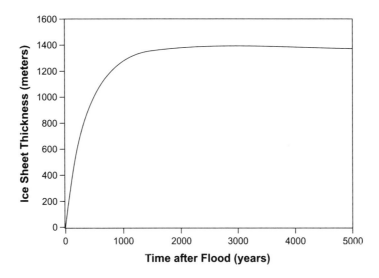

Figure 3.17 The thickness of the Greenland Ice Sheet at Camp Century as a function of time after the Flood (after Vardiman, 1993, p. 44).

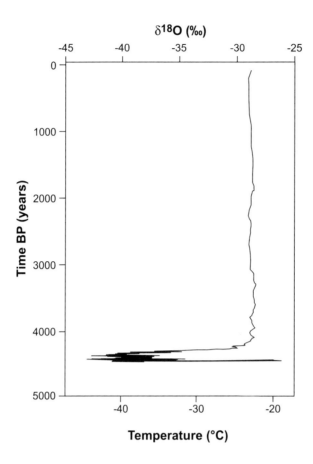

Figure 3.18 Oxygen isotope ratio versus time after the Flood for the Camp Century core, Greenland (after Vardiman, 1993, p. 48). Compare this plot with figure 3.15.

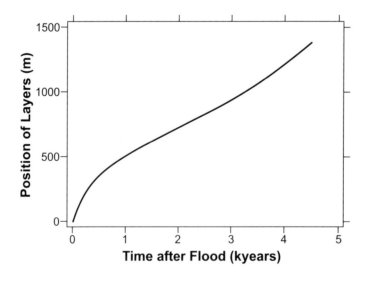

Figure 3.19 Position of ice layers at Camp Century as a function of time after the Flood (after Vardiman, 1993, p. 47). Compare this plot with figure 3.16.

The Creation-Flood model's postulated thickness of the annual layers with depth within the present Greenland Ice Sheet is shown in the upper curve in figure 3.14. One readily sees that in the lower part of the core, creationists would predict annual layer thicknesses perhaps a hundred or a thousand times the corresponding annual layer thicknesses from the Evolutionary-Uniformitarian model. The top curve in figure 3.14 was constructed by assuming that the annual layer thickness at the top of the building ice sheet was equivalent to 6 meters per year of ice during the 500-year buildup phase of the Ice Age, an amount which decreased rapidly during the 200 year deglaciation and the post–Ice Age period. I kept the annual layer thickness constant during the buildup phase of the Ice Age, because decreasing availability of moisture for snow, caused by gradually decreasing sea surface temperatures, would generally be balanced by greater orographic precipitation as the height of the ice sheet increased. A different curve for the Creation-Flood model, such as an exponentially decreasing annual layer thickness with time, could also have been used (Vardiman, personal communication).

Figure 3.14 can be thought of as the predicted annual layer thicknesses in the present Greenland Ice Sheet according to the two models. A similar annual layer thickness prediction can be made for the Antarctic Ice Sheet. Deeper down in the ice cores, the predictions become much different. The Evolutionary-Uniformitarian model has worked out an elaborate scenario based on their predicted annual layer thinning with depth that seems to verify their assumptions about the ice sheets. This is why they claim to have *measured* 110,000 annual layers down to 2,800 meters in the GISP2 ice core. They also continued dating below 2800 meters and arrived at an age of around 161,000 years at the 3030-meter level but later repudiated the dating of this section of the core because of widespread evidence of disturbance in the ice structure (Meese et al., 1997, p. 26,420). We will examine the Evolutionary-Uniformitarian dating methods and will explain the raw data in terms of the Creation-Flood model, focusing especially on the predicted annual layer thicknesses with depth.

At the end of the Ice Age, the Greenland Ice Sheet was not as high as today and would be expected to be warmer due to its lower elevation. However, the winters were probably colder during the deglaciation period, which likely offset the tendency for warmer temperatures with a lower ice sheet. Thus, the climate during deglaciation or immediately after deglaciation was similar to the climate today at the GISP2 and GRIP core sites. The small number of melt layers in very early Holocene ice (Alley and Anandakrishnan, 1995) could be evidence of the "big chill" during rapid deglaciation (Oard, 1990, pp. 109–114). After the disappearance of the Laurentide, Scandinavian, and Cordilleran Ice Sheets, and with a lower ice sheet, I would expect warmer temperatures in the GISP2 core. It is interesting that there is an increase in the number of melt layers from the late early Holocene to the mid-Holocene in the Summit cores and cores from ice caps in the Canadian Arctic (Alley and Anandakrishnan, 1995; Jouzel et al., 1997, pp. 26,474–26,475). This would be expected in the Creation-Flood model. These melt layers could be an indication, not of the "hypsothermal" period within the Evolutionary-Uniformitarian model, but—as the Creation-Flood model indicates—of a lower Greenland Ice Sheet after the other Northern Hemisphere ice sheets melted.

The reader must remember that mainstream glaciologists have had the time, money, and manpower to build their model. Obviously, they have collected the data, and thus have interpreted the data within their paradigm. In the process, they address certain problems of interest, and so these data and results are published. On the other hand, the Creation-Flood model depends upon the data provided by the mainstream scientists. It could be that crucial data needed to verify some aspect of the Creation-Flood model may not have been collected and, if collected, may still not be published. So, the Creation-Flood model is operating at a disadvantage when it comes to explaining the origin of the Greenland and Antarctic Ice Sheets and being able to distinguish which model is better. Regardless, a Creation-Flood model has been developed to explain the data, and in some instances the models can be tested (see chapter 11).

Chapter 4

THE EVOLUTIONARY-UNIFORMITARIAN DATING OF ICE SHEETS

Glaciologists need a chronology of the ice cores in which to place their measurements:

> The crucial prerequisite in the study of ice cores is the accurate determination of the age of the specimens. Without these data, scientists could not build an overall chronology in which to place their other measurements (Alley and Bender, 1998, p. 81).

The need for accurate dates of the ice sheet is essential for all kinds of questions in glaciology, meteorology, climatology, geology, volcanology, atmospheric chemistry, etc. Once scientists derive a chronology, they can then place the many deductions from the cores into their earth history model. Mayewski et al. (1993b, p. 12,839) state: "Understanding the climate system remains one of the major intellectual challenges faced by science." The scientists also think that if they can discover accurate inferences about the past climate, they will be able to predict future climate change such as the consequences of the greenhouse effect.

The various methods for dating ice cores fall into four general categories: (1) annual layer counting by visual observation of the core or by analyzing several of the measured variables, (2) glaciological flow modeling, (3) use of reference horizons or the correlation with other dated time series, and (4) comparison with the Milankovitch insolation changes (Paterson, 1981, pp. 328–349; Parrenin et al., 2001, p. 31,837). Direct dating by carbon-14 has been applied, but it is more in the experimental stage (Lal et al., 1997). Because of its importance, much of the remainder of this monograph will be devoted to a critique of the Evolutionary-Uniformitarian dating of the ice sheets. I will briefly describe the methods in this chapter and will analyze them in more detail in subsequent chapters.

Annual Layer Counting

The first main group of dating methods is annual layer counting. Each year of snow deposited on top of an ice sheet provides a seasonal cycle in many of the variables measured in the cores (Hammer et al., 1978; Hammer, 1989; Shoji and Langway, 1989). There are seasonal cycles in oxygen and deuterium isotopes, various chemicals that land on the ice sheets, dust, and climatic properties of the snow that can be detected in the ice and are called *visual stratigraphy.* These seasonal cycles are similar to yearly tree growth rings that can simply be counted to determine the age of a tree. Seasonal cycles show up well at the top of Greenland cores, but rarely are they found in Antarctic cores due to the much lower annual snow accumulation and blowing snow that mixes the snow. Cores drilled near the Antarctic coast, where snow accumulation is much greater than in the interior, are the main locations that show annual fluctuations. For instance, annual layers show up well on Law Dome, an isolated ice cap 100 km from the coast in Wilkes Land, East

Antarctica (figure 2.12). Law Dome receives 70 cm of water equivalent of snow a year (Morgan et al., 1997; Palmer et al., 2001a), which is more accumulation than at any core location, including Greenland.

One of the first variables used to date by annual layers, mainly on Greenland, is the seasonal cycle of the oxygen isotope or deuterium isotope ratio (see chapter 2). The oxygen isotope ratio is the main variable used to infer Holocene ice in the top portion of the ice core and ice from the ice age lower in the core, as well as to measure short period oscillations (see chapter 10). Because of annual layer thinning with depth, it is not practical to use the oxygen isotope method deeper down in the cores.

Between 1971 and 1974, three approximately 400-meter long cores were drilled at Dye 3, Milcent, and Crete on the Greenland Ice Sheet (Reeh et al., 1978) (see figure 1.1 for locations). Measurements were close enough so that the seasonal oscillations showed up well, especially at Milcent where the annual water-equivalent accumulation of 50 cm/yr with relatively low melting produced distinctive seasonal cycles (figure 4.1). Oxygen isotope annual layer dating will be explored in depth in chapter 5.

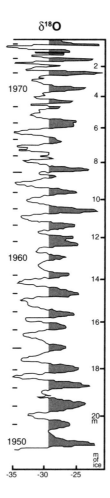

Figure 4.1   Annual oxygen isotope ratios down the top of the approximately 400-meter-long Milcent core, which was drilled from near the top of the Greenland Ice Sheet. Note the well-defined annual oscillations in the oxygen isotope ratio (after Hammer et al., 1978, facing page 12).

A second variable used to distinguish annual layers is visual stratigraphy (Langway, 1967). This method relies upon non-uniform variations in the physical properties of the snow or ice with depth that often is related to the seasonal cycle. Such variations include melt layers, depth hoar, wind crusts, forest fire layers, dust, and volcanic ash. This *bedding* or *stratigraphy* is observed by passing light through the core. It is especially the depth hoar that has been used for annual layer dating of the upper half of the new GISP2 core (Alley, 1988; Alley et al., 1990, 1997a; Meese et al., 1997). Depth hoar is a low-density, coarse-grained firn snow containing large, faceted, often cup-shaped ice crystals. Depth hoar formation occurs mainly in summer due to vapor transfer caused by temperature gradients at the top of the snow pack. Winter snow is denser and more homogeneous. As the snow becomes denser and turns to ice with depth in the core, the summer depth hoar and winter fine-grained snow will appear as bands of bubbles with alternating number and size. A visual dust stratigraphy is also seen deeper in the core, based on alternating cloudy and clear bands of ice. Sometimes the cloudy bands cannot be seen by the naked eye, so instruments are used to detect them. Using visual stratigraphy for deriving annual layers will be analyzed in depth in chapter 6.

Many other methods for detecting annual layers in ice cores have been developed over the years. These other methods can be grouped together into what can be called *chemical stratigraphy*. In this method, trace particles or ions that have a seasonal variation in the present climate can be traced down the core. These trace particles or ions consist of atmospheric dust or its ions, such as calcium, various sea salt ions, several acids, and variations in such substances as hydrogen peroxide (H_2O_2). Dating by chemical stratigraphy is the subject of chapter 7.

All these seasonal dating methods come with problems, but the use of more than one method is believed to provide a more solid basis for dating. Much attention has been focused on the annual layer dating method in Greenland cores. This method is considered the most scientific, and the resolution of one year is an earth science dream come true. With such resolution, the scientists believe they are able to date many events of earth history to a similar accuracy. Based on multiple annual layer methods, the GISP2 ice core was dated by counting 110,000 annual layers down to a depth of 2,800 meters (Meese et al., 1997). An extension of the layer counting down to 3,030 meters with an age of 161,000 years was later considered inaccurate due to ice disturbance. Ice core stratigraphy, dust bands, and acidity changes are the main annual layer dating methods used in the GISP2 core, since the oxygen isotope seasonal oscillations surprisingly gave out at only 300 meters (Alley et al., 1997a; Meese, et al., 1997). The annual layers below 2,800 meters are assumed to be too thin to measure, so the age of this ice depends upon how far a glaciologist wants to extrapolate the extreme thinning. Most believe the bottom 200 meters of ice is many hundreds of thousands of years old (Dansgaard et al., 1993), possibly even as old as 2.4 million years (Souchez, 1997).

Annual layer methods, more than any other method, seem solidly in favor of the Evolutionary-Uniformitarian model of the ice sheets. Who can argue with the simple counting of annual layers? The results of many variables, as well as the dating methods, appear very consistent—so consistent that it seems that the Evolutionary-Uniformitarian model is the true model of earth history.

How good is annual layer dating? Why do so many systems agree with each other? How can we test the model? We need to apply I Thessalonians 5:21: "Prove all things; hold fast that which is good" (KJV). Since annual layer dating is the most scientific of all the other methods, it is, therefore, necessary to spend the next three chapters on these annual layer dating methods.

Glaciological Flow Models

Glaciological flow models use the properties of ice and its deformation mechanisms to work out a dating scheme. This dating scheme uses as input the current annual amount of snow added to the ice minus the outputs due to melting, sublimation, and iceberg calving. A constant annual precipitation used to be assumed, but the more sophisticated models have been refined to include precipitation changes between glacial and interglacial climates. This causes the height of the ice sheet to change also, which was not allowed in previous models. Regardless, such annual precipitation changes result in only a slight change from the equilibrium assumption. Such flow modeling is especially used to date deep Antarctic cores, such as Vostok, which are believed to show three to seven or more glacial/interglacial sequences (Jouzel et al., 1996, p. 513). Flow models have been used to show that the ice has been accumulating for hundreds of thousands of years.

Reference Horizons

The third main dating technique is the use of reference horizons or time markers of known date. Ice cores show distinctive signatures, such as the change between a glacial to an interglacial climate or a spike in [10]Be (beryllium-10 is a radioactive isotope formed by cosmic rays, which also form radioactive carbon-14). These noteworthy events can be compared to other dated climate records in which the signature also appears. In this way a date for the reference horizon can be obtained for the ice core. For instance, the thermo-nuclear bomb tests in the 1950s and 1960s produced a number of chemicals that ended up on the ice sheets and were buried in the snow. These chemicals act as reference horizons with maximums in 1955 and 1965 (Karlöf et al., 2000, p. 12,472). When such reference horizons are located in an ice core, the snow or ice can be dated relative to these events. Other reference horizons include volcanic ash or dust bands (Hammer, Clausen, and Dansgaard, 1980), regional melt features, and unusual annual snowfall events. By knowing the dates on two or more reference horizons, the ice core between horizons is not only dated, but also the number of annual layers between horizons can be deduced.

Reference horizons have been extended to events of the Ice Age. Some of these time markers are the Younger Dryas (YD) cold event, which occurred during the last deglaciation at about 11,500 years ago and can be seen in the oxygen isotope ratios; [10]Be spikes at about 40 and 65 kyr ago; and the warm peak of the last interglacial at about 120 kyr (Raisbeck et al., 1987; Indermüle et al., 2000; Jouzel et al., 2001; Schwander et al., 2001; Delmonte, Petit, and Maggi, 2002).

The YD event, a return to near glacial conditions during the last deglaciation, was at first defined around the North Atlantic but is now found over much of the earth (Mayewski et al., 1993a). It is seen quite well in the oxygen isotope profile with depth in Greenland ice cores (Mayewski et al., 1996). There is a similar deviation during deglaciation in the oxygen isotope profile in Antarctic ice cores, called the *Antarctic cold reversal* (ARC); but it is three times weaker and dated 1,000 years before the YD (Mayewski et al., 1996; Jouzel et al., 1995). As a result, glaciologists have suggested that the Northern and Southern Hemisphere acted out of phase during millennial scale climate oscillations during the ice age (Rohling, Mayewski, and Challenor, 2003).

Flow models, as well as reference horizons, will be analyzed in depth in chapter 8. Rapid climatic oscillations, such as the Younger Dryas, will be discussed in chapter 10.

Milankovitch Insolation Changes

The fourth main dating method for dating ice cores is the changes in solar radiation with time caused by the astronomical theory of the ice ages or the Milankovitch mechanism. This mechanism is based on calculated changes in solar radiation absorbed at the surface due to the changing orbit of the earth around the sun (Imbrie and Imbrie, 1979). Extrapolated back in time millions of years, these changes are cyclical and thought to cause regular, repeating glacial and interglacial sequences, as well as stadials, interstadials, and other climate oscillations. The climatic oscillations are usually reflected in large-scale oxygen isotope ratio changes that act like time markers that can be related to the dates of the calculated insolation changes. Often, these oxygen isotope changes can be traced to other climatic time series from anywhere on the globe. The Milankovitch insolation changes are applied mainly to the older portion of the Greenland ice cores and to the longer Antarctic ice cores. For instance, Landwehr and Winograd (2001, p. 31,853) date the oscillating deuterium isotope ratio in the Vostok deep core to over 400,000 years by matching to the 500,000-year oxygen isotope chronology from the Devils Hole, Nevada, chronology. This latter chronology was based on the Milankovitch insolation mechanism. A critique of this ice core dating method will be provided in chapter 9.

Chapter 5

Annual Layer Dating
from Oxygen Isotope Ratios

The oxygen isotope ratio down an ice core is used to determine the large-scale features of the core, such as what part is glacial and what part is post-glacial (see chapter 2). Since the oxygen isotope ratio is generally proportional to surface temperature (other complicating variables are listed in appendix 1), it also has a seasonal contrast proportional to the difference between summer and winter temperatures. The ratio is lower in winter than in summer. This seasonal contrast has been used to determine annual layers in ice core.

At first Dansgaard et al. (1969, p. 377) stated that oxygen isotope seasonal dating in the Camp Century core was good for only a few thousand years. Later, they claimed the method could be applied down to 8,300 BP (before present) (Johnsen et al., 1972). The part of the core below the depth corresponding to 8,300 BP is expected to be much older, especially in view of extreme annual layer thinning as described by the Evolutionary-Uniformitarian model.

How solid are such old dates based on oxygen isotope seasonal contrasts? Can these annual layer measurements be simply counted downward like counting rings in a tree to determine the age of the tree? In order to answer these questions, we need to first understand how the seasonal contrast in $\delta^{18}O$ changes down an ice core and then what measurements have actually been obtained.

The Seasonal Contrast Diminishes down the Core

The seasonal cycle of oxygen isotopes shows up well at the top of the Greenland ice cores (see figure 4.1). So, it seems plausible when glaciologists claim that these seasonal cycles can be traced deep down an ice core. It must be remembered that $\delta^{18}O$ annual layers can be counted down only in the Greenland cores and the coastal cores from Antarctica. Coastal Antarctic cores are not that deep, so their age is not nearly as great as the long cores from Greenland.

Cores from the higher areas of Antarctica sometimes show annual layers at the very top. Ciais et al. (1995) report well-developed annual oxygen isotope ratios from 2- and 5-meter deep snow pits at the South Pole with an annual accumulation of 9 cm/yr. However, these annual layers are not expected to continue with depth below 5 meters. A new Byrd core drilled only to 164 meters showed well-defined seasonal $\delta^{18}O$ oscillations near the surface, which began to fade below 2.5 meters due to vapor diffusion (Langway et al., 1994). For these reasons, most of the research emphasis has been on the cores from Greenland. The dating of the interior Antarctic cores is therefore by other means and will be discussed in chapters 8 and 9.

Although the $\delta^{18}O$ seasonal cycle shows up well at the top of the Greenland cores, the seasonal contrast, or amplitude, diminishes down core. This causes the annual signal to become more confused with depth, leading to a greater chance of misinterpretation. The amplitude of $\delta^{18}O$ decreases because of molecular diffusion hastened by vertical thinning of annual layers due to overburden pressure:

> Unfortunately, various processes tend to diminish the isotopic gradients in snow and ice. For example, molecular diffusion in the firn and solid ice, hastened by the progressive plastic thinning of the layers with depth, gradually obliterates the oscillations that remain after firnification (Dansgaard et al., 1969, p. 377).

Molecular diffusion causes the water molecules to mix, smearing out the original annual isotopic amplitude.

Four types of diffusion that occur in the ice sheet (Whillans and Grootes, 1985) are: vapor diffusion through the pores between the ice crystals, vapor-ice surface diffusion, ice surface-ice interior diffusion, and solid diffusion within ice (figure 5.1). The third and fourth apply to the ice while the first and second apply mainly to the vapor in the firn. Vapor diffusion is much faster than solid diffusion (Johnsen and Robin, 1983). Diffusion mixing starts right away at the top of the firn (Langway et al., 1994, p. 42) and is faster the less dense and warmer the firn (Whillans and Grootes, 1985, p. 3,912). Diffusion mainly takes place in summer and seems to be related to the process that forms depth hoar (see chapter 6). Vapor diffusion ends by the time the firn is transformed into ice at about 70 meters depth. Below 70 meters, very slow solid diffusion aided by the thinning annual layers with depth will slowly wash out the seasonal oxygen isotope ratios in the ice.

The length of vapor diffusion in the firn has been determined to be about 8 cm (Johnsen, 1977; Johnsen and Robin, 1983). Based on this length, the $\delta^{18}O$ seasonal amplitude just below the firn-ice transition will be diminished 30% for an annual layer accumulation of 60 cm/yr of ice, 75% for an annual accumulation of 30 cm/yr, and 96% for an annual accumulation of 20 cm/yr (Johnsen and Robin, 1983, p. 57). Since diffusion in ice is orders of magnitude slower, glaciologists have determined an annual layer thickness threshold of 20 cm/yr as the threshold for the detection of annual layers below the firn-ice transition. Some believe such annual layers with 20 cm/yr annual accumulation may still be detected down to 8,000 years BP within the Evolutionary-Uniformitarian framework (Hammer, Clausen, and Tauber, 1986, p. 284). So, it is believed that the main diffusional mixing of $\delta^{18}O$ occurs in the firn with very little occurring in the ice.

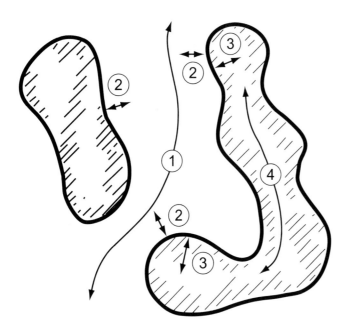

Figure 5.1   Four types of diffusion in ice sheets (after Whillans and Grootes, 1985, p. 3,911).

Oxygen Isotope Annual Layers Not Measured Continuously Down Cores

From the previous section, it is expected that cores with an annual accumulation greater than 20 cm/yr of ice will show seasonal oxygen isotope ratios to considerable depths. Therefore, it may surprise the reader to know that continuous seasonal $\delta^{18}O$ measurements have been made for only the top portion of Greenland cores. Such measurements have not been continued downward to the bottom of the Holocene, the theoretical limit of such measurements.

Continuous measurements were supposed to have been made down to around 10,000 years BP in the Dye 3 core (Reeh, Johnsen, and Dahl-Jensen, 1985). With an annual accumulation of 56 cm/yr, this task should have been straightforward but tedious. To identify an annual layer, *eight measurements per annual layer* are required (Johnsen et al., 1972, p. 429), and as the annual layers thin considerably with depth in the Evolutionary-Uniformitarian model, the number of measurements increase geometrically with depth. By 1985, $\delta^{18}O$ seasonal layers had been measured only down to about 1,000 meters or around 3,000 years BP in the Dye 3 core (Dansgaard et al., 1984, 1985). Hammer, Clausen, and Tauber (1986) state that measurements were made down to near 1,700 meters depth, dated about 8,500 BP, where the $\delta^{18}O$ variations became chaotic. It is likely measurements were not continuous to this depth but incremental (Hammer, 1989, p. 102).

It was expected that oxygen isotopes ratios would be measured continuously down the Holocene section of the new GRIP or GISP2 cores from the Summit area of the Greenland Ice Sheet. The annual accumulations for GRIP and GISP2 are 24 cm/yr, so theoretically their goals should have been met. However, the $\delta^{18}O$ seasonal oscillations surprisingly gave out around *300 meters* (Meese et al., 1997, p. 26,412). Johnsen et al. (1997, p. 26,400) exclaim:

> The progressive reduction of the annual δ cycle amplitude with depth was unexpected, due to the low temperatures at Summit, and indicates that processes other than self-diffusion in single crystals [Ramseier, 1967b] are responsible for a strong interstrata mixing.

I lean toward the idea that there probably is something wrong with the theory of isotopic diffusion, most likely that diffusion occurs faster than expected. Another possibility is that the measurements were coming up with unexpected results. Regardless, seasonal oxygen isotope ratios gave out much shallower than expected. Therefore, oxygen isotope measurements have *never* been continuously measured down the Holocene part of any Greenland ice core. Thus, the Creation-Flood model for the ice sheets has little explaining to do with regard to $\delta^{18}O$ seasonal measurements down ice cores. The claimed annual layers for various increments between 1,000 to 1,700 meters (3,000 to 8,500 BP) in the Dye 3 core can just as well be subannual layers, as will be discussed below.

Deep $\delta^{18}O$ Increments and Deconvolution

Despite their failure to provide a continuous $\delta^{18}O$ sequence down to the ice age boundary, glaciologists have claimed to have measured very short "increments" deep in the cores that show oxygen isotope oscillations at just the frequency expected from their thinning model. Moreover Sigfus Johnsen has claimed to be able to "regenerate" or deconvolute the $\delta^{18}O$ oscillations from low amplitude, chaotic-seeming $\delta^{18}O$ measurements (Johnsen, 1977; Johnsen et al., 1972, 1997; Hammer et al., 1978). Is there any significance to these claims?

On both the Camp Century and Dye 3 cores, there are short increments where $\delta^{18}O$ measurements show what looks like seasonal oscillations beyond the Scriptural timescale (Johnsen et al., 1972, p. 430; Dansgaard et al., 1982, p. 1,274). These incremental measurements of $\delta^{18}O$ annual layers were recorded to ages of 8,300 BP at Camp Century and to 8,500 BP at 1,700 meters deep at Dye 3. These annual layer increments seemed to agree with the annual layer thicknesses expected from flow model dating. Glaciological flow models are relied upon more and more the deeper the ice from which a core section is derived, and hence they constrain the annual layers to a certain range of thicknesses. Hammer (1989, p. 100) and Reeh (1989) admit that flow models provide a first guess to the annual layer thickness. These flow models end up producing a tremendous bias towards a large number of annual layers deep in the cores. It is difficult to know whether these increments were published just because they agreed with what was expected. It is possible that at this depth these oscillations are subannual cycles.

Johnsen's deconvolution method is essentially a "reverse diffusion" exercise in which a computer program regenerates the original seasonal oxygen isotope cycle from when the snow first fell at the top of the ice sheet (Johnsen, 1977, pp. 216–218). He developed a "transfer function" that depends upon the assumed annual layer thickness, which is determined by other methods, such as flow models. So, the Evolutionary-Uniformitarian model is built into this deconvolution scheme, which is really not an objective technique. Johnsen (1977, p. 218) shows a deconvoluted section of the Camp Century core (figure 5.2) in which slight changes of inflection are treated as annual layers with an annual layer thickness assumed to be 1.8 cm. This annual layer thickness, of course, was determined by the flow model. He obtained six oxygen isotope annual layers from this interval. However, after he decreased the annual layer thickness to 1.2 cm, he obtained ten, instead of six, annual layers (Johnsen, 1977, p. 219). This shows how sensitive the deconvolution technique is to differences in presumed annual layer thickness.

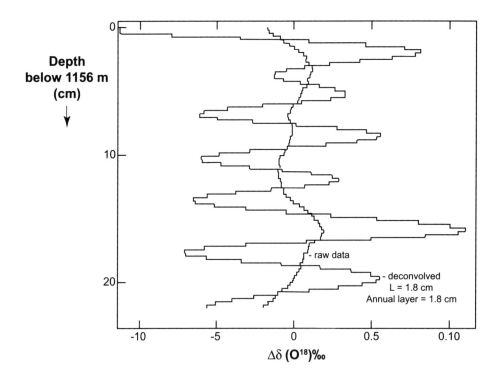

Figure 5.2 $\delta^{18}O$ profile and its deconvolution from the Camp Century deep ice core from about 1156 meters depth with an assumed age of 12,000 years and an annual layer thickness of 1.8 cm (after Johnsen, 1977, p. 218).

60

Johnsen et al. (1997, p. 26,400) show a "deconvoluted" section between 715 and 720 meters in the GRIP core (figure 5.3). However, it appears that there are eight to ten cycles in the raw $\delta^{18}O$ measurements, depending upon how one determines a $\delta^{18}O$ maximum. These cycles would correspond to an annual accumulation of about 50 cm/yr, double the present average. Johnsen's method, however, based on the *presumed* annual layer thickness, produced about 26 cycles. He picked up many more annual layers than indicated in the $\delta^{18}O$ plot. His results indicate an annual accumulation of 19 cm of ice per year, which is close to expectations in the Evolutionary-Uniformitarian model, as shown in figure 3.14.

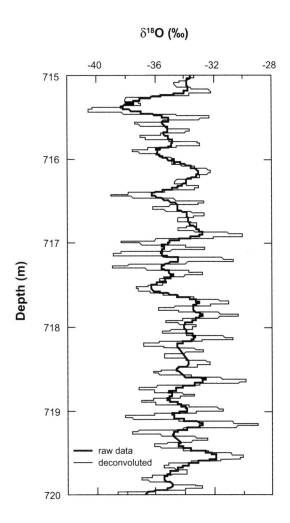

Figure 5.3 $\delta^{18}O$ profile for a five meter increment in the GRIP core showing about eight to ten cycles, corresponding to an annual accumulate of about 50 cm of ice per year. Superimposed is the deconvolution of this increment showing about 26 cycles, or an annual accumulate of about 20 cm/yr, which is more congenial to the expect annual layer thickness in this layer (see figure 3.14).

These two examples demonstrate that the measured data can support different supposed annual layer increments. So, deconvolution is a subjective exercise which depends upon the assumed annual layer thickness; and almost any number of annual layers can be tweaked out of a rather chaotic oxygen isotope interval. The raw data between the 715- and 720-meter increment in the GRIP core (figure 5.3) seems to better support the Creation-Flood model of increasing annual thickness of ice with depth in the core.

Subannual δ¹⁸O Oscillations

It is quite possible that the $\delta^{18}O$ oscillations obtained in the short core increments deep in the cores represent subannual $\delta^{18}O$ cycles instead of annual cycles. It is known that subannual cycles are imprinted in oxygen isotope measurements and other seasonal indicators at the *top* of the cores:

> The isotope record initially contains temperature information from many times of the year. . . . and they also demonstrate that the snow in this area initially contains temperature and chemical records with sub-annual resolution (Shuman et al., 1998, p. 21).

Usually, these are small oscillations within the larger seasonal cycle. These subseasonal oscillations are usually caused by individual storms or short period weather cycles of weeks, months, or seasons.

It is interesting to note that a storm has variable oxygen isotope ratios, depending upon a number of factors, such as the oxygen isotope ratio of the vapor entrained into the storm and the temperature of condensation (Hammer et al., 1978, p. 13). For instance, it has been shown that large oxygen isotope variations often exist in samples taken from within a single winter storm (Langway, 1970, p. 44; Gedzelman and Lawrence, 1982). In fact, the variation in one storm can be as large as the entire seasonal variation (Epstein and Sharp, 1959, p. 91). Gedzelman, Rosenbaum, and Lawrence (1989) measured the stable isotopic composition of snow and water vapor from a huge northeaster that hit New York February 11-12, 1983. They measured oxygen isotope ratios ranging from −9.52‰ to −9.87‰. The lowest ratios occurring at the beginning of the storm were believed to be due to high-level condensation where cold temperatures and water vapor of low oxygen isotope ratio occur. Such low oxygen isotope ratios are also favored by snow from more stable stratiform snow (Gedzelman and Arnold, 1994). This storm showed a larger range in $\delta^{18}O$ than the seasonal variation for the Milcent ice core (figure 4.1). In addition to large $\delta^{18}O$ contrasts occurring in only one storm, the average oxygen isotope ratio can vary from storm to storm adding more $\delta^{18}O$ variability during a one-year period (Gedzelman and Lawrence, 1982).

Many of these subannual cycles have been recorded in shallow pits during wintertime warm events that cause a cycle in the oxygen or deuterium isotope ratio. Figure 5.4 shows three years of deuterium isotope fluctuations in a 2-meter deep snow pit (Shuman et al., 1995). There is an extra oscillation of the same amplitude as the seasonal cycle recorded at about 0.35 meter deep. The other years have oscillations midway between the seasonal maximums that are of less amplitude.

High oxygen or deuterium isotope fluctuations during winter can occur from strong warm advection from much lower latitude, as long as there is snow to record the isotope fluctuation. Sustained warm air advection has been observed to warm the winter temperature at the South Pole from −100°F to −30°F in four days (Hogan, 1997). Palmer et al. (2001a, p. 28,090) have observed that occasional autumn through spring storms advect precipitation from warm low latitudes leaving a signal in one or more parameters in the Law Dome ice core, mostly commonly in $\delta^{18}O$. These subannual signals are preserved mainly because of the high accumulation rate of 70 cm/yr at Law dome (Morgan et al., 1997). These day-to-day or week-to-week $\delta^{18}O$ variations can

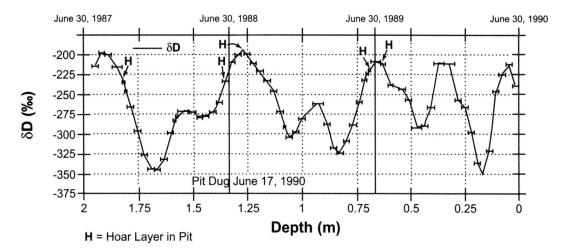

Figure 5.4   Continuous δD measurements from a snow pit showing subannual oscillations. Note the two minor subannual oscillations deeper in the pit and the one major oscillation at 0.35 meters deep with an amplitude as large as the seasonal cycle (after Shuman et al., 1995).

result in secondary peaks below the firn/ice transition (Grootes and Stuiver, 1997, p. 26,457). The warmer air advected from low latitude with heavy precipitation can look like a summer cycle in oxygen isotope ratio but has occurred during the winter. This is especially true in high precipitation areas. Down the core such storms would produce two or more cycles per year.

The weather also runs in cycles of colder or warmer-than-average temperatures for various periods within a year. A cold spell may last a week, two weeks, a month, or a season. Warm spells have similar periods. Such varying warm and cold spells would have differing oxygen isotope ratios that would be reflected in the ice down the core.

At the annual accumulation rates observed today on top of the Greenland Ice Sheet, diffusion is expected to mostly erase these subannual cycles with depth. Hence, Evolutionary-Uniformitarian scientists believe that storm and longer-period weather cycles are washed out by molecular diffusion, so that the main seasonal cycle is all that remains. In their model, this is a reasonable assumption since they assume the same precipitation rate as today for the Holocene and a reduced rate for the glacial portion.

The Law Dome core with its high annual accumulation of ice, on the other hand, illustrates what can happen with higher precipitation rates, such as those during and a little after the Ice Age in the Creation-Flood model. Since diffusion is mainly effective in the firn to 8 cm or possibly a little longer, an annual accumulation greater than 50 cm/yr would cause subannual layers to be *recorded* below the firn-ice transition. If the annual accumulation were 1 m/yr or 2 m/yr or even more, which is reasonable for the Ice Age ice and the immediate post–Ice Age ice in the Creation-Flood model, *many* subannual cycles could easily remain after the firn diffusional process. Figure 5.5 is a schematic to illustrate how a small number of subannual oscillations within the Evolutionary-Uniformitarian model would be almost totally erased at an ice accumulation of 20 cm/yr and almost totally preserved at 2 m/yr. In the latter, short period subannual oscillations should be superimposed on the longer period annual oscillation. Furthermore in the Creation-Flood model, there is less annual layer thinning and less time for diffusion of isotopes in ice. Solid diffusion can be neglected in the short creationist timescale; it will be mainly the thinning of the ice layers that will weaken the signal.

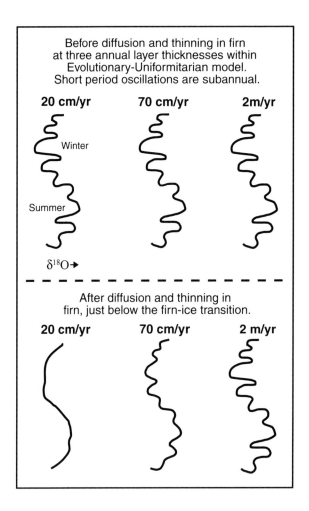

Figure 5.5   Schematic illustrating that more subannual oscillations due to storms and weather cycles on a timescale of a week, month, or season remain after firn diffusion with higher annual accumulations of ice. Note that with an annual accumulation of two meters, very little erasing of subannual layers occurs, but there are shorter period oscillations superimposed on a longer period oscillation.

These factors would all tend to preserve subannual cycles that Evolutionary-Uniformitarian scientists would count as annual cycles. Remember that these scientists assume similar temperature and precipitation as today, and that the annual layer thickness down the core *must thin* with time. They could easily misinterpret the oxygen isotope measurements because the finer the scale of measurements down the cores, the more isotope wiggles will be found.

Since winters are warmer and summers cooler for the early part of the Ice Age in the Creation-Flood model, there would be little seasonal contrast of oxygen isotope ratios and most $\delta^{18}O$ cycles would be due to non-seasonal oscillations. In the later part, there should be more and more of a seasonal contrast as winters became colder. A strong seasonal contrast would have occurred during deglaciation and immediately after the Ice Age. In the Creation-Flood model, the ice sheet would also be thinner during most of the Ice Age buildup, so precipitation would be heavier on the top of the still-growing ice sheet; and storms from the far south would contain relatively warm air with high $\delta^{18}O$. Furthermore, a thinner ice sheet is expected to cause more meltwater that could result in more $\delta^{18}O$ cycles (see appendix 1). For this reason, one would expect a mix of subannual and annual cycles preserved at mid- and lower portions of the cores.

It is possible that shorter subannual cycles would be superimposed on a longer annual cycle late in the Ice Age and soon afterwards, but there are no continuous $\delta^{18}O$ measurements just above the Ice Age portion of the core to check whether this is true. One deep increment in the Dye 3 core, above the Ice Age ice, hints at such a superimposed sequence of cycles. Figure 5.6 seems to show short period oscillations superimposed on a long period oscillation of about 0.4 meters of ice. Since this is just one short segment, it is suggestive only.

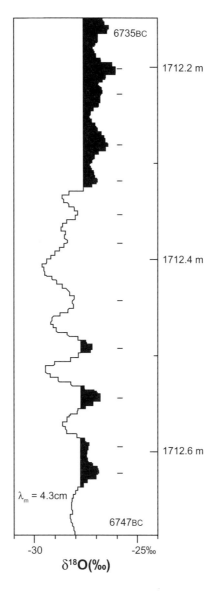

Figure 5.6 $\delta^{18}O$ profile about 1,712 meters deep in the Dye 3 core. Note that there appears to be shorter period oscillations superimposed on a longer period oscillation of about 0.4 meters of ice. Since this is just a short segment, it is not statistically significant and is suggestive only. The longer period oscillation may also be a subannual layer (from Hammer, Clausen, and Tauber, 1986, p. 286).

Six increments in the GISP2 core show a distinctly longer period of $\delta^{18}O$ oscillations that cover many supposed years in the Evolutionary-Uniformitarian timescale (figure 5.7) (Grootes and Stuiver, 1997, p. 26,467). The first three increments, *a* to *c*, are after the Ice Age; increments *d* to *f* are in Ice Age ice. Increments *a* and *b*, from only 1500 years ago, show what looks like seasonal oscillations; but when compared to the claimed years, there are not enough. Figure 5.7*a* shows 8 to 10 $\delta^{18}O$ maximums in a supposed 20-year period from 590 to 610 A.D. At face value, it appears that the annual cycle at this level is twice that postulated by the uniformitarian scientists. Figures 5.7*c* to *f* appear to contain shorter $\delta^{18}O$ cycles superimposed on a larger $\delta^{18}O$ cycle. These figures show the five-year interval in the Evolutionary-Uniformitarian model. However, figure 5.7*c*, from just above the Ice Age ice, shows one major oscillation in about a five-year period. Figures 5.7*d* to *f* seem to show $\delta^{18}O$ maximums longer than five years. Even these longer-period cycles could be subannual cycles in the Creation-Flood model. We would need to see a continuous profile of $\delta^{18}O$ with depth to know for sure. Grootes and Stuiver (1997) consider these long-period oscillations as "decadal cycles," but they could easily be annual cycles or subannual cycles within the Creation-Flood model. Regardless, it is likely that the annual layers suggested by the Evolutionary-Uniformitarian model are much too thin in the middle and lower portion of the GISP2 ice core.

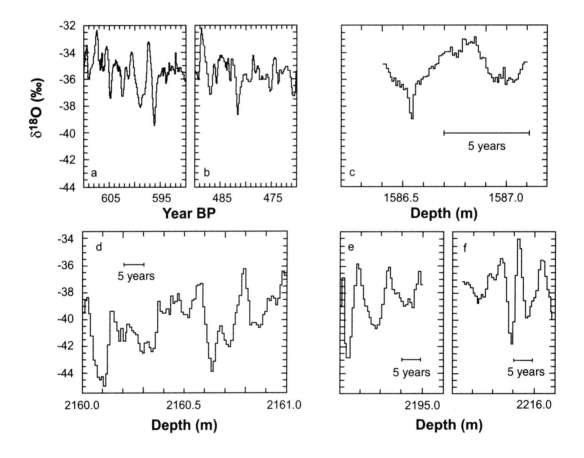

Figure 5.7   Six $\delta^{18}O$ increments down the GISP2 core showing finer-scale oscillations superimposed on large-scale cycles. They also show that the large-scale oscillations, which could be annual layers in the Creation-Flood model cover many years in the Evolutionary-Uniformitarian timescale (after Grootes and Stuiver, 1997, p. 26,467).

Chapter 6

ANNUAL LAYER DATING BY VISUAL STRATIGRAPHY

The second main method for determining annual layers in ice cores is visual stratigraphy. This method is actually one of the oldest methods, and like the oxygen isotope method, is applied mainly to Greenland cores. It is sometimes applied to coastal Antarctic cores, for instance on Siple coast, West Antarctica. Alley and Bentley (1988) observed depth-hoar layers in snow pits between ice streams B and C. Because the oxygen isotope method surprisingly gave out at 300 meters in the Greenland cores from Summit, visual stratigraphy became the main method for annual layer dating of these cores (Shuman and Alley, 1993). As briefly mentioned in chapter 4, visual stratigraphy depends upon surface phenomena that cause differences in the character of the ice that can be observed visually, usually by shining a light through the core. It is based on the simple observation that summer snow and winter snow look different. It is known that these visual markers can occur annually. The main seasonal visual markers are depth hoar and dust bands. A major advantage of visual stratigraphy over other methods is that annual layer dating is easy, rapid, and can be used for the ice even in the brittle zone, which is between 700 and 1,400 meters in the GISP2 core (Gow et al., 1997).

Depth Hoar Layers

Depth hoar is defined by Alley (1988, p. 284) as low-density firn or snow containing large, faceted, often cup-shaped ice crystals. It is very coarse-grained with low densities of 100 to 300 kg/m^3 and forms within 10 centimeters of the snow surface (Alley et al., 1997a). Depth hoar develops when a large, vertical temperature gradient causes vapor to sublimate, diffuse, and crystallize in a layer (Colbeck, 1991; Sturm and Benson, 1997). During fair weather and light winds in summer, the sun shines on the snow surface warming the upper few centimeters more than the temperature of the air above and the snow below (Colbeck, 1989; Alley et al., 1990). Periodic summer warm periods also increase the near surface temperature gradient. Vapor diffusing out of this surface layer migrates primarily upward into the free atmosphere, but some vapor is transported downward into deeper layers. The resultant mass loss of up to 50% produces low snow densities. During rapid vapor flux, large faceted snow crystals condense in the low-density layer, which starts about one centimeter below the surface (Shuman and Alley, 1993).

Surface hoar frost also develops on the ice sheet. Radiative cooling at night sometimes produces fog. The fog deposits a surface hoar frost on top of the snow.

After the period of surface and depth hoar formation, usually during calm, clear weather, a synoptic storm develops with winds usually greater than 10 m/sec. The wind and snowfall cover and protect the hoar frost with a wind crust or wind slab. During gusty winds, the wind breaks the ice crystals into small shards and rounds off the edges (Colbeck, 1991, p. 83). The net result is a higher-density, finer-grained accumulation above the depth hoar.

This sequence can repeat many times during a summer, producing a depth hoar *complex*. These depth hoar layers are widespread on the Greenland Ice Sheet and can be detected by satellites over a few hundred square kilometers (Shuman, Alley, and Anandakrishnan, 1993; Shuman et al., 1995, 1997). Although wind crusts occur in summer, winter produces more frequent wind and a thicker wind crust. Thus, as observed in snow pits, an annual layer develops composed of a hoar frost complex separated by a non-hoar frost winter layer (figure 6.1).

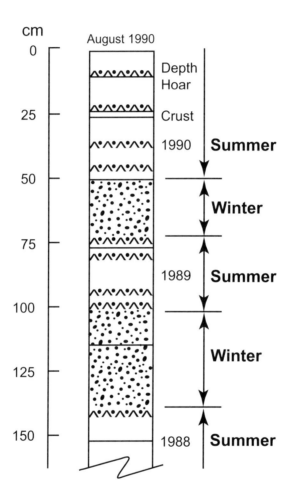

Figure 6.1   Depth hoar complex from a snow pit on the Greenland Ice Sheet (after Meese et al., 1997, p. 26,412).

As the snow piles up each year, the summer depth-hoar complexes and winter layers become compressed more and more with depth. The firn increases density from 100 to 300 kg/m^3 near the top to 830 kg/m^3 near the pore close-off depth in which the air in the pores becomes trapped into bubbles within the ice. At this point the firn has changed to ice (Alley and Bentley, 1988, p. 3; Schwander et al., 1997; Watanabe et al., 1999).

During the process of deep burial and densification, other diagenetic processes reduce the contrast between the seasonal layers. However, the annual density changes are retained in the ice as variable bubble densities and ice grain sizes that affect light transmission and reflection (Alley et al., 1997a). The grain size variations cause summer layers below pore close-off depth to typically have fewer but larger bubbles with more variability than winter layers.

The visual stratification of the ice from depth hoar can still be seen until about halfway down the GISP2 ice core where the bubbles disappear due to the formation of an air/ice clathrate. As the core relaxes, these clathrates are replaced by air bubbles, so the depth hoar complex visual stratigraphy can be continued deeper. Depth hoar complexes have become the most useful and prominent annual layer dating method in the upper half of the GISP2 core.

Dust Bands Date GISP2 to 110,000 Years BP

In the early Holocene and glacial portion of the GISP2 core, annual "dust or cloudy bands" are the most prominent annual layer marker. These bands can often be seen visually. However, some can only be identified nonvisually by a high signal in a laser beam or through lowered electrical conductivity (Alley et al., 1997a, p. 26,368). The method using a laser beam is called *laser-light scattering* (LLS). The electrical conductivity method (ECM) will be discussed in chapter 7, since it measures chemical cycles.

Laser-light scattering (LLS) can detect dust concentrations either in ice or in melt water from the ice. LLS is not strictly a visual stratigraphic method, since the dust sometimes cannot be seen with the naked eye, but it will be discussed here because it is a method to aid visual stratigraphy. LLS actually extends the method of visual stratigraphy lower in the core than the depth in which visual stratigraphy can be used. The LLS method originally proposed by Hammer (1977) is based on the fact that the dust particles in the water or ice will scatter the light from the laser beam (Ram and Illing, 1994). The amount of scattered light at right angles to the beam is proportional to the amount of dust. The reason ice needs to be melted for the LLS method is because bubbles in the ice also scatter the light in the upper portion of the core. The bubbles disappear about 1,400 meters down the core as they change into air/ice clathrates. The LLS method applied to water is time consuming and destroys the ice, so the method is not widely used for the upper half of the core. The solid LLS method was mainly used to sample ice in GISP2 below 1,700 meters, the Ice Age portion of the ice. It is sometimes applied to increments elsewhere in the core as a comparison to other annual layer methods. The technique applied to ice, however, is fast with a very high resolution of 1 mm or less (Ram et al., 1995).

Cloudy bands are much more significant and more easily seen in the glacial portion of the ice, since the quantity of dust is much greater than in post-glacial ice. Cloudy bands observed visually have correlated to depth hoar bands where they overlap in the early Holocene. That the presumed annual layers matched fairly well gave the glaciologists confidence that the cloudy bands were annual dust oscillations with a maximum in spring (Alley et al., 1997a, p. 26,376). Annual layer dating from cloudy bands is the main dating method in the lower portion of the GISP2 core (figure 6.2). It has been claimed that 110,000 annual layers have been detected down to 2,800 meters (Meese et al., 1997). In fact Meese et al. (1997, p. 26,420) believe they were able to count 50,600 more annual layers with an accuracy of 24% from 2,800 to 3,000 meters. Within the Evolutionary-Uniformitarian timescale, this would put the age of the ice at 3,000 meters at about 161,000 years. This figure is still a far cry from those researchers who believe that the ice below 2,800 meters is many hundreds of thousands of years old to possibly a few million years old. However, this lower layer is believed to have been distorted by ice flow and the extension to 3,000 meters is considered invalid.

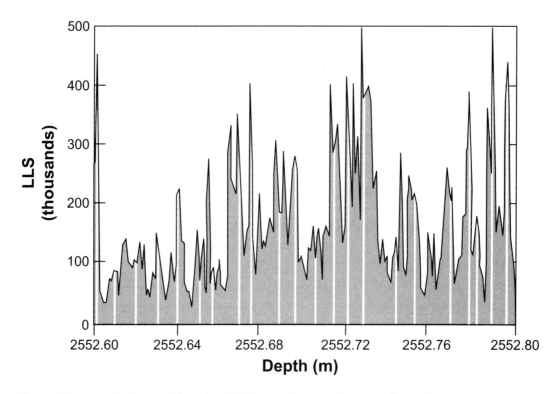

Figure 6.2   An LLS record from the GISP2 core about 2,552 meters deep (after Meese et al., 1997, p. 26,417). The white lines are the determined annual layer peaks, but note that there are many more LLS peaks than claimed annual layers.

Subjective Interpretation of Visual Stratigraphy

I s visual stratigraphy so straightforward that it is like counting the rings to determine the age of a tree? Are there really 110,000 annual layers in the GISP2 core? There actually are a number of significant problems in using visible stratigraphy for annual layer counting that make the method questionable:

> Various stratigraphic features 'observed' are difficult to categorize explicitly. The peculiarities of weather add to the difficulty by making it nearly impossible to rely on the cyclical recurrences of certain stratigraphic indicators. The indicators or features listed in table 1 are generally diagnostic and useful only when considered in relationship to the whole. To a great extent, interpreting physical stratigraphy is an art dependent upon experience and foreknowledge of the contemporary environmental conditions at the site (Shoji and Langway, 1989, p. 164).

This method is easily conformed to the expected annual layer frequency determined by preconceived beliefs.

Two practical difficulties with the method are the poor observational conditions and a rough core surface with numerous breaks that can hamper the counting process (Alley et al., 1997a, p. 26,377). The visible signal also is not purely an annual signal; there are multiple depth hoar layers and cloudy layers during summer and a few layers even during the winter, as will be discussed below. There is also much variability in the visual stratigraphic signal down a core:

70

In common with all other methods of layer counting, visible stratigraphy has certain weaknesses. Probably the biggest weakness is that the signal is variable along the full core length (sometimes subtle, sometimes obvious); unless the observer is careful and persistent, it is likely that large errors will result (Alley et al., 1997a, p. 26,377).

This demonstrates that the signal is quite variable, so misinterpretation of annual layers can result—or worse, preconceived ideas can bias the results. So, the practice of counting annual layers down an ice core is an "art" or a "trial and error procedure" (Alley et al., 1997a, pp. 26,370–26,371).

There are differences among various researchers in deducing the number of annual layers (Alley et al., 1997a, p. 26,378). One researcher consistently counted 20% more LLS annual layers in the lower portion of the GISP2 core than other researchers (Meese et al., 1997, p. 26,419). Furthermore, those that count the annual layers must be "careful" and "persistent," indicating that there is a strong subjective element in deciphering annual layers through visual stratigraphy. At one time, visual stratigraphy was considered accurate to no more than 200 years ago with an accuracy of 10% (Hammer et al., 1978, p. 5; Alley et al., 1997a, p. 26,367). But now, accuracy is claimed to be much better:

> The ice at 2800 m is dated at 110,000 years B.P. with an estimated error ranging from 1 to 10% in the top 2500 m of the core and averaging 20% between 2500 and 2800 m (Meese et al., 1997, p. 26,411).

The method applied to the Holocene ice is considered to have an accuracy of 1%. However, despite these optimistic error ranges, there is enough variability and subjectivity in counting "annual layers" that practically *any* age scale can be defended, as will be shown below.

Multiple Hoar Layers Can Form Each Year

It has been observed from snow pits that many depth-hoar/wind-slab couplets can form each summer (Alley et al., 1990; Shuman and Alley, 1993; Shuman, Alley, and Anandakrishnan, 1993). This is why the summer layer is called a *depth hoar complex*. Shuman and Alley (1993) report four depth hoar events in two years at the top of the Greenland Ice Sheet, while Shuman et al. (1997) find six in another two-year period. In figure 6.1, Meese et al. (1997, p. 26,412) show as many as four depth-hoar layers in summer. It is possible that if depth hoar complexes were widely spaced in the summer, as seen in figure 6.1 for the summer of 1990, two or more annual layers would be deduced in an ice core within the Evolutionary-Uniformitarian model (Shuman and Alley, 1993, p. 2,643). Alley and colleagues measured about 15 alternating depth-hoar/finer-grained wind crusts per year in snow pits at the top of the Greenland Ice Sheet (figure 6.3) (Alley, 1988; Alley and Koci, 1988). These layers were observed to have formed by individual storms (Alley and Koci, 1988). It is recognized that the visible annual signal from depth hoar is confusing at the top of the ice sheet:

> Fundamentally, in counting any annual marker, we must ask whether it is absolutely unequivocal, or whether non-annual events could mimic or obscure a year. For the visible strata (and, we believe, for any other annual indicator at accumulation rates representative of central Greenland), it is almost certain that variability exists at the subseasonal or storm level, at the annual level, and for various longer periodicities (2-year, sunspot, etc). We certainly must entertain the possibility of misidentifying the

deposit of a large storm or a snow dune as an entire year or missing a weak indication of a summer and thus picking a 2-year interval as 1 year (Alley et al., 1997a, p. 26,378).

Notice that *all* the annual indicators contain much variability at many scales.

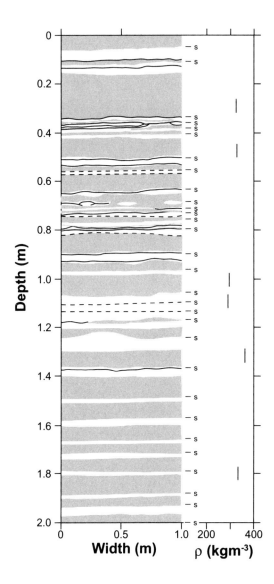

Figure 6.3 Fifteen storm layers per year in a snow pit from Site A, Greenland (after Alley and Koci, 1988, p. 2). Fine-grained firn is patterned, coarse-grained firn is white, crusts are shown by solid lines, and indistinct crusts are shown by dashed lines. Bases of individual storms are labeled with an "s."

Although considered rare today, winter depth hoar layers can also form, but they are normally thin and discontinuous (Alley, 1988; Alley et al., 1990, p. 2,393; 1997, p. 26,368; Shuman et al., 1995, p. 9,166). Winter depth hoar layers can be distinguished today in snow pits at the top of the ice sheets but can complicate observations at greater depths in a core. Langway (1967, p. 16) recognizes that significant depth hoar layers develop at the lower altitude, higher accumulation

Site 2 in northwest Greenland during winter: "Unfortunately for polar stratigraphic purposes depth hoar layers may develop at any time of the year that a steep temperature gradient exists . . . "

In the Evolutionary-Uniformitarian model, the annual accumulation in the past is assumed to be similar or less than today. So, the visual stratigraphic signal from depth hoar complexes that can be observed today at the very top of the ice cores, which are often annual, is expected to be faithfully recorded deeper in the ice.

However, in the Creation-Flood model, the climate would be different. Since depth hoar complexes are significant only in the post–Ice Age ice, the snowfall rate was likely greater than now for awhile after the Ice Age. So, it is likely that glaciologists could misinterpret a storm layer or a series of storm layers for annual layers. A storm has a warm and cold sector. The warm air above cold snow may cause strong enough of a temperature gradient in the top ten centimeters of the ice sheet for depth hoar to form during storms. Or it is possible that depth hoar complexes could form between major storm periods. It is more likely that a depth hoar layer formed by storms or other weather oscillations would be counted as an annual signal, if the snowfall were significantly higher in the past, as in the Creation-Flood model. So, in the Creation-Flood model, many depth hoar layers could form with more frequent storms and heavier snowfall, especially for awhile after the Ice Age. These would be subannual layers that would be interpreted as annual layers within the Evolutionary-Uniformitarian model. This tendency to multiply the number of annual layers would not only occur with depth hoar layers, but also with other annual dating techniques as well.

Multiple Dust Bands Can Form Each Year

Just as many depth hoar layers can form in one year and be misinterpreted as a multiyear sequence, so many dust bands can also form in a year and be counted as many annual layers. This is especially true during the Ice Age. Figure 6.2 shows significant subannual dust bands recorded by LLS even within the Evolutionary-Uniformitarian model. There appear to be twice as many peaks as annual layers. Furthermore, there also appears to be a longer-period cyclicity. Even today more than one dust band can be recorded per year.

> Sometimes, we observe more than one relatively strong-looking cloudy band per year, and a secondary fall peak is not unusual. . . . Although dust delivery to the GISP2 site must be related to the seasonality of dust sources and of weather patterns, occasional "odd" weather patterns or volcanic eruptions could produce dust deposition at the site at almost any time of year (Alley et al., 1997a, pp. 26,376–26,377).

Meese et al. (1997, p. 26,412) also admit:

> However, an increased particulate concentration may not be restricted to the spring or summer and additional influxes of dust may occur during any part of the year, creating additional peaks of a nonannual nature.

In a recent article in the journal *Science*, a picture of recent firn revealed multiple cloudy bands per year with the number of bands variable for each year (Kerr, 1999, p. 29).

It is known that the dust during the Ice Age was much greater, especially during the glacial maximum. In the GRIP core, the dust was 40 times greater in the glacial maximum than it was in the Holocene within the Evolutionary-Uniformitarian timescale (see the curve for calcium in figure 7.2) (Maggi, 1997, p. 26,725). In the new NorthGRIP core, the dust was one hundred times greater in the glacial maximum as it was in the Holocene (Ruth et al., 2003). There are three main causes for such large dust concentration:

The main causes of the high dust content of glacial age ice is a combination of three effects which characterize this time period: enhanced aridity (increased [sic] the desert areas), stronger winds (augmentation of the dust production), and stronger atmospheric circulation (facilitating the long-range transport of atmospheric particles toward polar regions). An additional factor, until now not taken into account, is the increase of the lifetime of aerosols as a function of the decreased precipitation rates (Delmas and Legrand, 1989, p. 335).

After much uncertainty, it is now believed that dust in the Ice Age portion of the Greenland cores originated from eastern Asia (Biscaye et al., 1997, p. 26,765; Svensson, Biscaye, and Grousset, 2000). There is not as much dust in the Ice Age portion of the Antarctic Ice Sheet, and this dust is believed to have been derived from southern South America east of the Andes Mountains (Grousset et al., 1992; Basile et al., 1997).

In the Creation-Flood model, annual dust concentrations would be greater than the numbers measured by the uniformitarian scientists, because the annual layer thickness was greater. So storms would be very dusty, especially at the end of the ice age and during the deglaciation period. In such a dusty environment, it is likely that multiple dust bands can be laid down even in one storm by several methods. For instance, during the showery phase of a storm, the varying intensity of snowfall could result in oscillations of the dust content. In the Evolutionary-Uniformitarian model, such oscillations would be interpreted as annual layers deep in the ice core; in contrast, in the Creation-Flood model, they would be interpreted as multiple cycles within one storm, adding up to many oscillations during one year.

The finer the scale of measurement, the more cycles would be expected to show up (figure 6.4). Ram et al. (1995, p. 3,527) admit:

> In principle, the smaller the [LLS] beam size the higher the resolution. In practice, however, a small beam size leads to a noisy signal since dust in the spring/summer layers is *not uniformly* distributed and its concentration can *vary significantly over a small distance* [emphasis and brackets mine].

They go on to say that indeed they did reduce the resolution to 1 mm because they *believed* the annual layers were paper thin.

This indicates that presumed annual layer thickness produces a strong bias, and that cycles will be found to "prove" expectations. For instance, in a dust concentration profile at the 1,213 meter depth level in the Camp Century core, Thompson claimed an annual layer thickness of about 10 centimeters using a measuring interval of 1.7 centimeters, while Hammer and colleagues found an annual layer thickness of only 1 centimeter using a finer scale (Hammer et al., 1978, pp. 12–13). The fact that cycles can be found to "prove" preconceived expectations was dramatically shown again when Meese et al. (1993, 1994) at first dated the 2,800-meter level of the GISP2 core at 85,000 years BP by visual stratigraphy. However, this date disagreed with the timescale based on deep-sea cores (see chapter 9), so the layer between 2,300 and 2,800 meters was "remeasured" by a finer-resolution laser beam of 1 mm thickness instead of 8 mm thickness as before (Meese et al., 1997, pp. 26,417–26,419). They found 25,000 more years in this layer, so that the 2,800-meter level was dated at 110,000 years BP, just as expected from the chronology from deep-sea cores!

Besides measuring the dust at a very high resolution, researchers also counted every peak, including some peaks that were barely discernible. In a study of the dust profile in the Ice Age portion of the GISP2 core, Ram and Koenig (1997) counted every LLS peak as an annual layer

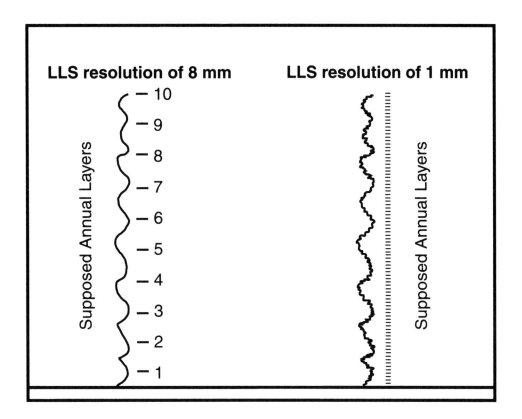

Figure 6.4   Schematic of how more "wiggles" in dust show up when measured at finer resolution, for example between a laser beam width of 8mm and one of 1 mm. Annual layers indicated by short horizontal lines. Although many years are indicated in both curves, such profiles with variable dust wiggles can represent one annual layer or part of an annual layer in the Creation-Flood model.

although the amplitude of the peaks varied considerably, especially in the Ice Age portion of the core. Even "hidden" peaks were counted, so desirous were scientists of more annual layers:

> In addition, as discussed by *Ram et al.* [1995], "hidden" peaks can reveal themselves as shoulders in another peak when the laser beam diameter is not sufficiently small compared to the distance between annual dust layers. We looked for such "hidden" peaks in the deeper ice and included them in our annual layer counting. We have confidence in our dating approach since the depth-age scale we obtain for pre-Holocene ice down to a depth of [sic] ~2,808 m agrees very well with the independent gas-age chronology of *Bender et al.*, [1994] (figure 4) (Ram and Koenig, 1997, p. 26,643).

The subjectivity of the LLS procedure is obvious. The chronology of Bender et al. (1994) is tied to the deep-sea core timescale through the Vostok $\delta^{18}O$ of atmospheric oxygen in the ice bubbles (Meese et al., 1997, p. 26,417).

In conclusion, the 110,000 years of annual layers claimed for the GISP2 core are a result of preconceived ideas on the age of the core, rather than being simply like counting tree rings to determine the age of the tree. In contrast, in the Creation-Flood model, oscillations in dust would be interpreted as variability within and between storms during dusty periods of the Ice Age.

Chapter 7

ANNUAL LAYER DATING FROM CHEMICAL "STRATIGRAPHY"

Many sources produce dust and chemicals in the form of aerosols and gases which eventually are deposited on top of the Greenland and Antarctic Ice Sheets (figure 7.1). These chemical *species*, as they are called, are then incorporated into the ice with time and represent a measure of the trace pollutants in the atmosphere at about the time of deposition. Appendix 2 briefly describes some of the many processes that occur and the variables that interact with a chemical species between the time it leaves its source to the time it becomes locked within the ice.

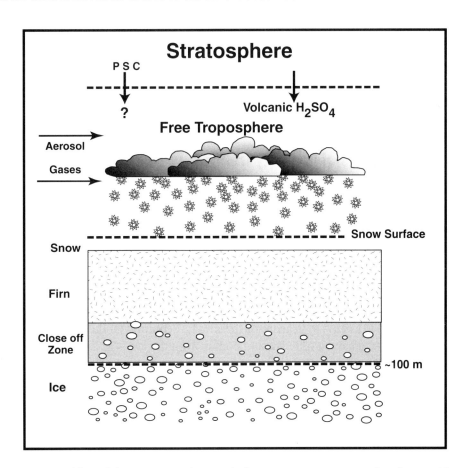

Figure 7.1 Deposition of dust, gases, and aerosols from many sources on an ice sheet and incorporated into the ice below the firn/ice transition (from Delmas, 1992, p. 2). PSC stands for polar stratospheric clouds.

With respect to low and midlatitudes, except coastal locations where sea-salt components predominate, most polar precipitation is actually depleted in chemical species. For this reason, the analytic procedures must be able to detect trace amounts of impurities in the ice. Both soluble and insoluble impurities are measured. Besides measuring chemicals in the ice, researchers also measure gas molecules, such as CO_2 and CH_4, in the air bubbles (Fischer et al., 1999; Sigman and Boyle, 2000; Chappellaz et al., 1997; Brook et al., 2000). Even the oxygen isotope ratio of the oxygen in the air bubbles is measured. These bubble variables are showing promise in being able to correlate the ice in time between the Greenland and Antarctic Ice Sheets, since these gases are expected to be well mixed between hemispheres (Bender et al., 1985; Sowers, Bender, and Raynaud, 1989; Sowers et al., 1991; Bender, Sowers, and Labeyrie, 1994).

Chemical species are measured down an ice core to see how they have changed with time. They show large-scale changes related to the climate. For example, although little dust and few chemicals occur in the post–Ice Age portion of the core, they increase markedly in the glacial ice. During the last few hundred years, pollution has increased in the atmosphere above the ice sheets, especially the Greenland Ice Sheet; and this pollution shows up as increased chemical species in the top of the cores (Peel, 1989; Pearman et al., 1989). Each chemical species provides different information about the past climate. Altogether, forty-two chemical species have been measured down the GISP2 core. Large-scale trends in several impurities will be shown in the next section.

Many of these foreign constituents in the ice show seasonal contrasts. Dust especially has a pronounced seasonal oscillation on the ice sheets with a winter/spring maximum. Furthermore, dust is not altered by burial in the firn and the formation of ice, as are many of the soluble chemical species. Dust, therefore, makes an excellent seasonal dating technique in today's climate. It is the main variable analyzed deeper in the ice cores by visual stratigraphy of cloudy bands aided by the LLS method, but the Ice Age was much dustier than today, resulting in complications. I will analyze the soluble species that are used for annual layer dating in this chapter.

General Impurity Trends down Ice Cores

Because of the many complications in understanding the processes in which chemical species and bubble gases are incorporated into the ice sheet (see appendix 2), glaciologists usually use an analysis of the top layers of the snow as a baseline for interpreting the deeper firn and ice. From this baseline, they can interpret broad trends in species and gases down the core. However, because of the many complications involved, there is no guarantee that their extrapolations are correct, especially for the Ice Age portion of the core.

Figure 7.2 shows the raw concentration of sodium and calcium as a function of depth compared with the oxygen isotope ratio for the GRIP core. Sodium is mostly a measure of the marine particle input, and calcium is mainly a measure of the input of continental dust, although a little calcium originates in the ocean and a little sodium comes from the land (Röthlisberger et al., 2002a, p. 1). Although both sodium and calcium concentration are small during the Holocene, or post-Ice Age portion of the core, they were much greater during the Ice Age. The Ice Age concentrations are likely due to significantly stronger surface winds and/or a more efficient meridional transport between middle and high latitudes (Legrand and Mayewski, 1997, p. 238). The large oscillations superimposed on the Ice Age concentration will be discussed in chapter 10. These oscillations in the Ice Age portion show a strong inverse correlation between $\delta^{18}O$ and the terrestrial and sea-salt species records (Mayewski et al., 1997).

In figure 7.3, correlations (within the Evolutionary-Uniformitarian timescale) for the new, deep Vostok ice core are shown between δD (curve *a*), atmospheric gases CO_2 and CH_4 trapped in air

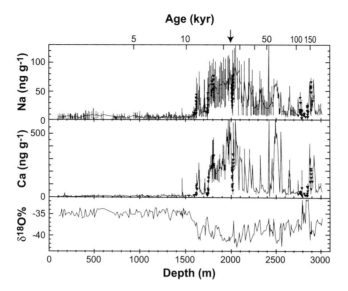

Figure 7.2 The sodium (Na) and calcium (Ca) concentration compared with the oxygen isotope ratio in the GRIP core (after De Angelis et al., 1997, p. 26,682).

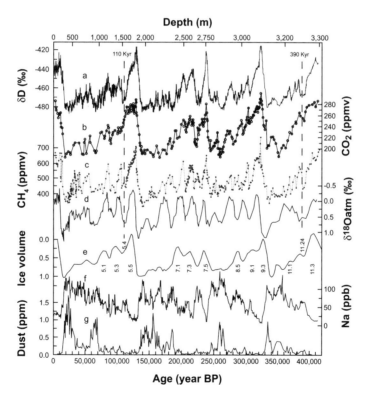

Figure 7.3 Correlations within the Evolutionary-Uniformitarian timescale between δD (curve *a*), atmospheric gases CO₂ and CH₄ trapped in air bubbles (curves *b* and *c*), the δ¹⁸O of the oxygen in the air bubbles (curve *d*), ice volume (curve *e*), sodium (curve *f*), and dust (curve *g*) for the new, deep Vostok ice core (from Kotlyakov et al., 2001). Ice volume is a simple correlation with δD, so is really not an independently measured variable in the ice.

bubbles (curves *b* and *c*), the $\delta^{18}O$ of the oxygen in the air bubbles (curve *d*), ice volume (curve *e*), sodium (curve *f*), and dust (curve *g*). Changes in ice volume are simply correlated to δD, so it really is not an independently measured variable in the ice. The inverse correlation between δD and sodium is remarkable. The dust correlation is generally anticorrelated with the lowest δD, but there are long periods with little dust. So the dust correlation is more on the broad scale and not in detail. The $\delta^{18}O$ of the oxygen in the air bubbles correlates well with δD to about 2,000 meters depth, but does not seem to correlate as well below 2,000 meters.

Electronic Measurement of Chemical Species

Many chemical and gaseous species have seasonal trends in the high latitude atmosphere and on the Greenland and Antarctic Ice Sheets today (Fischer, 2001) (figure 7.4). Some of these seasonal trends continue down in the ice cores and some do not. For instance, hydrogen peroxide (H_2O_2) shows a strong seasonal trend in the atmosphere and the surface snow today, being ten times greater in summer than winter due to photochemical processes in the atmosphere (Delmas, 1992, p. 9). However, the H_2O_2 concentration decreases down core, with very little remaining in the Ice Age portion of the core (Neftel, Jacob, and Klockow, 1986; van Ommen and Morgan, 1996; McConnel et al., 1998). The sharp seasonal contrast essentially disappears in the firn since H_2O_2 is very reactive (Delmas, 1992, p. 9). It would be very laborious to chemically measure any of these species down a core to produce seasonal trends, especially with the extreme thinning postulated in the Evolutionary-Uniformitarian model. Therefore, annual layer dating by chemicals is almost exclusively done by fast electronic means. Chemical measurements are performed at times to check the electronic measurements.

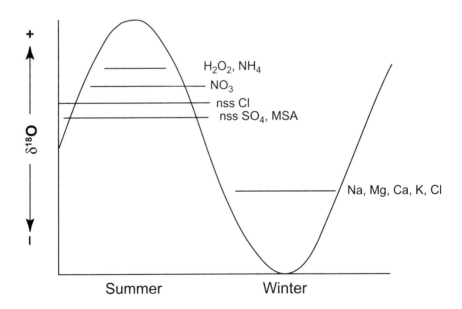

Figure 7.4   Seasonal distribution of many chemical species on the top of the Antarctic Ice Sheet (modified from Whitlow, Meyewski, and Dibb, 1992, p. 2,048). The seasonal difference is represented by a simplified seasonal change in $\delta^{18}O$. nssCl and nssSO$_4$ represent non-sea-salt chloride and sulfate, respectively. The seasonal distribution is similar for the Greenland Ice Sheet.

Two electronic measuring techniques have been developed that continuously measure mainly the acid concentration down a core. It is the seasonal trends in acid concentration, therefore, that are used to date the ice core by counting annual layers. I will focus the rest of this chapter on annual layer dating of acids, after I briefly discuss the two electronic methods used to measure the acids. These methods are the electrical conductivity method (ECM) and the dielectric profiling method (DEP).

The electrical conductivity method (ECM) measures the direct-current electrical conductivity of the ice core. The ECM signal is measured by passing two electrodes lengthwise down the surface of a clean, fresh core face and digitally recording the resulting signal (Hammer, 1980; Neftel et al., 1985). Moving at a few cm/sec to 20 cm/sec, the electrodes travel down the core face in a zigzag fashion to reduce the effect of sources of poor contact, such as air bubbles on the surface of the ice. An electrical potential difference of 1,250 volts or more over a distance of one centimeter is passed through the ice.

The dc electrical current recorded between the electrodes measures the acidity between the electrodes (Hammer, 1983; Moore et al., 1992). It is particularly useful in defining annual layers because of the high resolution of the measurements and in detecting volcanic horizons, which produce a large sulfuric acid peak (Hammer, 1980; Maccagnan et al., 1981). However, the ECM signal tends to saturate at high acidities, resulting in inconsistent responses to the amount of acid (Fujita et al., 2002a,b). The direct current is conducted by the movement of protons associated with the hydrogen ions [H^+] of strong acids. The strength of the current is proportional to the concentration of acids and inversely proportional to the concentration of bases, since bases neutralize acids. Chemicals that neutralize acids include ammonia from biomass burning or other sources (Legrand et al., 1992; Chylek et al., 1995) and alkaline dust from continental sources (Wolff et al., 1997). The resolution of ECM is 1 mm in the GRIP and GISP2 cores (Taylor et al., 1992, 1993, 1997a; Wolff et al., 1997).

The Greenland Ice Sheet is acidic in the post-glacial portion, where the amount of dust is very low, but is predominantly basic in the glacial portion due to the great concentration of wind blown dust (Hammer et al., 1985; Wolf et al., 1997). However, in the Ice Age portion of the Antarctic Ice Sheet, there is not enough alkaline dust to neutralize the acidic ice, so the ice sheet is acidic throughout, since precipitation is slightly acidic. This acidity of precipitation is mainly caused by atmospheric SO_2 that is oxidized to sulfuric acid (Jaffrezo et al., 1994, p. 1,241). In the GISP2 core from Greenland, where 110,000 annual layers are claimed, the ECM technique was applied mainly to the post–Ice Age acidic ice. The ECM technique was also applied to certain less dusty and more acidic intervals, called the *strong interstadials*, found in the glacial ice down to 2,500 meters (Wolff et al., 1997; Meese et al., 1997). Because Antarctic ice is acidic throughout, Hammer, Clausen, and Langway (1985, 1994, 1997) were able to measure 50,000 supposed annual layers in acidity down to a depth of 1,910 meters in the old Byrd core.

The dielectric profiling method (DEP) is an ac method that picks up not only ice core acidity, but also some of the bases as well (Moore, 1988; Moore, Mulvaney, and Paren, 1989; Moore et al., 1992; Taylor, 1995). Besides acids, the particular ions picked up by DEP are the ammonium and chloride ions (Wolff et al., 1995, 1997). This method is not used as much as ECM, probably because of the bases it also measures. The DEP method, however, has an advantage in that it requires no special ice surface preparation and no physical contact between the electrodes and the ice, unlike ECM. It has a resolution to 3 mm (Moore, 1993). A potential difference of one volt is all that is needed. A new device has recently improved the technique (Wilhelms et al., 1998; Wolff et al., 1999). By using both ECM and DEP together, one can deduce the amount of certain bases by subtracting the former from the latter.

Annual Layer Dating Using Acids

A cids show a strong seasonal trend (see figure 7.4) that shows up in the snow that falls on the ice sheets:

> Climatologists can also detect the annual layers by measuring the acidity of the ice, which is generally higher for summer snow for reasons that remain somewhat obscure (Alley and Bender, 1998, p. 81).

The major acids recorded in ice cores are sulfuric acid (H_2SO_4) and nitric acid (HNO_3). Minor amounts of hydrochloric (HCl), hydrofluoric (HF), and methanesulfonic acid (CH_3SO_3H), or MSA, are also present in the ice. HCl can form in the Antarctic atmosphere by the reaction of sea salt with other acids, mainly sulfuric acid (Legrand and Delmas, 1988b; Wagnon, Delmas, and Legrand, 1999, p. 3,426). It can also originate from volcanic eruptions (Hammer, Clausen, and Langway, 1997). HF is detected in small portions and likely originates from volcanoes (De Angelis and Legrand, 1994; Wagnon, Delmas, and Legrand, 1999, p. 3427). MSA is the end product of the oxidation of gaseous dimethylsulfide (DMS) given off to the atmosphere by certain marine phytoplankton (Saigne and Legrand, 1987; Gibson et al., 1990). It is interesting that MSA is only produced by the oxidation of DMS and therefore is an ice core measurement of past marine biogenic activity. MSA has been observed to increase in Antarctica during El Niño events, possibly due to higher sea surface wind speeds leading to more efficient air-sea exchange of DMS (Legrand and Feniet-Saigne, 1991). Another plausible explanation for this correlation is increased sea ice extent or duration (Welch, Mayewski, and Whitlow, 1993; Legrand and Mayewski, 1997, p. 236; Curran et al., 2003).

The ECM and DEP technique only measure the bulk acidity. If glaciologists want to measure the particular negative ion or anion of such acids as HCl, HF, HNO_3, H_2SO_4, and MSA, chemical analysis is required. Enough measurements have been made to know the general proportion of acids in the cores. I will concentrate on the ECM measurements of the major acids that are used for annual layer dating, since DEP's measurement of a few bases confuses the issue. Although ECM is a measure of sulfuric and nitric acids, it is expected that the minor acids contribute substantially to the total acidity from time to time. This will, of course, confuse the deductions.

ECM measures the H^+ ion. This ion is balanced mainly by the negative $_{nss}SO_4$ and NO_3 anions (Delmas, 1992, p. 5). $_{nss}SO_4$ is the non-sea-salt sulfate that is found by the following equation:

$$_{nss}SO_4 = SO_4 - 0.121 \, [Na^+] \tag{7.1}$$

where SO_4 is the total sulfate measured in the ice, $[Na^+]$ is the measured sodium ion assumed to be contributed from sea salt, and 0.121 is the SO_4/Na^+ bulk seawater ratio. Sea salt in the atmosphere is produced by the bursting of bubbles at the sea surface and wave crest disruptions. So, by subtracting the sea salt component of sulfate, the remaining non-sea-salt sulfate is assumed to be due mainly to sulfuric acidic deposition from the other sources. As it turns out, sea salt sulfate is only 10% of the total sulfate, except at coastal sites that receive large amounts of sea salt (Delmas, 1992, p. 5). This formula is supposed to eliminate the sulfate contributed by seawater. However, there are several other sources for sulfate besides seawater:

> Sulphate has a number of sources in Antarctic ice cores, including sea salt, volcanic emissions, the oxidation of dimethyl sulphide (DMS) and a minor influence from anthropogenic activities (Curran, Van Ommen, and Morgan, 1998, p. 388).

The sources of sulfate are shown in figure 7.5.

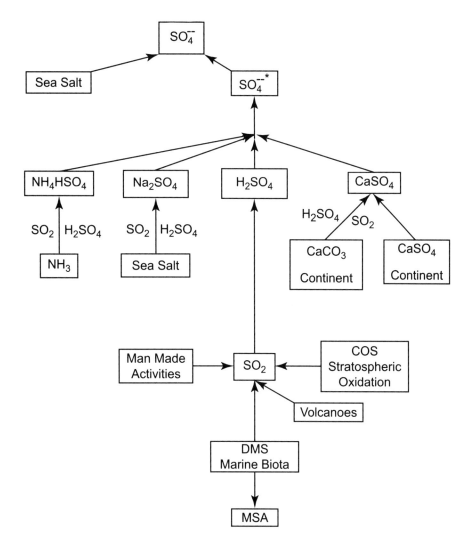

Figure 7.5 Flow chart showing possible sources of sulfate in polar ice (from Legrand, 1995, p. 98).

We are interested in the origin of the sulfuric acid represented in the ice cores. There are two main sources of sulfuric acid as indicated in the quote above, not including the minor influence of anthropogenic activities. One is sulfuric acid from rather rare volcanic eruptions (Hammer, 1980; Moore et al., 1992). The eruptions usually cause a well-defined spike in sulfuric acid that can usually be subtracted out in the seasonal dating. Sulfuric acid spikes can be used to date the core when the year of the eruption is known (see chapter 8).

The second main source of sulfuric acid is from DMS, especially in the Southern Hemisphere. The oxidation of DMS is suppose to be the main source of the sulfuric acid, but 20% of the sulfuric acid is believed to originate in the stratosphere and is not associated with volcanism (Legrand, 1995). DMS has a strong summer maximum in the top layer of the mid- and high-latitude oceans. This DMS must be released to the atmosphere; and the amount released depends upon several complex variables, such as wind speed, sea ice coverage, plankton blooms, and the DMS molecular diffusivity (Bates et al., 1992; Legrand et al., 1997; Minikin et al., 1998; Berresheim et al.,

1998). DMS first forms as a gas but is photochemically changed into very small aerosol particles called *Aitken particles,* some of which also serve as condensation nuclei (Ito, 1989). But this oxidation process forms not only sulfuric acid, but also MSA, which is not a sulfate but a minor acid in the cores. Although the majority of DMS is changed to sulfuric acid, the proportion of the DMS oxidized to sulfuric acid instead of MSA is variable (Ivey et al., 1986). The understanding of all these variables is still in its infancy:

> Chemical interpretations of ice cores will rely on very crude assumptions and there is still a limited understanding of DMS chemistry and its relationship to MSA and sulfuric acid (Berresheim and Eisele, 1998).

The second main acid measured in cores is nitric acid. Most of the nitrate chemically measured in the core is believed to be mainly from nitric acid deposition, but nitrate in small quantities can be present as neutral salt from terrestrial dust (Wolff, 1995). Nitric acid can come from many sources and essentially is the end product of the oxidation of various oxides of nitrogen that are trace gases in the atmosphere (Delmas, 1992, p. 7).

Acids Presently Deposited on the Ice Sheets

On Antarctica it has been found that the major acid incorporated into the ice is sulfuric acid, H_2SO_4. Studies have shown that 80 to 90% of the aerosol mass deposited on the Antarctic Ice Sheet consists of fine particles, less than one micron, of non-sea-salt sulfate (Berresheim and Eisele, 1998, p. 1619). However, nitric acid can be a major component in inland Antarctica (Osada, 1994; Wolff, 1995, p. 206). Unfortunately, the strong seasonal sulfuric acid trend cannot be applied to the very low accumulation of the East Antarctic Plateau cores, such as Vostok, Dome C, and Dome F.

Nitric acid is the main acid that falls on the Greenland Ice Sheet (Wolff et al., 1995); but sulfuric acid, or at least the sulfate anion, is a close second (Legrand and Meyewski, 1997). The Greenland ice of the past two centuries has been contaminated with anthropogenic pollution and biomass burning. These sources have added more acids, including nitric acid, to the ice sheet of late. In order to find the background nitric acid deposition, this anthropogenic source must be eliminated.

Too Many Unknown Variables

The present trends in acidity have been extrapolated to explain seasonal wiggles down the ice cores. Seasonal cycles measured by the ECM and/or DEP on Antarctica have been applied to the Byrd core and high accumulation coastal cores, such as Law Dome (Aristrarain, Delmas, and Briat, 1982; Hammer, Clausen, and Langway, 1994; Morgan et al., 1997; Kreutz et al., 1999; Palmer et al., 2001b). The GISP2 core annual layer chronology to 110,000 years included acidity oscillations during the Holocene and only in certain less dusty sections in the Ice Age portion of the core (Meese et al., 1997). However, too many unknown variables can change with time, thus making seasonal dating by acids equivocal. Too many sources for sulfuric and nitric acids can vary with time and complicate the seasonal cycle. I will first discuss the variables that can affect the sulfuric acid seasonal cycle and comment on measurements in the Byrd ice core.

1) Sulfuric Acid Variables

As stated above, the seasonal cycle with a summer maximum and winter mininum in sulfuric acid and/or $_{nss}SO_4$ is quite complicated (Legrand, 1995). First, the seasonal cycle itself is not so simple. At Alert in the high Canadian Arctic, Li, Barrie, and Sirois (1993) discovered two warm season MSA peaks, a larger April to May spring peak, and a smaller July to August peak. MSA and sulfuric acid originate from the same source. So, a double maximum should be expected in sulfuric acid or $_{nss}SO_4$. However, such a double maximum in $_{nss}SO_4$ was not correlated to MSA, because $_{nss}SO_4$ has been overwhelmed by the modern anthropogenic component of $_{nss}SO_4$ (Li and Barrie, 1993; Whung et al., 1994). It is of interest that snow at Mizuho Station, Antarctica—about 2,200 meters high and with very little modern pollution—had a double sulfate, as well as nitrate, maximum in spring and late summer, a result similar to Alert (Osada, 1994). In a survey of surface snow in Dronning Maud Land, Antarctica, a double peak in $_{nss}SO_4$ was also found (Goktas et al., 2002).

It is likely that with much greater snowfall, such as in the Creation-Flood Ice Age model, such a double max in one year would be counted as two annual acidity maximums in the Evolutionary-Uniformitarian scheme. In the former model, with much warmer sea surface temperatures, multiple phytoplankton blooms could have occurred during the entire year, sending warm season subannual pulses in $_{nss}SO_4$ to the ice sheet—a reasonable conclusion since Greenland is located in an area with intense seasonal biological productivity involving blooms of major DMS producing species (Whung et al., 1994, p. 1,147). In the ocean surrounding Antarctica, such blooms could also have occurred more frequently than they occur today, possibly producing multiple subannual sulfuric acid peaks in the ice sheet.

Greater snowfall obscures volcanic acid deposition (Delmas et al., 1985), so that multiple maximums could occur within one year just due to volcanism. High volcanism and greater snowfall would be typical of the Creation-Flood Ice Age model. Such a pattern would be expected to result in multiple subannual sulfuric acid peaks.

Another variable that can determine the amount and seasonal oscillation of sulfuric acid deposition on the Greenland Ice Sheet is non-eruptive volcanic sulfur emissions from Kamchatka, Iceland, and the Aleutian Islands (Legrand, 1995; Legrand and Mayewski, 1997, p. 237). These emissions are of the same order of magnitude as DMS sources of sulfuric acid in the Northern Hemisphere and are expected to be random over the year. This variable would add much variance to sulfuric acid deposition in Greenland cores. Two shallow cores drilled on an ice cap on Berkner Island, coastal Antarctica, indicated that volcanic peaks were difficult to distinguish from sulfuric acid peaks (Mulvaney et al., 2002). In the Creation-Flood Ice Age model, volcanism during the Ice Age is much more intense than today. Non-volcanic sulfur emissions should also be more active. Volcanic peaks deposited in the ice during the past 200 years are generally seen as spikes, but during the Ice Age sulfuric acid deposition from both volcanism and non-eruptive volcanic emissions as well as much greater snowfall could have resulted in many subannual sulfate peaks, depending upon the fineness of the measurements.

Another variable neglected due to uniformitarian bias is that melt layers could significantly change the acidity signal (see appendix 2). It is well known that melt layers absorb CO_2 and acids. This is known to be a problem in the Dye 3 core in southern Greenland, an area warmer than the summit area:

> In addition, at some Greenland locations, such as Dye 3, an average of almost 6% of the annual accumulation layers consist of summer melt features . . . , which also complicates the acidity record (Hammer, Clausen, and Langway, 1994, p. 116).

So, each melt layer could end up being an acidity max down the core. As stated in appendix 2, melt layers strongly absorb acids, and multiple melt layers in a summer would cause multiple acidity wiggles. In the Creation-Flood Ice Age model, the winters would have been much warmer

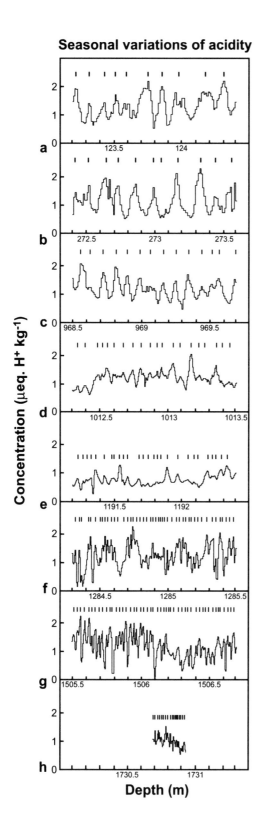

Seasonal variations of acidity

Concentration (μeq. H$^+$ kg^{-1})

Depth (m)

in Antarctica than they are today. During the Ice Age, summer melting or even winter melting due to strong warm air advection along with heavy precipitation could cause multiple melt layers and acidity peaks. Meltwater also has fewer air bubbles, so hopefully glaciologists have been able to detect high acid layers caused by meltwater; but it is not known whether this is the case, especially in the lower half of the ice where an air hydrate formed when the bubbles disappeared.

Hammer, Clausen, and Langway (1994) claim to have counted 50,000 annual acidity layers in the Byrd core. Figure 7.6 represents acidity plots for several intervals in the Byrd core. The interval between 300 and 880 meters has very few measurements because the ice is brittle. The counting of peaks looks fairly straightforward down to the 1,013-meter interval where it starts to become a little more chaotic. In the graphs, the assumed annual layers for the intervals around 1,192 and 1,285 meters are questionable. A case can be made for fewer annual layers in the longer period oscillations. The annual layers represented by the graph for the interval around 1,506 meters look rather chaotic. Hammer, Clausen, and Langway (1994, p. 118) do admit to a certain amount of subjectivity in identifying these annual layers. Furthermore, these peaks do not mean that they are annual. Many of the peaks could be due to the double max in sulfuric acid during the warm season, melt layers within the Evolutionary-Uniformitarian model, or some other process. Greater volcanism, especially during the Ice Age, could add to the number of ECM peaks. Within the Creation-Flood model, multiple subannual wiggles would be expected in the mid- to lower portion of the ice core.

Figure 7.6   Acidity wiggles in several intervals from the Byrd core (from Hammer, Clausen, and Langway, 1994, p. 117).

2) Nitric Acid Variables

The nitrogen cycle in the atmosphere is highly complex with a number of variables affecting the nitrate that ends up in the ice (Röthlisberger et al., 2002b):

> The atmospheric nitrogen cycle is highly complex and there is a wide range of factors that can affect the nitrate level in polar ice (Curran, Van Ommen, and Morgan, 1998, p. 389).

Wolff (1995, p. 195) corroborates:

> However, the [nitrate] data are not easy to interpret, and we do not have an adequate knowledge of even the present-day sources of nitrate in polar snow, nor of the deposition processes that control the concentrations seen.

The main cause of spring/summer maximum and winter minimum in nitric acid production, other than anthropogenic, is unknown. I will discuss several variables that likely impact the nitric acid wiggles in ice cores. I will focus on the GISP2 core measurements that represent mostly nitric acid wiggles, since this core is the one used for the long annual layer chronology to 110,000 years; but the comments also apply to the other Greenland cores.

In the Holocene part of the GISP2 core, the dominant seasonal ECM current is caused by seasonal variations in the nitrate budget (Taylor et al., 1997a, p. 26,511). The sources and sinks of nitric acid include biomass burning, soil exhalation, lightning, NH_3 oxidation, stratospheric oxidation of N_2O, solar activity, the ionospheric dissociation of N_2, solar proton events, galactic cosmic rays (Legrand and Kirchner, 1990; Delmas, 1992, p. 7; Taylor et al., 1997a, p. 26,512; Legrand and Mayewski, 1997; Palmer et al., 2001b), and even possibly supernovae (Risbo, Clausen, and Rasmussen, 1981). Legrand and Kirchner (1990, p. 3493) state: "Sources and sinks of NO_x (and HNO_3) are highly variable in time and space." NO_x represents the oxides of nitrogen.

Of all these sources, mid- and low latitude lightning and stratospheric chemical production are considered to be the main sources of nitrate for the polar ice sheets (Röthlisberger et al., 2000). Some authors have favored lightning as the primary source for nitric acid, followed secondarily by poleward transport and oxidation of N_2O in the lower stratosphere (Legrand and Delmas, 1986, 1988a; Legrand and Kirchner, 1990; Legrand, Wolff, and Wagenbach, 1999; Wagenbach et al., 1998b). Glaciologists have generally switched opinions and presently believe that the major source of nitrate is from the stratosphere (Meese et al., 1997, p. 26,412; Wagenbach et al., 1998b; Wolff, Legrand, and Wagenbach, 1998). However, the chemistry of nitrogen oxides is closely related to the amount of stratospheric ozone, thus complicating the situation (Bottenheim and Barrie, 1996).

Another recently discovered, important variable in the nitrogen cycle is that the Scotch pine (*Pinus sylvestris*) exudes nitrogen oxides (Morgan, 2003). Other types of trees or vegetation may be a source of nitrogen oxides, especially in relatively unpolluted air.

The variables that determine the nitrogen cycle are expected to be constant after the Ice Age, but during the Ice Age the different climate likely caused the sources of nitrogen oxides to change and thus affect the well-defined seasonal cycle observed in the atmosphere today.

One sink for atmospheric nitrate, as well as chloride, is believed to be strong volcanic eruptions. It is surmised that the great Toba eruption, which occurred at about 72 kyr in the Evolutionary-Uniformitarian timescale, depleted 94% of the nitrate in the atmosphere (Yang et al., 1996). It has been reported from the South Pole that nitric acid decreases due to sulfuric acid deposition from strong volcanic eruptions (Wolff, 1995, p. 211). Such sulfuric acid spikes can also displace the nitrate in the core (Röthlisberger et al., 2000, p. 20,566). So it is possible that variable volcanic effects may modulate the amount of nitric acid in the air and hence available to be deposited on the ice sheet.

There are also nonseasonal inputs of nitrogen oxides that indicate that subannual peaks sometimes occur:

> Although ECM is an excellent seasonal indicator, as stated above, nonseasonal inputs from other sources may cause additional peaks which could be confused with the annual summer signal (Meese et al., 1997, p. 26,412).

For instance, stratospheric effects cause a secondary nitric acid peak in late winter in Antarctica (Wagenbach et al., 1998b). Just like with sulfuric acid, such a double maximum would be interpreted as two annual layers if the snowfall were greater in the past.

One non-seasonal input could be melt layers. As already stated, nitric acid peaks occur in the Dye 3 core and other warmer areas of the Greenland Ice Sheet (Clausen and Langway, 1989; Wolff, 1995, p. 202). In the Creation-Flood model with a lower ice sheet and warmer temperatures, especially early in the Ice Age, melt features should be more common. Melt features could be as common as the number of storms, since each storm has a warm and a cold sector. Although the ECM method is used sparingly in the glacial part of the core during warmer intervals, Wolff (1995, p. 202) warns that the nitric acid signal may be subannual or peak in a season other than summer in the glacial part:

> There is a need for caution in using it [summer nitrate maximums] for dating in the last glacial, where we currently have no information on whether nitrate peaked in summer, or indeed whether its signal varies annually.

Subannual nitric acid peaks could also be caused by depositional and post-depositional processes (see appendix 2 for all the many variables involved from the chemical's source to its being locked in ice). Nitric acid is quite volatile and can form a gas in the firn of the ice sheet (Wolff, 1995, pp. 218–219). Wolff (1996, p. 2) states:

> However, there has been a growing realization that depositional and post-depositional processes confuse the interpretation for many species, and this workshop is the culmination of that awareness.

Snow pit studies indicate a fair amount of nitric acid loss that seems to be inversely related to accumulation rate (Legrand and Barrie, 1996, p. 648). Because of other factors, such as increased dry deposition during times of reduced precipitation, this inverse relationship is weak (Wolff, 1995). Consequently, such post-depositional movement fouls up the seasonal cycle and can cause subannual cycles:

> Post-depositional processes in most cases do not significantly alter long-term average concentrations, but can affect short term (i.e. subannual scale) fluctuations, as well as the amplitude and timing of chemical signal seasonality (Kreutz et al., 1998, p. 371).

It has recently been discovered in Dronning Maud Land, Antarctica, that the seasonal cycle of nitric acid is wiped out in the firn (Goktas et al., 2002, p. 351).

In summary, assuming that every acidic oscillation down the GISP2 core is annual is fraught with difficulties. The ECM technique that measures acidity in ice cores, and also the DEP technique, could have multiple subannual peaks because:

> The concentration of strong acids is a composite of various acids which do not vary seasonally in the same way, and volcanic eruptions and other phenomena may add to the acidity (Hammer, 1989, p. 108).

Furthermore, ECM is strongly influenced by other seasonal indicators that bias the results:

> Only together with other continuous records such as $\delta^{18}O$ and dust and ion concentrations, do they allow correct dating of the ice and characterizing of the incorporated impurities (Neftel et al., 1985, p. 38).

Considering the Creation-Flood Ice Age model with its greater snowfall, warmer ocean temperatures, and a much different climate, there are a number of possibilities for producing subannual acidity peaks in ice cores.

Multiple Methods Are of Little Help

The glaciologist realizes that each method has difficulties, but he applies more than one annual layer dating method in the hope that more is better, as indicated in the quote above by Neftel et al. (1985). Kreutz et al. (1999, p. 38) believe:

> Each of these techniques, used independently, has an associated error (identifying a year where one does not exist, or omitting a year where one does exist), which increases with depth or age (Alley and others, 1990). Therefore, combining several of these techniques in a multi-parameter dating approach provides a more accurate means for reconstructing accumulation histories and interpreting chemical variability through time.

This multiple variable approach was applied to the GISP2 core by Deborah Meese and colleagues (1997) to arrive at their 110,000 years. Figure 7.7 shows the use of the various methods to come up with 110,000 annual layers with a crude extension to 161,000 years in the GISP2 core. *S* is the visual stratigraphic method, *D* the oxygen isotope method, *E* stands for ECM, *L* is the LLS method for dust, and *V* stands for volcanic markers. The asterisk indicates the method is secondary and was not applied on a continuous basis in that core interval.

How well do the various intervals compare? Figure 7.8 shows the comparison of four methods for the interval between 270 and 275 meters. Even though this interval, which is not that deep, should show distinct annual layers, there is ambiguity even this shallow in the core. It was assumed that visual stratigraphy, shown by the vertical black lines, will determine the annual layers. The white vertical lines define annual layers in $\delta^{18}O$, ECM, and LLS. There are obvious differences between the black and white lines. One can even question the definition of annual layers in these other three records. For instance, one can question the lines just before the 271-meter depth in the $\delta^{18}O$ record. Although this 5-meter interval represents twenty years, ECM had 22 and LLS had 23 counted peaks. But, a case can be made for even more peaks than these. For instance, a double peak in LLS at 272.3 meters was counted as one annual peak.

Based on comparisons near the top of the ice sheet, the glaciologists were able to justify the use of multiple methods deeper in the core by analyzing the annual layer oscillations in the well-behaved upper 600 meters of the GISP2 core, especially the top 300 meters where oxygen isotopes were also used. Such use allowed them to determine what they believed to be the precise characteristics of each annual signal, a determination that was applied with confidence deeper in the core:

> Our ability to intercalibrate multiple annual indicators in the upper part of the core and learn their signal characteristics allowed us to retain considerable confidence

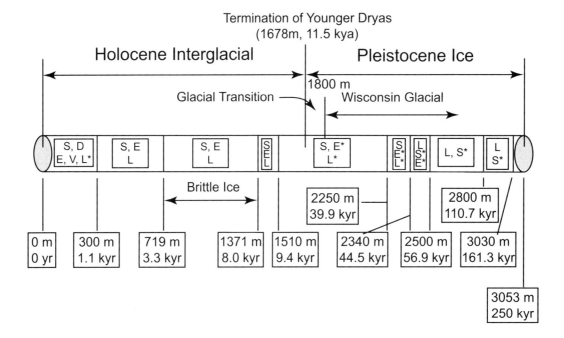

Figure 7.7 Multi-parameter dating of the GISP2 ice core (from Meese et al., 1997 and redrawn by Vardiman). Dates are in years before 1950. The dating methods used for each section of ice are shown: S = visual stratigraphy, D = oxygen isotopes, E = ECM, L = LLS, and V = volcanic markers. The 250-kyr-age estimate at 3053 meters was obtained from the nearby GRIP glaciological flow model, not by annual layer dating. An asterisk means that the method was used as a secondary backup but not on a continuous basis.

in our interpretations even after some indicators were lost with increasing depth (Meese et al., 1997, p. 26,413).

Still, the claimed accuracy of these methods deteriorates with depth; it is 1-10% in the top 2,500 meters and averages 20% between 2,500 and 2,800 meters (Meese et al., 1997, p. 26,411).

The neighboring GRIP core was not subjected to such in-depth analysis of annual layers by multiple methods as the GISP2 core was, especially in the Ice Age portion of the core. It was dated by "annual layers" above 14,500 BP and by glaciological flow models below 14,500 BP in the Evolutionary-Uniformitarian timescale (Johnsen et al., 1992a). The scientists took a short cut in determining the annual layers at the top by indirectly deriving the annual layers to 8,600 BP by comparison of volcanic reference horizons in the Dye 3 core to 1,380 meters. Between 8,600 BP and 14,500 BP, seasonal variations were found by using mostly different methods than those used on the GISP2 core. The researchers used what are believed to be seasonal cycles in Ca^{2+}, microparticles, NH_4^+, and nitrate. By flow modeling, the bottom of the GRIP core was dated at 250 kyr, which was also assumed to be the date for the bottom of the neighboring GISP2 core.

Within the Evolutionary-Uniformitarian paradigm, all the seasonal indicators discussed in chapters 5 through 7 have problems:

All four seasonal indicators have problems. The ECM has non-seasonal components superimposed on the annual signal; for example, the volcanic peak at 101.5 m [in the

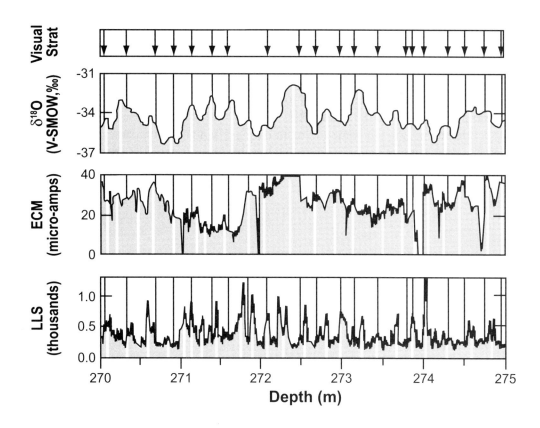

Figure 7.8 The comparison of four annual layer methods applied to the 270 to 275 meter interval in the GISP2 core. The white vertical line represents the annual markers for δ¹⁸O, ECM, and LLS, but it is the black vertical lines based on visual stratigraphy that were assumed to separate the interval into annual layers (from Meese et al., 1997, p. 26,415).

GISP2 core] may be misinterpreted as an annual peak, while the anomalous low at 103.8 masks an annual peak. Diffusion of isotopes may obscure some years in the δ¹⁸O record . . . The particulate record also has non-seasonal contributions such as volcanic particulates . . . Visual stratigraphy can also be misleading due to erratic firnification or depositional events and becomes less clear with increasing age and depth owing to densification and other physical changes (Taylor et al., 1992, p. 331).

They go on to conclude that multiple seasonal methods can still improve the annual layer dating:

However, when several of the above methods are compared, the discrepancies become fairly clear. . . . It is, thus, possible to count annual layers in the upper part of the GISP2 core (and probably other cores) rapidly using only ECM, particulates and visible strata. If only two records are available, counting annual layers becomes less certain because there is no way to reconcile discrepancies between records. . . . If only one record is available, it is not even possible to recognize problem areas and dating the core by counting annual layers becomes speculative (Taylor et al., 1992, p. 331).

I am not sure of the logic of adding a third imprecise method to two other imprecise methods to come up with the "real" annual layer within the Evolutionary-Uniformitarian model, especially in the mid- and lower parts of the ice cores. Even within the Evolutionary-Uniformitarian model, it has been shown that between 270 and 275 meters, even using four variables is questionable.

If the Creation-Flood Ice Age model assumptions replace the Evolutionary-Uniformitarian model assumptions, even more discrepancies in annual layer dating will occur, especially in the mid- and lower portions of the GISP2 and GRIP cores. I doubt whether the annual layer methods, alone or in combination, can overcome the main dating bias that encompasses *all* annual layer methods and constrains interpretation. This dating bias becomes apparent in the use of flow models as a first guess, which will be the subject of chapter 8.

CRITIQUE OF FLOW MODELS AND REFERENCE HORIZONS

Annual layer dating is *not* the primary dating method for ice cores but depends upon glaciological flow models:

> This property [the strain rate three times higher during the last glaciation than the Holocene] has important implications for ice-sheet modeling, the *most frequently used* method for dating ice cores (Paterson, 1991, p. 75) [emphasis mine].

It is the flow model that determines the *expected* annual layer thickness, and there are always enough variations at many scales, whether millimeters or centimeters, to "verify" the presumed annual layer thickness. What is the basis of these flow models?

Old Age Built into Ice Sheets by Flow Models

It is natural for the Evolutionary-Uniformitarian glaciologists to view the Greenland and Antarctic Ice Sheets as products of long periods of time. Since they view every process in nature this way, they assume these ice sheets have existed for millions of years. Thus, these glaciologists have assumed that the ice sheets have been more or less in equilibrium for all this time. This assumption determines how they view the ice sheet (see figure 3.12). Based on equilibrium, they have constructed a preliminary timescale based on a *steady-state snowfall and glaciological flow for hundreds of thousands to millions of years*. Dansgaard et al. (1969, p. 377) state in referring to the Camp Century core:

> The approximate age of different sections of the core can be obtained by (i) considering the generally accepted glacial flow outline . . . , and (ii) making certain assumptions concerning the parameters that influence it. Correlation of the time as a function of depth (timescale) discussed here is calculated on the basis of simple assumptions such as unchanged rate of accumulation *a* [35 cm of ice per year], unchanged thickness of the ice sheet, *H*, and unchanged flow pattern back in time.

This is the equilibrium assumption that contributed to the early glaciological flow model for the dating of the ice sheets. More sophisticated modern flow models include more variables, such as less snowfall during the ice age and a thinner ice sheet, but these differences are small and have little impact on the equilibrium assumption. For instance, the maximum change in altitude of the Antarctic Ice sheet between glacials and interglacials is 150 meters in the Evolutionary-Uniformitarian model (Ritz, Rommelaere, and Dumas, 2001). If the ice sheets built up rapidly during the Ice Age but growth slowed during the modern climate, as in the Creation-Flood Ice Age model, the assumptions that undergird the Evolutionary-Uniformitarian flow models would be erroneous, especially as applied to the mid- and lower portions of the ice.

Essentially, the Evolutionary-Uniformitarian paradigm is assumed and built into the dating procedure right from the beginning. Then the flow model provides the first guess for annual layer dating:

> Preliminary modeling for the age distribution should be carried out *before* the drilling and the core analysis, to give an *initial* indication of the age depth relation, which can later be improved with the additional ice core data (Budd et al., 1989, p. 178) [emphasis mine].

Hammer (1989, p. 100) corroborates this important assumption to the derived timescale for ice cores:

> During ice flow, the thinning of annual layers can be described fairly well by modeling. Thus, favorable conditions exist allowing models to be refined using the information obtained from analysis of the core, e.g., from information on the flow properties of the ice and on general changes in the annual layer thickness.

Since the flow model provides a *first guess*, there is a certain amount of give-and-take between the flow model and the subsequent annual layer measurements. The annual layer measurements *refine* the flow model. But, the flow model acts as a *constraint to determine the approximate bounds of the annual layer thickness* (Reeh, 1989). For instance, it takes eight measurements per presumed annual layer to resolve the oxygen isotope annual layer cycle. Thus, flow models restrict how fine these eight measurements will be for the ice core. If the flow model suggests an annual layer thickness of 20 cm, measurements must be made every 2.5 cm. If the model suggests it is 1.6 cm, measurements must be every 2 mm. It is quite likely that wiggles at any scale will be picked up. The flow model also constrains the first guess for other variables (Reeh, 1989).

A glaciological flow model was applied right away to the dating of the very first deep ice core on Greenland—the Camp Century core drilled in 1966 (Dansgaard and Johnsen, 1969a; Dansgaard et al., 1969, 1970, 1971). This core was drilled 1,390 meters to bedrock in northwest Greenland, 225 km east of Thule Air Force Base (figure 8.1). Using the oxygen isotope method, scientists discovered annual layer oscillations to a few thousand years down to the middle of the core. If the annual layers did not thin further with depth below where the last oxygen isotope measurement was made, the ice sheet at the location of Camp Century would be only about 4,000 years old (figure 8.1, see also figure 3.17).

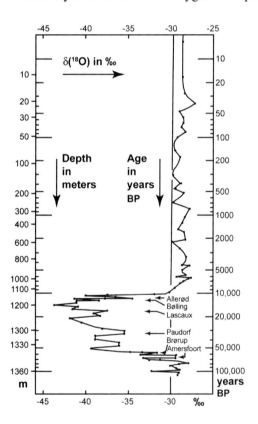

Figure 8.1   Oxygen isotope ratio of Camp Century ice core with time according to a glaciological flow model. Note how the timescale on the right is tremendously compressed, mainly for the bottom half (from Dansgaard and Johnsen, 1969a, figure 6).

94

There is certainly enough time within the Creation-Flood Ice Age model to account for the ice on Greenland. Because of the radical thinning assumed for the annual layers, mainly in the lower half according to the glaciological flow model, the bottom of the core was dated at over 100,000 years. The annual layer of ice thins so much that the bottom 25 meters of the core represents a period of 50,000 years! This is how flow models based on the equilibrium assumption greatly expand the assumed age for the middle and lower portion of an ice core.

Glaciological flow models were also applied to Antarctica. The second deep ice core was drilled into the West Antarctic Ice Sheet in 1968 soon after the Camp Century core. This is called the *Byrd deep core*, which was drilled 2,164 meters to till or gravel just above bedrock. Figure 8.2 shows the oxygen isotope ratios with time in the core. This core was also dated by flow models in the same way as the Camp Century core (Gow, Ueda, and Garfield, 1968; Epstein, Sharp, and Gow, 1970). The bottom half of the core is the Ice Age portion represented by the low oxygen isotope ratios. The bottom of the ice is dated at about 75,000 years ago and the higher oxygen isotope ratios match the ending of the last interglacial period, according to the Evolutionary-Uniformitarian ice age scheme. To show the arbitrary nature of flow model dates, one early paper suggested the bottom of the core was no older than 27,000 years within the Evolutionary-Uniformitarian system (Gow and Williamson, 1976, p. 1671). This is one-third the estimate by flow modeling. It all depends upon how much thinning one believes has occurred, which is based on other assumptions as will be discussed in chapter 9.

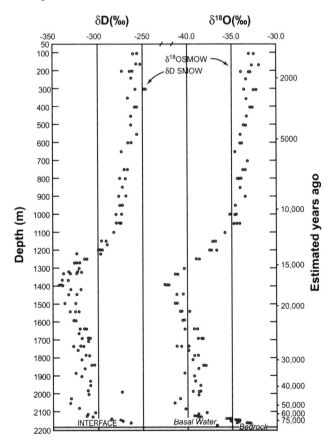

Figure 8.2   Deuterium and oxygen isotope ratio of the Byrd ice core with time (from Epstein, Sharp, and Gow, 1970). Notice how about half the ice has been deposited within the last 2,000 years.

A typical flow model, shown in figure 8.3, was constructed upstream of the Dye 3 ice core (Reeh, Johnsen, and Dahl-Jensen, 1985). The Dye 3 borehole was drilled to bedrock 2,035 meters deep in southern Greenland in 1981. The flow model was difficult to design because of the location of Dye 3 about 40 km from an ice divide, the hilly bedrock, and the irregular accumulation of snow (Dansgaard et al., 1982, p. 1,274; Reeh, Johnsen, and Dahl-Jensen, 1985). The Dye 3 core was also dated by curve matching to the Camp Century core (Dansgaard et al., 1984, p. 290).

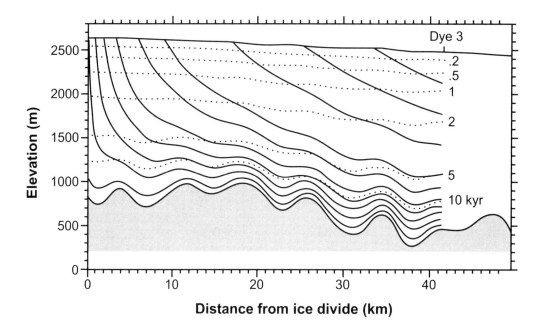

Figure 8.3   Ice flow model derived for the Dye 3 core (Reeh, Johnsen, and Dahl-Jensen, 1985, p. 60).

Flow models are believed to be especially accurate for the top of the ice core (Dansgaard et al., 1982, p. 1,275). The top of the core is where annual layer methods are also good, so this is no surprise. But where annual layer methods are quite vulnerable in the middle and lower portions of the core, flow models, tied to reference horizons, often provide the *only* chronology. For instance, the long Vostok core recently drilled to 3,623 meters was dated to over 400,000 years *only* by flow modeling tied to reference horizons (Parrenin et al., 2001). The GRIP core drilled at the very top of the ice sheet in central Greenland was dated by a steady state flow model beyond 14,500 years ago in the Evolutionary-Uniformitarian timescale (Castelnau et al., 1996; Souchez, 1997, p. 26,322). Of course the GRIP flow model was tied to the Younger Dryas reference horizon at 1,678 meters depth and assumed to be about 11,640 years old. Further down the core, an oscillation in $\delta^{18}O$ was tied to marine isotope stage 5d at about 110,000 years ago (Souchez, 1997, p. 26,322). The bottom of this core is considered to be about 200,000 to 250,000 years old (Gow et al., 1997; Hammer et al., 1997), but could be as old as 2.4 million years old as some claim (Souchez, 1997, p. 26,317).

Even cores close to the coast are dated by flow models. For instance, the shallow 325 meter deep Renland ice core (see figure 2.7) drilled to bedrock in east-central Greenland was dated by flow modeling (Johnsen and Dansgaard, 1992). It is interesting that the top two-thirds of this core,

200 meters, accumulated within only 1,000 years! Then there seems to be a very compressed chronology in the next 100 meters down to the top of Ice Age ice, determined by the oxygen isotope ratio. The bottom 20 meters represents 90,000 years of time! This unnaturally compressed chronology seems to be simply fitted to preconceived ideas of Evolutionary-Uniformitarian ice age chronology; it does not even conform to typical flow models. A similar situation seems to show up on the Law Dome core (see figure 2.12) in that the top half of the ice was deposited in a little more than 1,000 years with a greatly expanded chronology deeper in the core.

It is interesting that regardless of the stretched out dating of the bottom of ice cores by flow models, the ice core represents only a small portion of the millions of years assumed for the age of the ice sheets. Glaciologists expected to find much older ice in areas with no basal melting. For instance, the GRIP and GISP2 cores were expected to penetrate more than one glacial cycle near the bottom, which is well below freezing, but only one definite cycle was drilled with the very bottom ice likely disturbed (Yiou et al., 1997b, p. 26,441). Early ice flow models for the GRIP and GISP2 cores even predicted that the ice 100 meters above bedrock would be older than 200,000 years (Schøtt, Waddington, and Raymond, 1992). This prediction failed. They would love dearly to find those missing hundreds of thousands or millions of years at the very bottom of the ice sheets. Dansgaard et al. (1969, p. 379) hoped that the thin annual layers in the bottom several meters of the Camp Century core could represent several previous glacial and interglacial periods that cycle every 100,000 years. There is, of course, no proof of this. On the other hand, the bottom of the ice core could possibly be disturbed due to its proximity to the bedrock, as some glaciologists claim.

Other reasons for the difference in time within the Evolutionary-Uniformitarian model are that the bottom ice could have either melted by geothermal heat over hundreds of thousands to millions of years, or that the very old bottom ice could have flowed away. But since the ice is much colder than freezing at the bottom of the Camp Century, GRIP, and GISP2 cores, retarding basal flow, these suggestions do not seem correct. Besides GRIP was drilled at the very top of the ice and GISP2 just to the west, in which case the ice is supposed to sink straight down with time and hardly flow laterally at all (see figure 3.12). In regard to the Camp Century core, Dansgaard et al. (1985, p. 73) do not believe the basal ice flowed much. Therefore, presumably no ice from previous ice ages should have been melted or transported away, assuming steady state, of course. So, where is the evidence of previous glacials and interglacials? Remember these deductions are all within the Evolutionary-Uniformitarian model, assuming equilibrium ice sheet flow for a very long time. Since there is essentially only one ice age cycle found in Greenland cores, the data of the cores is open to the reinterpretation of only one Ice Age within the Creation-Flood model (Oard, 1990), especially in view of the arbitrary assumption of flow model dating.

"Verification" of Flow Models by Ice Age Reference Horizons

As previously stated, the Evolutionary-Uniformitarian glaciological flow models are based on the *assumption* that ice sheets have been more or less in equilibrium for a few million years or more. The assumption of old age is built into the flow model right from the start. In developing the flow model, glaciologists incorporate various strategic reference horizons in the ice cores and compare them to other geophysical and geochemical systems of "known" dates. These supposedly known dates from other climatic and dating systems are used as "reference horizons" for the flow model. The use of reference horizons is the third main method of dating ice cores:

> Some large and well-documented past atmospheric perturbations can be used as 'reference horizons.' They represent an independent way to scale the counting of years provided by stratigraphy methods. Furthermore, such horizons are of special

interest for dating ice cores from low-accumulation areas when the aforementioned stratigraphic methods are not as useful (Legrand and Mayewski, 1997, p. 222).

These reference horizons are touted as "accurate and independent" of other ice core dating methods.

In the first flow model applied to the Camp Century core, Dansgaard et al. (1969) were able to match oxygen isotope wiggles to warmer temperatures over the earth in the 1920s and 1930s, cooler temperatures during the Little Ice Age in the seventeenth and eighteenth centuries, and the warmer climatic optimum around A.D. 1000. This is good so far. They then matched the large change in oxygen isotope ratio at 1,100 meters to the end of the ice age, which itself is a reference horizon. Other climatic records date the end of the ice age at about 10,000 years ago at this high latitude, so the 1,100-meter level was dated at 10,000 years in the flow model, and the ice above was interpolated to the climatic optimum about A.D. 1000 (see figure 8.1). There are a number of methods that date the end of the ice age as well as other glacial/interglacial transitions, such as deep-sea cores, varves, coral terraces, pollen profiles, etc. (Dansgaard et al., 1982, 1985; Oeschger, 1985; Hammer, Clausen, and Tauber, 1986; Shoji and Langway, 1987; Dansgaard and Oeschger, 1989, p. 126).

Furthermore, the transition from an ice age climate to the modern climate around 1,100 meters is punctuated by several $\delta^{18}O$ oscillations, called (from top to bottom) the *Younger Dryas, Allerød, Older Dryas,* and *Bølling* periods. These events are all assumed to have standard dates within the Evolutionary-Uniformitarian ice age model. Dansgaard and colleagues were able to match Camp Century to these late ice age events. They continued to match rapid changes in the $\delta^{18}O$ ratio within the ice age itself, such as the so-called Plum Point and Port Talbot interstadials and the Brørup and Amersfoort stadials. The Camp Century core matches fairly well events derived from pollen cores, carbon-14 dated glacial events in the Ontario and Erie basins, and a generalized temperature curve for surface waters of the central Caribbean, based on oxygen isotope ratios of fossil shells (Emiliani, 1966). The high oxygen isotope ratio near the bottom of the ice core concurs with the end of the Sangamonian (United States terminology) or the Eemian (European terminology) interglacial period. The events of this period, punctuated by warm and cold stages, are dated in the Evolutionary-Uniformitarian ice age model to around 70,000 to 130,000 years. No wonder the glaciological flow model for Camp Century thinned so much at the very bottom—the dates were adjusted to match the previous "interglacial."

Flow modeling and curve matching to deep-sea core $\delta^{18}O$ profiles showing multiple glacial/interglacial oscillations are how the many cores drilled on top of the East Antarctic Ice Sheet, especially Vostok, have been dated from the very beginning (Jouzel et al., 1987, 1993, 1996; Jouzel, Petit, and Raynaud, 1990; Waelbroeck et al., 1995; Parrenin et al., 2001). Interpolation between the various reference horizons does not exactly match up between the ice cores and the marine records, but it is usually close (Ruddiman and Raymo, 2003, p. 142). Lorius et al. (1985, p. 591) state: "Indirect dating techniques, based on the comparison of $\delta^{18}O$ profiles in ice cores and in deep-sea cores have recently been used." Lorius, Jouzel, and Raynaud (1993, p. 133) later add:

> Second, beyond the Holocene period, absolute dating of the [Vostok core] ice is not possible and ice core chronologies are then established either by using *glaciological [flow] models or by comparison with other paleorecords* with inherent limitations in accuracy [emphasis and brackets mine].

In these procedures, oscillations of high $\delta^{18}O$ deep in the ice sheet are tied to the interglacial stages 5 and 7 in the deep-sea record (Waelbroeck et al., 1995). The latest Vostok core chronology is further tied to the older deep-sea glacial/interglacial oscillations (stages 8 to 11):

The EGT4 chronology is based on ice flow modeling, with the constraint [sic] of a few control points (at 110 and 390 kyr B.P.), which put Vostok in phase with marine isotopic records (Yiou, Vimeux, and Jouzel, 2001, p. 31,876).

This is how evolutionists arrive at an age of over 400,000 years for the 3,300-meter level of the recently drilled deep core at Vostok (Petit et al., 1997, 1999)! This time represents four supposed glacial/interglacial stages. Dome Fuji has also been dated by curve matching to glacial/interglacial cycles, and the $\delta^{18}O$ curve is very similar to the δD curve of Vostok (Watanabe et al., 2003), which is not surprising since they both lie on top of the East Antarctic Ice Sheet. So accurately dating the ice cores, especially on Antarctica, depends upon the validity of the dating of deep-sea cores. This subject will be explored in more depth in chapter 9.

These other deep-sea records generally have been dated by various Quaternary radiometric dating methods, including the ^{14}C method and the uranium series dating methods (Dansgaard et al., 1971, p. 40). Dansgaard and Johnsen (1969a, p. 222) summarize the agreement between their flow model-dated Camp Century ice core with ice age reference horizons from elsewhere by saying:

> Secondly, when stable oxygen-isotope data for about 1600 samples from the core were plotted against the age of the ice in our time scale, they showed a variation which was in complete agreement with practically all known climatic changes with the last 70000 or 100000 years . . .

This matching of the Camp Century ice core with other data supposedly provides powerful "confirmation" for the flow model applied to the Camp Century core. It also supposedly justifies their Evolutionary-Uniformitarian assumptions and their belief that the ice sheets have been in equilibrium for a few million years or more. But this procedure is just circular reasoning, since they assumed these reference horizons in the first place. They tie all paleoclimatic records to their assumed chronology and ice age history.

Volcanic Reference Horizons

A few reference horizons are considered especially accurate. In this section and the next, I will discuss two of the main reference horizons: volcanic markers and ^{10}Be spikes.

As mentioned in the previous chapter, volcanic eruptions show up as sulfuric acid spikes in the ice cores. These show up well by ECM and DEP. Occasionally even tephra layers are observed in cores, as in the Byrd and Dome Fuji ice cores (Gow and Williamson, 1971; Ageta et al., 1998). These tephra bands are likely from local Antarctic volcanic eruptions (Delmas et al., 1985). Figure 8.4 shows the acidity profile for the 400-meter deep Crête core on Greenland (Hammer, Clausen, and Dansgaard, 1980). The spikes in acidity have been correlated to eruptions of known date, such as Krakatoa, Tambora, and Laki. From the dates of these eruptions, one can deduce the annual layer thickness between eruptions. This method has the potential to determine the annual layer thickness and the age of the ice much deeper in the deep ice cores. For instance, the gigantic Toba eruption is used as a reference horizon at 72,000 years (Legrand and Mayewski, 1997, p. 225). The ice age Toba eruption in Sumatra, Indonesia, was strong enough to block out most of the sunlight from the entire earth for several months (Froggatt et al., 1986; Rampino and Self, 1992, 1993). This eruption gives us an idea of the strength of some Ice Age eruptions in the Creation-Flood Ice Age model.

However, there are a number of problems with using volcanic spikes to date ice cores (Hammer, Clausen, and Dansgaard, 1980, Hammer, 1986; Cole-Dai et al., 2000). First, only the most significant volcanic eruptions can deposit acids on the ice sheets (Svensen, Biscaye, and Grousset,

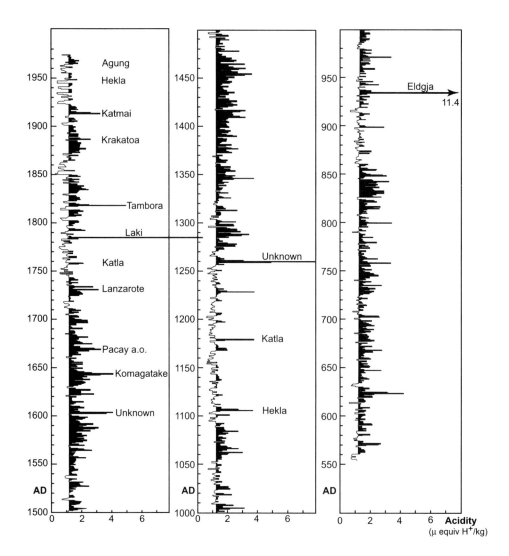

Figure 8.4   Acidity of the 400 meter Crête ice core from Greenland shows several acidity spikes that can be correlated to volcanic eruptions (from Hammer, Clausen, and Dansgaard, 1980, p. 230).

2000, p. 4652). Second, eruptions from one hemisphere often do not produce a significant acidity spike on the ice sheet in the other hemisphere (Cole-Dai et al., 2000). Third, eruptions close to the ice sheets confuse the global signal:

> Only large equatorial volcanic eruptions produce global signals, but due to the local eruptions from Iceland and coastal Antarctic regions, the identification of global signals is a challenging task and has so far only been possible for a few events (Schwander et al., 2001, p. 4,243).

In regard to the Greenland Ice Sheet, Iceland is close enough that even modest eruptions can result in high acidity (Grönvold et al., 1995). Fourth, Ice Age ice on the Greenland Ice Sheet is too alkaline to pick up many volcanic acidity spikes. Fifth, intermediate acidity maximums may be due to either to an especially strong annual or subannual acidity maximum (Delmas et al., 1985). Sixth, some acidity spikes can be due to meltwater. Clausen et al. (1997) believe some of the acidity spikes in the Dye 3 core are due to high nitric acid levels caused by melt layers. Seventh, "ghost acidity peaks" can be caused by reworking of deposited snow by wind (Delmas et al., 1985, p. 12,909).

Even more significant, volcanic history is really known accurately only to *200 years* (Clausen et al., 1997)! A few large eruptions are known beyond 200 years, but with all the other acidity spikes and difficulties mentioned above, it is difficult to match the eruption with a spike in the ice cores. So, the volcanic reference horizons become more and more sketchy the further one goes beyond 200 years in the past. It is very difficult to pin a precise date on *any* acidity peak beyond 2,000 years ago (Zielinski et al., 1994; Grönvold et al., 1995; Meese et al., 1997, p. 26,413; Cole-Dai et al., 2000; Basile et al., 2001, p. 31,915). Hammer (1989, p. 114), who first wrote of volcanic reference horizons, admits that the method is not used much for two reasons:

> The use of volcanic reference horizons in ice cores, however, has not been widely used. The reason is twofold: First, before volcanic horizons could be used for dating purposes it was necessary to establish a time scale independent of any subjective interpretations of the volcanic signals (by seasonal variations). Second, the information on past volcanic eruptions is limited and the dating of the eruptions is not very precise, apart from certain well-documented historical eruptions.

As for the so-called acidity reference horizon for Toba at 72,000 years, this can only be due to attributing a strong Ice Age spike in ice cores that has already been dated by other methods. It is subjective to attach this event to one of the innumerable ice age acidity spikes.

Beryllium-10 Reference Horizons

Beryllium-10 is a cosmogenic radioactive isotope formed by cosmic rays in the same manner carbon-14 is formed (McHargue and Damon, 1991). The very small amount of beryllium-10 formed *in situ* by cosmic rays striking the ground or ice is insignificant to ice core dating (Stauffer, 1989). Beryllium-10 has a half-life of 1.5 million years, although it was once measured to be 2.7 million years (Yiou and Raisbeck, 1972). Beryllium-10 is routinely measured in ice cores today. Chlorine-36 is another cosmogenic radioactive isotope that is sometimes measured and applied to reference horizons in ice cores (Wagner et al., 2000).

Beryllium-10 is important for ice core dating because of two spikes at about 35,000 and 60,000 years ago, within the Evolutionary-Uniformitarian timescale, at Vostok, Antarctica (figure 8.5). Each spike supposedly lasted one to two thousand years. These spikes are also found in deep-sea cores (Yiou et al., 1985; Raisbeck et al., 1987). Figure 8.5 shows that the spikes are about twice the background level of measured beryllium-10. There is also a general broad-scale correlation between high ^{10}Be and low δ^{18}O, although the spikes themselves do not seem to be correlated. Beryllium-10 decreases dramatically from the Ice Age to the post–Ice age period.

The well-developed spikes in ^{10}Be from the Vostok core can be used to date other ice cores by correlation, since the ages of the spikes are supposedly known from other climatic data sets. But the peaks are not always found in other ice cores and are sometimes found at the *wrong* times—a hint that the Antarctic and Greenland deep ice cores may *not* correlate. For instance, the 35,000-year peak in the Vostok core does not show up well in the Camp Century core, and the 60,000-year peak in Vostok could not be found in the Byrd, Camp Century, GRIP, or GISP2 ice cores (Beer et al., 1992; Baumgartner et al., 1997, 1998). Part of the problem could be due to inadequate sampling. Another possibility is that the Ice Age timescale in Antarctica is greatly expanded compared to Greenland (see chapter 10). The 60,000-year spike from Vostok was used to date coastal cores

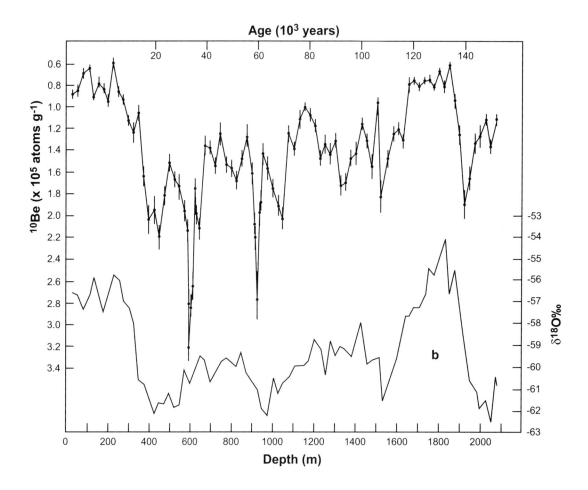

Figure 8.5   Beryllium-10 concentration and $\delta^{18}O$ as a function of depth in the Vostok ice core. Note the inverted scale of ^{10}Be that facilitates comparison between the two records (from Raisbeck et al., 1987, p. 275).

on Greenland, but because the spike is missing for some reason in the GRIP and GISP2 cores, the coastal cores had to be "redated" (Reeh, Oerter, and Thomsen, 2002).

There are further mismatches. The youngest peak in the GISP2 core was dated at 40,000 years, which is 5,000 years too old (Yiou et al., 1997a). Correlations between ice sheets, however, may be confused with other spikes. For instance, a spike of a little more than double the background level of ^{10}Be occurring at 1,850 meters in the Dye 3 core is dated at 13,000 years within the Evolutionary-Uniformitarian dating system (Beer et al., 1985, p. 69). This could be the same spike dated at 35,000 years in Antarctic cores, since the Antarctic ice core timescale is stretched out much more than Greenland cores. Then the spike dated as 60,000 years in Antarctic cores would correspond to the 40,000-year spike in Greenland cores. This would make the spikes global phenomena that really are correlated, but the Antarctic timescale must be greatly compressed.

In order to understand the cause of the ^{10}Be spikes as well as the broad-scale trend, one must understand the global geochemistry of ^{10}Be (McHargue and Damon, 1991; Morris, 1991). The beryllium trend in ice cores could be caused by (1) changes in production rate, (2) changes in the atmospheric circulation, or (3) changes in the precipitation rate (Beer et al., 1985, p. 69). The geochemical cycling of ^{10}Be is quite complicated with a number of minor inputs and variations (Finkel and Nishiizumi, 1997). The formation of beryllium-10 in the atmosphere depends upon (1) variations in primary cosmic ray flux, (2) changes in solar modulation, and (3) changes in geomagnetic field intensity (Raisbeck et al., 1987, p. 275). There is a latitudinal difference in [10]Be formation with much more produced above polar regions (Lal, 1987, p. 787). Approximately 70% of the production is in the stratosphere and 30% in the troposphere (Beer et al., 1983; Morris, 1991, p. 315). From its formation, [10]Be is quickly scavenged by submicron particles—unlike carbon-14, which remains in the atmosphere a long time as carbon dioxide. Beryllium-10 can especially be scavenged by sulfates after volcanic eruptions (McHargue and Damon, 1991, p. 142). Residence time in the stratosphere is a little less than one year but is about only three weeks in the troposphere. In addition, the residence time of [10]Be depends upon stratosphere-troposphere exchange, which is greater during the spring in the midlatitudes. It also depends upon intertropospheric mixing. So there is both a tropospheric and stratospheric source for [10]Be, which could have been different in the past. To complicate matters, [10]Be is recycled from dust and soil particles into the atmosphere (McHargue and Damon, 1991, p. 142). Such complications make the interpretation of [10]Be in ice cores difficult and open to the possibility that conditions were different during the Ice Age.

Deposition of [10]Be on the earth's surface is especially dependent upon precipitation, which is related to the general circulation of the atmosphere. The greater the precipitation, the more the [10]Be deposition (Masarik and Beer, 1999). However, a dilution effect has been observed in areas of high rainfall, which complicates this correlation. There is also dry deposition of [10]Be that would compensate for lack of snowfall in some areas, further complicating the correlation with precipitation (see appendix 2 for a discussion of wet and dry deposition). Most of the [10]Be deposited at low accumulation sites on the Antarctic Ice Sheet is by dry deposition (Steig, Stuiver, and Polissar, 1995). So, even though Camp Century has more than ten times the snowfall as Vostok, Camp Century has only 25% more [10]Be (Raisbeck and Yiou, 1985). Furthermore, there is much variation in [10]Be deposition in individual rain- or snowstorms. Some storms result in the deposition of up to 20 times more [10]Be than the average (Morris, 1991, p. 322). Such large inputs could be due to increased stratospheric mixing. Measurements of [10]Be concentrations in monthly rainwater in France vary by up to a factor of three (Beer et al., 1985, p. 68).

Some researchers believe that polar climatic changes account for the beryllium-10 record in ice cores, while others favor the idea that the [10]Be production rate changed (Lal, 1987; Beer et al., 1988; Mazaud, Laj, and Bender, 1994; Muscheler et al., 2000). The broad-scale trend in the ice cores, two to three times greater [10]Be deposition during glacial maximum than during the Holocene, is assumed to be caused by much less ice age precipitation (Raisbeck et al., 1981; Oeschger et al., 1984; Yiou et al., 1997a). However, the [10]Be increase during the ice age could also be due to dry deposition. The trend could also be due partially or wholly to other variables.

The spikes at 35,000 and 60,000 years are not attributed to decreased precipitation because there is no correlation with $\delta^{18}O$ in Antarctic cores. However, there is a positive correlation with the [10]Be peak and relative $\delta^{18}O$ maximum in the Camp Century and GRIP cores (Yiou et al., 1997a). The spikes are believed to have been caused by geomagnetic excursions that allowed increased cosmic rays to impact the earth (Wagner et al., 2000). But the increased [10]Be is greater than that predicted by a zero dipole field (Raisbeck et al, 1987). Other possibilities include long-period changes in solar activity, increased number of galactic cosmic rays, a supernova, or increased amount of glacial meltwater (McHargue and Damon, 1991, p. 144–145, Sonett, Morfill, and Jokipii, 1987). Oeschger (1985, pp. 14–15) noted that [10]Be production was 1.6 times the 800-year average during the Maunder minimum in sunspots about A.D. 1700 (figure 8.6).

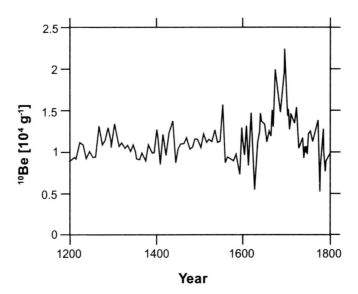

Figure 8.6   Beryllium-10 concentration in 10^4 atoms/g of ice as a function of age in the Milcent ice core, Greenland (after Oeschger, 1985, p. 14).

In summary, many variables are too poorly known to make any claims about the broad-scale distribution of ^{10}Be in ice cores. Furthermore, the ^{10}Be spikes cannot be used to correlate between the two ice sheets, unless the timescale for Antarctic cores is significantly reduced.

Within the Creation-Flood Ice Age model, there are at least three possibilities for explaining the two ^{10}Be spikes. One possibility is that intense volcanic eruptions may be the source of the two major ^{10}Be spikes as well as other spikes. Such a global cause of the spikes is supported by the spikes showing up in the ice cores on both Antarctica and Greenland. Alternatively, in the compressed timescale in the Creation-Flood model, the spikes could be due to increased solar modulation due to fewer sunspots, such as in the Maunder minimum when ^{10}Be nearly doubled (Oeschger, 1985, p. 14). Evidence for this suggestion is provided by the fact that beryllium-10 is strongly correlated with the 11-year sunspot cycle (Steig et al., 1996). A third possibility is that a stormy period on a decadal scale caused by a period of relatively violent volcanic eruptions (see chapter 10) could cause a greater influx of stratospheric air that contained more ^{10}Be.

Does the Ice Core Bubble Data Support an Equilibrium Ice Sheet?

I have been making a case that the Greenland and Antarctic Ice Sheets have *not* been in equilibrium for millions of years or even 10,000 years. The evidence for 110,000 annual layers in the GISP2 core is based mainly on the assumption of old age, and there are alternative ways to explain the observed data. The Creation-Flood Ice Age model proposes that the Greenland and Antarctic Ice Sheets formed rapidly in a 700-year Ice Age and experienced further growth in the post–Ice Age climate (figure 8.7). So, the ice that is now low in the ice cores did not originate near the top of the ice sheet and sink to a lower level, but was deposited on a growing ice sheet at low to intermediate levels (Vardiman, 1993).

Glaciologists measure the pressure, volume, and temperature of the air bubbles in the ice. Since the pressure is related to altitude, the measurements can be used as an ancient altimeter

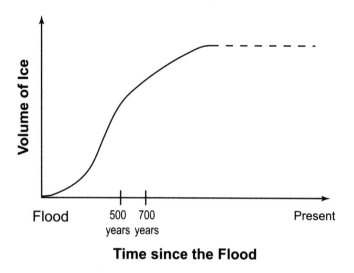

Figure 8.7 Buildup of the ice on Greenland and Antarctica since the Flood.

(Raynaud and Lorius, 1973, 1977; Raynaud and Lebel, 1979; Raynaud et al., 1979, 1982; Raynaud and Whillans, 1982; Raynaud, 1983; Jenssen and Radok, 1982; Jenssen, 1983). From these measurements, scientists have deduced that the ice in the lower portion of the cores was deposited at nearly the same height as the current ice sheet. This lends support for their equilibrium model and is contrary to the Creation-Flood model. Is this bubble data proof of ice sheets in equilibrium for millions of years or is the observed bubble data equivocal and open to different interpretations?

The bubbles in ice are formed as firn snow that contains much air becomes denser with depth until the pores close off and ice forms, trapping air bubbles. This occurs around 50 to 100 meters deep in the ice sheets. Near the pore close-off depth at 56 meters in the Byrd core there are 150 to 200 bubbles per cm^3 (Gow, Ueda, and Garfield, 1968, p. 1,012). The bubbles disappear around 1,200 meters, being compressed so much by the overlying ice that the bubbles form an air hydrate with the ice (Miller, 1969; Shoji and Langway, 1982). Upon melting of this ice, the air in the hydrate is released, possessing almost the same volume as when the air first became trapped in the ice.

Researchers measure the volume (V_c), pressure (P_c), and temperature (T_c) of the air in the bubbles for when the air bubbles closed off, where the subscript c applies to the core measurements. These measurements are then reduced to standard temperature and pressure at sea level by the following equation, where V is the resulting volume of air reduced to standard sea level pressure (P) at 1013 mb, and standard temperature (T) at 273°K (Raynaud and Lebel, 1979):

$$V = V_c \times P_c / T_c \times T / P \qquad (8.1)$$

This equation assumes a constant pore volume at bubble close-off in equilibrium ice sheets. Figure 8.8 presents an early result relating the volume of air measured versus temperature and elevation; 90% of the change in V_c is caused by pressure, while 10% is caused by temperature (Martinerie et al., 1988).

105

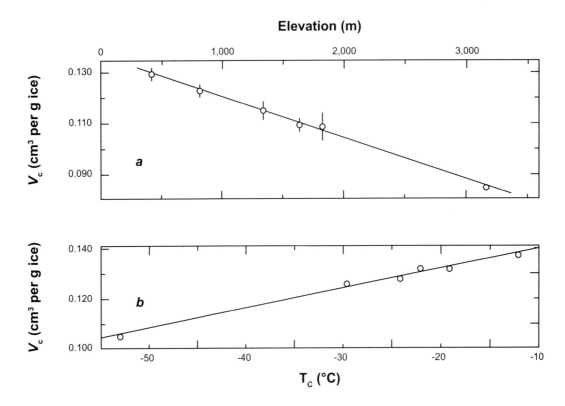

Figure 8.8 Relationship between (a) the volume (V) reduced to standard pressure and temperature with ice sheet elevations of the measurements, and (b) the measured volume (V_c) and measured temperature (T_c) (after Raynaud and Lebel, 1979, p. 289).

The relationships look impressive, but Raynaud and Lebel (1979) did discover some strange results that indicate problems with the method. For instance, the Greenland Ice Sheet was supposedly 1,200 to 1,400 meters *higher* during the ice age than at present; researchers now believe it was 100 to 200 meters *lower* than at present! The gas content in the basal ice of the Camp Century ice core is 50% of the volume measured at the top of the core. This would imply that the ice sheet was *four* times its current height during the ice age according to equation 8.1 (Herron and Langway, 1979, 1987). These are significant errors. The researchers postulate that some of the basal ice is due to the freezing of melted basal ice that would lose some or all its air content. So, there are complications with the use of bubble data for an ancient altimeter.

One of the more significant problems is that a lot of scatter occurs in their volume measurements. Raynaud et al. (1997, p. 26,067) inform us:

> At a given site, short-term V variations are observed. Their amplitudes can reach up to about 20% of V. They essentially reflect a seasonal type of V_c variability that has been associated either with the seasonal variations of the surface snow temperature [*Raynaud and Lebel*, 1979; *Raynaud and Whillans*, 1982] or with the fact that the high-density winter layers close their bubbles at shallower depth and thus prematurely isolate the summer layers from the free atmosphere.

Such seasonal or short period variations are up to 20% (Herron and Langway, 1987, p. 286), while figure 8.8 shows that the volume variations from near sea level to 3,000 meters represent a difference of 25–30%. Seasonal changes in wind speed, melt layers, depth hoar, ice crystal size, and radiation crusts cause much of the seasonal contrast (Paterson and Hammer, 1987, p. 97; Sowers et al., 1992; Martinerie et al., 1994; Delmotte et al., 1999; Krinner et al., 2000). Melt water that later refreezes loses most of the air in the snow (Herron and Langway, 1987, pp. 286–287). To complicate matters further, measurements performed on adjacent horizontal layers may show volume differences as great as 20–25% (Martinerie et al., 1988). Bubble volume measurements of Holocene ice in Law Dome varied from 0.114 to 0.128 with an average of 0.118 cm^3/gm (see figure 2.12) (Delmotte et al., 1999). Such variability is attributed to the formation of depth hoar. The bubbles in the Ice Age ice near the bottom of Law Dome core averaged 0.110 cm^3/gm, suggesting that this ice formed at a higher altitude than the dome's current height of 1,200 meters. This is a distinct possibility (see chapter 1). On the other hand, lower ice age values of air content could also be due to other factors (Delmotte et al., 1999). This leaves open the possibility that a changing climate can account for a fair percentage of the altitudinal variability.

There are a number of variables that have a relatively small effect on the bubble volume but added up could have a significant impact on the volume and interpreted altitude of the ice. These variables also contribute to the scatter in the measurements and are expected to be different in the past, especially during the ice age:

> The interpretation of ice core air content in terms of past ice sheet elevation over the last glacial-interglacial cycles is not simple because the interpretation depends on several parameters, each of them being variable with time. . . . To correctly interpret the air content of the ice in terms of past ice sheet elevation changes, the variations of these parameters must therefore be known (Krinner et al., 2000, p. 2059).

Because some of the bubbles are cut during processing, 1–10% of the air can escape, depending upon the size of the bubbles (Martinerie, Lipenkov, and Raynaud, 1990). Colder sites tend to have a larger number of small bubbles and vice versa. A correction is applied for the cut-bubble effect, but there is still a fair amount of uncertainty (Martinerie et al., 1992, p. 10).

Another variable is that pressure differences due to long-term atmospheric circulation changes over the ice sheet (such as during the Ice Age), can affect the volume in the bubbles (Martinerie et al., 1992). A stormier period with a greater number of low pressure systems will cause a bubble air volume reduction. This difference can result in an overestimation of the altitude by about 150 meters during the glacial period (Krinner et al., 2000).

Much of the bubble volume variability is likely related to conditions at pore close-off (Raynaud et al., 1997). These past conditions are relatively unknown:

> These results highlight the fact that variations in the porosity of close-off during past periods are not well constrained. . . . Furthermore the mechanism governing the present-day V_c variations are not fully understood, so V_c behaviour under glacial conditions is not well constrained (Delmotte et al., 1999, pp. 255–256, 260).

The variable conditions at bubble close-off are enough to account for *almost all the amplitude in the volume measurements*:

> Overall variability of the air content, observed along deep ice cores recovered in Greenland and in Antarctica has an amplitude up to 25% . . . On the other hand, an air-content signal with the same order of magnitude can be induced by variability of close-off porosity, V_c, associated with the stratigraphy of the ice sediments due to different weather conditions (causing very short-term variation within a few

centimeters of ice core) or with wind speed changes due to climatic variability (Lipenkov et al., 1995, p. 424).

Besides the seasonal variables mentioned above, the volume of air at pore close-off may depend upon the accumulation rate (Kameda et al., 1990; Raynaud et al., 1997), although others dispute such dependency (Martinerie et al., 1992, 1994). A change in seasonal precipitation is another factor that can change the volume of air trapped in the ice (Raynaud et al., 1997). More snow in winter will tend to reduce the volume, and vice versa for summer.

In the Creation-Flood model any one or all of the above variables would be different during the Ice Age and the immediate post–Ice Age period. We must remember that in the current ice sheet the ice from the Ice Age was originally higher because the layers have been compressed downward from when the snow was first deposited. Thus, the air volume during the Ice Age and immediately afterwards does not need to be 25–30% greater but rather approximately 15% greater than measured. In other words, to reconcile the measured bubble data claimed, by evolutionary scientists, to indicate a thick ice sheet in equilibrium, there needs to be climatic variables that reduce the amount of air to less than the measured variability. Many of the mainstream scientists that have studied the bubble data admit that the ice age climate was different and that the bubble data can be misinterpreted:

> Use of such measurements in old ice to estimate past surface elevations, on the other hand, rests on the assumption that the present rate of change of gas content with surface elevation is typical of the past, including the Ice Age. This is doubtful. . . .We do not use gas content data in this review because we believe that, although the method is potentially useful, the conclusions from most studies so far published are unreliable (Paterson and Hammer, 1987, p. 97).

Concerning specific variables that would cause lower gas contents in the middle and lower portions of the ice cores within the Creation-Flood model, table 8.1 shows seven possibilities. I believe that the factors of increased melt layers, stronger wind, and more dust alone would easily reduce the volume of air over that expected from present day conditions.

1.	Lower atmosphere pressure
2.	Colder temperatures
3.	Higher wind speed
4.	More dust
5.	More melt layers
6.	More "winter-type" snow
7.	Correction for cut bubble effect too high

Table 8.1 Variables that would result in an altitude overestimation from V_c, the measured bubble volume in ice cores.

I have discussed in this chapter the use of glaciological flow models and reference horizons to date ice cores. Before reference horizons can be used, the Evolutionary-Uniformitarian scientists need to deduce the dates of these events from other climatic records. How do scientists know the dates? The dates are obtained by assuming the astronomical theory of the ice age, also called the *Milankovitch mechanism*. This is the fourth dating method, and it is the actual dating method within the Evolutionary-Uniformitarian paradigm to which all other methods must conform. This method will be analyzed in the next chapter.

Chapter 9

CRITIQUE OF DATING BY MILANKOVITCH INSOLATION CHANGES

The last dating method discussed, which is actually the *main* dating method used to date ice cores, is the Milankovitch insolation changes caused by the Milankovitch mechanism or astronomical theory of the ice age. The Milankovitch mechanism sets the timescale for glaciological flow models and reference horizons. The flow model in turn was used as a first guess to determine the annual layer thickness for the GRIP and GISP2 Greenland cores. Moreover, the Milankovitch mechanism has set the timescale for deep-sea cores, pollen cores, lake cores, loess/paleosol sequences, and other Pleistocene climatic time series. Many of these events are used as reference horizons in dating ice cores. No one should be surprised that the bottom of the ice sheets date to hundreds of thousands of years, nor should they be surprised that these other climate systems are dated up to a few million years old. This is because they all *assume* the Milankovitch mechanism for glacial/interglacial oscillations. Believe it or not, the Milankovitch mechanism, supposed to work through changing ice volume, also has been applied to pre-Pleistocene sediment oscillations, which occurred at a time when little or no ice existed on the continents (Oard, 1997b)

The Milankovitch Mechanism

The Milankovitch mechanism is supposed to generate multiple ice ages resulting from differences in solar radiation due to cyclical variations in the geometry of the earth's orbit around the sun. There are three variations: (1) changes in the eccentricity of the earth's orbit, (2) the precession of the equinoxes, and (3) changes in the tilt of the earth's axis. The eccentricity and tilt cycles are caused by gravitational attraction between the earth and the other planets. The precession of the equinoxes is a result of the gravitational attraction between the sun and moon with the earth's equatorial bulge. Improvements over the years in the orbital data of planets have resulted in improvements in the equations of celestial mechanics. The calculations of Vernekar (1972) and Berger (1977a,b, 1978) are considered standard today. Berger's calculations are considered the most accurate, but Vernekar's results agree reasonably well with Berger's, especially for the past 400,000 years within the Evolutionary-Uniformitarian timescale. I will be using the data from Vernekar (1972) because he has published a monograph that separates the warm and cold half seasons (caloric seasons or half years) and graphed the data for all latitudes. Berger's results are published mainly for shorter periods, like the month of July for a particular latitude, and give the impression that the mechanism is much more significant. One must consider the whole warm season and a whole hemisphere to understand the real effect of the Milankovitch mechanism.

The earth's orbit around the sun is an ellipse, which is a slightly flattened circle (figure 9.1). Eccentricity is a measure of the ellipticity of the orbit with zero being a perfect circle and one being a straight line. The current eccentricity of the earth is 0.017 in which the sun is three million miles closer to the earth at perihelion on January 3 than at aphelion on July 4 (figure 9.1). Over the past, eccentricity is believed to have varied from zero to 0.06 with two major cyles, one that is 100,000 years and the other that is 413,000 years long. Figure 9.2 shows the variation of the eccentricity extrapolated backwards for the past two million years (Vernekar, 1972).

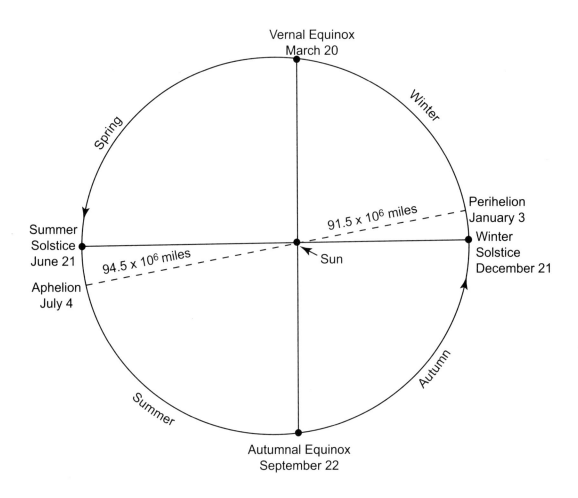

Figure 9.1   The current geometry of the earth's orbit around the sun (from Oard, 1984a, p. 67, redrawn from Imbrie and Imbrie, 1979, p. 70).

The precession of the equinox is the rotation of the orbital ellipse of the earth around the sun. The precession of the equinoxes has a period of around 22,000 years. The precession is only significant when the orbital eccentricity is greater than zero; the earth's orbit must be elliptical and not a perfect circle. With an elliptical orbit, the sun is closer to the earth at perihelion. Figure 9.3 shows how, in the Evolutionary-Uniformitarian ice age, perihelion changed by 180° between the model of 11,000 years ago and the present as seen from the fixed stars. Perihelion would have been in summer 11,000 years ago. Since the eccentricity of the earth's orbit modulates the precessional effect (the greater the eccentricity the greater the precessional effect on sunshine absorbed at the earth's surface), both are graphed in figure 9.4 for the past, supposed two million years.

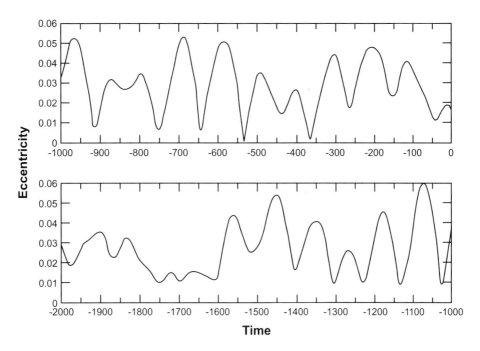

Figure 9.2 The variation in the earth's eccentricity for an assumed past two millions years. Units are in thousands of years (from Oard, 1984a, p. 67, after Vernekar, 1972, p. 4).

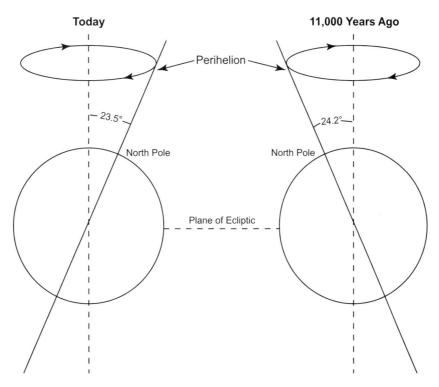

Figure 9.3 The change in the earth's axis as seen from the fixed stars between today and 11,000 years ago. Also included is the change in the tilt of the earth's axis in that time (from Oard, 1984a, p. 67, redrawn from Fodor, 1982, p. 111).

113

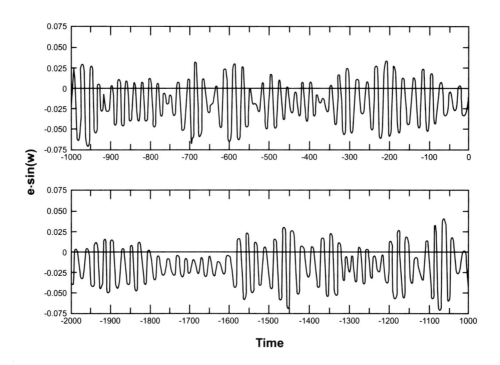

Figure 9.4   The variation of the precession of the equinoxes, modulated by the change in the eccentricity of the earth's orbit. Units are in thousands of years (from Oard, 1984a, p. 68, after Vernekar, 1972, p. 7).

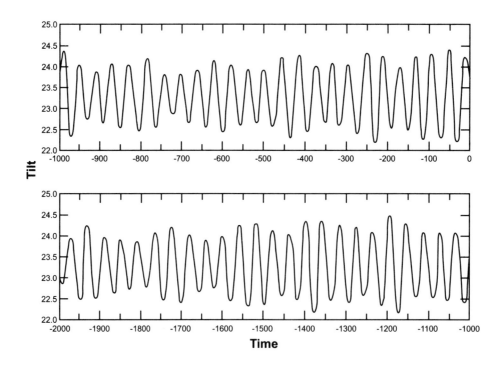

Figure 9.5   The variation in the tilt of the earth's axis for an assumed past two million years. Units are in thousands of years (after Oard, 1984a, p. 68, after Vernekar, 1972, p. 6).

The earth's tilt varies from 22.1° to 24.5° with a period of 41,000 years. Figure 9.3 also shows the slight change in the tilt between 11,000 years ago and the present. Figure 9.5 shows the variation of the earth's tilt extrapolated backwards for two million years.

The three orbital variations do not change the total radiation received by the earth over a year (Imbrie and Imbrie, 1979, p. 83). The Milankovitch mechanism only causes changes in the *seasonal and latitudinal distribution* of solar radiation. The tilt redistributes the solar radiation latitudinally in each hemisphere. The precession cycle affects the seasonal partition of solar radiation.

The changes in solar radiation for all three orbital influences are shown in figure 9.6 in units of *langleys* per day as a function of latitude for the top of the atmosphere calculated from 160,000 years ago to 50,000 years into the future. A langley is the amount of radiation in calories absorbed in one minute on one cm^2 perpendicular to the sun's radiation. Figure 9.6 is for the Northern Hemispheric caloric summer, the warmest six months, since this is the variable that supposedly determines multiple ice ages. The Northern Hemisphere summer radiational changes at 65°N are supposed to be the pacemaker of ice ages (Hays, Imbrie, and Shackleton, 1976; Imbrie and Imbrie, 1979, pp. 104–105). Figure 9.6 indicates a cooling 70,000 years ago (in the Evolutionary-Uniformitarian paradigm) of about 20 langleys/day at 65°N to initiate the "last" ice age, the Wisconsin ice age.

There is also a deficiency of about 20 langleys/day about 25,000 years ago that is supposed to have ushered in the last advance of the "last" ice age. This compares with the average radiation at 65°N for the six-month period from April 1 to September 30 of 750 langleys/day. These spikes in radiation at 65°N are only about 3% of the average. But notice on figure 9.6 that the deficiency in radiation is less in the middle latitudes and more over the poles. So, the net hemispheric change is significantly less than 3%. Therefore, the Milankovitch mechanism is inherently a small effect.

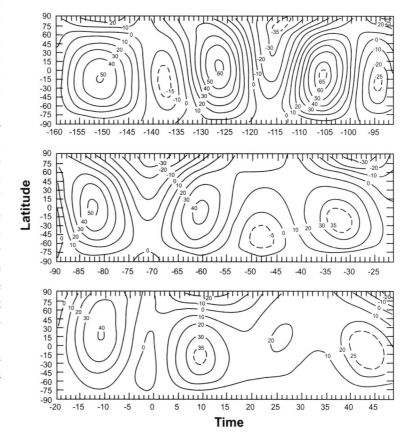

Figure 9.6   The net change in solar radiation in langleys per day received at the top of the atmosphere in the Northern Hemisphere caloric summer for an assumed time interval of 160,000 years in the past to 50,000 years in the future. Minus latitude is for the Southern Hemisphere. Units are in thousands of years (after Oard, 1984a, p. 69, after Vernekar, 1972, p. 19).

The Milankovitch Paradigm Determines Ice Age History

The Milankovitch mechanism is actually an old ice age hypothesis developed by Joseph Adhemar and James Croll in the mid-1800s (Oard, 1984a). However, the hypothesis was rejected because of a lack of understanding of the mechanism and poor celestial mechanics equations. After more detailed celestial mechanical calculations had been made in the early 1900s, Milutin Milankovitch, a Yugoslavian meteorologist, derived the secular changes in solar radiation with time. Most European geologists accepted Milankovitch's hypothesis, but it waned by the middle 1900s due to many dating contradictions and because the radiational changes are quite small.

The hypothesis was revived in the 1960s as a result of matching the Milankovitch radiational changes at 65°N with climatic changes deduced from deep-sea cores (Hays, Imbrie, and Shackleton, 1976). The scientists discovered that ice ages for the past 800,000 years have developed and waned to the 100,000-eccentricity cycle. Several scientists later found "proof" that ice ages before this time oscillated according to the tilt cycle of 41,000 years. The reason for this switch in the Milankovitch cycle is unknown. As a result of the statistical matches with deep-sea cores, most scientists came to believe that the Milankovitch mechanism had been proven. It is considered a "fact" now and has become a *ruling paradigm* in climate research in which all data sets are fit to the mechanism. Grootes and Stuiver (1997, p. 26,460) admit: "Deep-sea sediment cores have long provided the standard for past climatic developments."

Because the mechanism is considered a fact, scientists have used it as *input* into glaciological flow models and reference horizons to *date* the Greenland and Antarctic Ice Sheets. The Vostok ice core, for instance, shows four large cycles of oxygen or deuterium isotope ratio (see figure 2.11). This is viewed as representing four Milankovitch ice ages that repeat every 100,000 years. This asumption is the reason why the bottom of the Vostok core is dated to over 400,000 years old and the ice near the bottom of the new Dome C core is dated at 740,000! It is rather interesting that the glaciological flow models, the main method of determining Antarctic chronology, are a little off from the Milankovitch expectations (Salamatin et al., 1998). So, the age in the deeper part of the core is matched to marine isotopic stages that are based on the Milankovitch mechanism.

Since the Milankovitch mechanism is considered a fact, glaciologists now simply "tune" the Vostok timescale to agree with Milankovitch radiational oscillations at 65°N. Waelbroeck et al. (1995, pp. 113) inform us that they simply tuned the timescale when there were only two cycles in an earlier core (there are actually several deep Vostok cores):

> Taking advantage of the fact that the Vostok deuterium (δD) record now covers almost two entire climate cycles, we have applied the orbital tuning approach to derive an age-depth relation for the Vostok ice core, which is consistent with the SPECMAP marine time scale [from deep-sea cores].

The SPECMAP marine timescale was earlier tuned to the Milankovitch orbital changes:

> The deep-sea core chronology developed using the concept of "orbital tuning" or SPECMAP chronology . . . is now generally accepted in the ocean sediment scientific community (Waelbroeck et al., 1995, pp. 113–114).

Not only is the Vostok timescale derived from the Milankovitch mechanism, but other ice cores from both the Antarctic and Greenland Ice Sheets are ultimately also based on the Milankovitch mechanism. Watanabe et al. (2003, p. 512) state: "However, we can at present rely on orbital constraints derived from the ice $\delta^{18}O$ record only." Hondoh et al. (2002, p. 384) admit:

116

The geophysical metronome (Milankovitch components of the past surface temperature variations) and the isotope-temperature transfer function deduced from the borehole temperature profile at Vostok station, Antarctica, are applied to date the 2500 m deep ice core from Dome Fuji station, Antarctica.

These researchers go on to speculate that the ice at 3,000 meters is around two million years old, which is 1.7 million years older than the ice at 2,500 meters. This age deduction is based on the extreme annual layer thinning *assumed* for the bottom of all ice sheets.

The Milankovitch Mechanism Too Weak to Cause an Ice Age

This is not the place for a detailed critique of the Milankovitch ruling paradigm according to the Creation-Flood Ice Age model, since that would take a monograph in itself. Such an analysis would have to delve into deep-sea cores and Quaternary dating schemes. I will only briefly mention several of the more obvious problems with the Milankovitch mechanism (Oard, 1984a,b, 1985).

One of the most obvious problems that should be fatal to the hypothesis is that the radiational changes are much too weak to cause such a dramatic climatic change as an ice age:

Milankovitch cycles are the only known major climate forcing functions identified in ocean and ice cores. Yet despite the small resulting radiation changes, large climate changes occur. Thus, there are strong nonlinear and positive feedbacks in the system (Hecht et al., 1989, p. 384).

Notice that because evolutionists assume the very small Milankovitch mechanism is true, they need to postulate strong nonlinear feedbacks to account for the drastic climate change of an ice age. The oscillations in radiation shown on figure 9.6 when added up for the whole Northern Hemisphere are quite small compared with the average radiation.

Furthermore, these changes in figure 9.6 are almost totally due to the precession and tilt cycles. The ice ages, on the other hand, are supposed to have cycled according to the 100,000-year eccentricity cycle for the past 800,000 years. Scientists used to claim there were only four ice ages, but now they claim there were around 30 regularly repeating ice ages (Kennett, 1982, p. 747). The big problem with the 100,000 cycle is that the radiational change caused by the eccentricity cycle is extremely small! Jouzel, Petit, and Raynaud (1990, p. 353) lament:

However, the implied large amplification of this relatively weak forcing (the total insolation received by the planet has varied by less than 0.6% over the last 10^6 years), the observed dominant 100 ka cycle and the synchronized termination of major glaciations in the Northern and Southern Hemispheres cannot easily be explained.

Didier Paillard (2001, p. 325) corroborates:

Nevertheless, several problems in classical astronomical theory of paleoclimate have indeed been identified: (1) The main cyclicity in the paleoclimatic record is close to 100,000 years, but there is no significant orbitally induced changes in the radiative forcing of the Earth in this frequency range (the "100-kyr Problem").

How could such very small changes in radiation every 100,000 years produce such huge climatic changes—and produce many ice ages in regular succession? This was one of the original reasons for the early rejection of this old hypothesis. Researchers have been looking for strong nonlinear boosting mechanisms for several decades with little or no success; no significant feedback mechanisms have been found (Oard, 1984a). But lately, scientists have been occupied by abrupt climate changes, deduced from the ice cores, that some believe may have worked to trigger a sudden onset of an ice age, which is the basis of the current hyper-environmental concern over anthropogenic climate influences (Oard, 2004c) (see chapter 10).

The surprisingly miniscule radiational change of the Milankovitch mechanism is contrasted to the climate change required to cause an ice age. Larry Williams (1979) performed a computer experiment designed to find out what kind of temperature change was required for one inch or more snow to remain after the spring and summer melting period in Canada (Oard, 1984a, p. 72; 1990, pp. 4–6). Figure 9.7 shows that one inch or more snow was left only in northeast Canada after a summer cooling of 10–12°C. Furthermore, the experiment had a number of favorable features to keep the snow from melting: (1) summer sunshine was reduced to the strong solar radiation minimum in the Milankovitch mechanism at 116,000 years (see figure 9.6), (2) the altitude of the land was raised about 100 meters, (3) the moderating influence of Hudson Bay was taken out, and (4) the winter snowfall was doubled. Without these assumptions, even more cooling is required just for northeast Canada in Williams' experiment. For the snow and ice to built up over the northern United States, a cooling of at least 28°C is required in summer (Oard, 2004a, pp. 98–103).

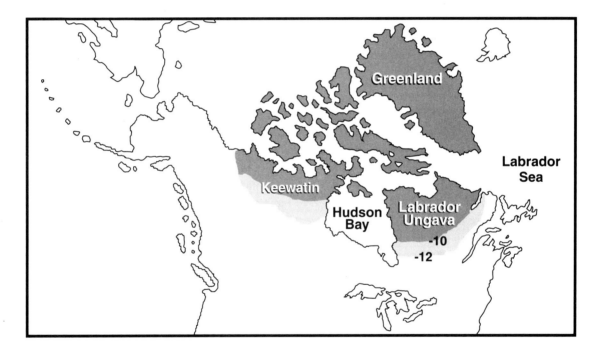

Figure 9.7   Boundaries of permanent snow cover in northeast Canada for a 10°C and 12°C spring and summer temperature decrease from the average (from Oard, 1990, p. 7, redrawn from Williams, 1979).

A second major problem, indicated in the information above, is that "ice ages" in the Northern Hemisphere are supposed to be caused by radiational changes at 65°N, but glaciation in the Southern Hemisphere is also caused by the *same* latitudinal radiational change. The ice age in each hemisphere is synchronous, but a look at figure 9.6 shows that when the summer radiation is negative in the Northern Hemisphere, it is mostly positive in the Southern Hemisphere! For example, the most recent global advance of the last ice age at about 25,000 years shows a positive radiational change in the Southern Hemisphere.

118

Why Do Deep-Sea Cores Show Milankovitch Oscillations?

I f the mechanism is so weak and problematic, then why do scientists believe in the Milankovitch mechanism? The Milankovitch mechanism was "verified" by finding Milankovitch oscillations in deep-sea cores. Because of the correlation of wiggles between radiational changes at 65°N and deep-sea core, oxygen isotope changes, most scientists simply succumbed to the correlation. The question can then be asked, why do scientists find Milankovitch oscillations in deep-sea cores? I will present only a brief description of a few problems in deducing such oscillations, since an in-depth study of this topic is beyond the scope of this monograph.

The Milankovitch oscillations are inferred from fluctuations in the oxygen isotope ratio in marine plankton shells from the ocean bottom. The main plankton group is the foraminifera, of which there are two types: planktonic foraminifera that float near the surface of the ocean and benthonic foraminifera that dwell at the bottom of the ocean.

One of the first problems encountered in evaluating the Milankovitch mechanism in deep-sea cores is that the equation that correlates the temperature with the $\delta^{18}O$ of foraminifera shell formation also has a third *unknown* variable: the $\delta^{18}O$ of the seawater in the past (Oard, 1984b). The only variable known is the measured $\delta^{18}O$ of the foraminifera shells. So, we have the classic problem of one equation with two unknowns. The problem is not trivial since the amplitude of $\delta^{18}O$ of the ocean water between no glaciation and glacial maximum is almost 2‰ (see appendix 1) whereas the amplitude of the foraminifera $\delta^{18}O$ variations is nearly the same (figure 9.8).

There are so many problems associated with the interpretation of $\delta^{18}O$ in foraminifera down deep-sea cores that it is difficult to see how Milankovitch cycles show up at all (Oard, 1984b). I will mention just two main problems. First, the $\delta^{18}O$ of the foraminifera shell depends significantly on the water temperature. There are horizontal temperature differences in the oceans caused especially by the seasons, but there are also strong vertical temperature gradients. In the present tropical and subtropical oceans, the upper layer of water is generally warm, but a little below the surface, the temperature begins to decrease markedly with depth. The most rapid decline is called the *thermocline* and its depth and rate of change vary from place to place. Figure 9.9 shows the thermocline for the eastern equatorial Pacific off Panama. This area has one of the most shallow and highest rate of change of

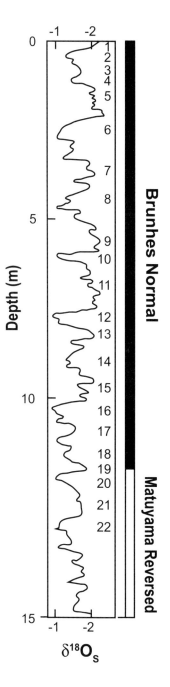

Figure 9.8 Oxygen isotope variations in deep-sea core V28-238 from the Solomon Plateau, Pacific Ocean, at a water depth of 3,120 meters. Magnetic declination of the core is shown at the right (from Oard, 1984b, p. 126, redrawn from Shackleton and Opdyke, 1973).

any thermocline in the ocean. The oxygen isotope ratio is very sensitive to temperature; a four-degree change in temperature results in a 1‰ change in $\delta^{18}O$. Just a change of 25 meters can make a huge difference in $\delta^{18}O$, especially in the thermocline. It is known that planktonic foraminifera often show large vertical ranges (Shackleton and Opdyke, 1973, p. 51; Duplessy, 1978). Therefore, the depth habitat of planktonic foraminifera needs to be known with precision not only in the present, but also in the past.

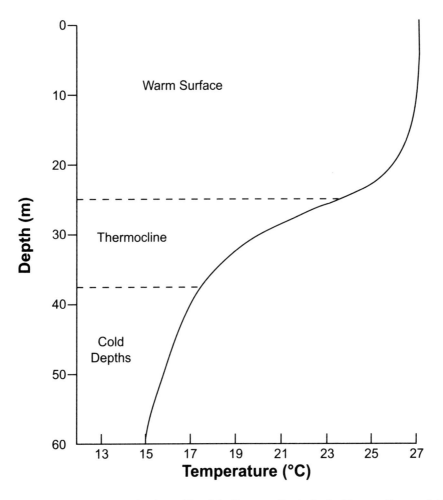

Figure 9.9   The temperature-depth profile of the Panama Basin in the Eastern Equatorial Pacific (from Oard, 1984b, p. 128).

A second problem is that foraminifera shells dissolve while sinking to the bottom, generally starting at about 3,000 meters and becoming almost totally dissolved by 5,000 meters (Oard, 1984b). However, there are a number of variables that change these depths. Moreover, the shell can continue to dissolve on the bottom or in the top layer of sediment. The significance of dissolution is that the calcite of the foraminifera shell has different $\delta^{18}O$ ratios. So, dissolution will change the total $\delta^{18}O$ of the shell. Moreover, dissolution is stronger on shells with a lower $\delta^{18}O$. Usually, oceanographers avoid shells that show any sign of dissolution, but this can sometimes be difficult to know (Oard, 2003b).

120

Recently, it has been found that dissolution and replacement of the shell can occur *without showing diagenetic changes in a binocular microscope* (Schrag, 1999; Oard, 2003b). The electron microscope reveals that secondary calcite of much greater $\delta^{18}O$ can be added to the *inside* of the shells or replace primary shell structure. When the electron microscope was used to pick unaltered planktonic foraminifera, the resulting temperature increase amounted to a whopping 15°C (Pearson et al., 2001). This amounts to about a 4‰ $\delta^{18}O$ difference, which is more than twice the amplitude of the supposed glacial/interglacial oscillations. This causes most research results using planktonic foraminifera to be suspect:

> We infer from this that *most* planktonic foraminifer stable isotope data from carbonate oozes and chalks are "suspect," and may represent a roughly equal combination of surface- and bottom-water signals. . . . We contend that *most* workers, including ourselves, have been misled to some extent by fine-scale recrystallization of planktonic foraminifer shells, which occurs at shallow burial depths in open ocean pelagic oozes and chalks. This process introduces a *much larger* component of diagenetic calcite than has generally been recognized, making such shells *unsuitable for sea surface palaeotemperature analysis* [emphasis mine] (Pearson et al., 2001, pp. 485, 486).

This result applies mainly to planktonic foraminifera and not to benthonic foraminifera, since the replacement of calcite in the latter would occur at nearly the same temperature as the bottom temperature where the foraminifera live. Much research has been done using planktonic foraminifera and most of the conclusions are now suspect.

There are other factors that can affect the $\delta^{18}O$ of calcite in benthonic foraminifera. Researchers sometimes assume the deep ocean temperature has remained unchanged through supposed glacial/interglacial cycles, so that $\delta^{18}O$ of benthonic foraminifera would not be affected by temperature. But this assumption is untrue (Oard, 1984b, pp. 127–128). Uniformitarian scientists now believe bottom temperatures fluctuate enough to account for half the $\delta^{18}O$ change in benthonic foraminifera (Ruddiman and Raymo, 2003, p. 153). In the Creation-Flood Ice Age model, the bottom of the ocean would start off quite warm and cool with time. There likely would be a huge overturn of the ocean as cool water produced at the surface of the ocean sinks. There would be multiple short-term oscillations in $\delta^{18}O$ of benthonic foraminifera superimposed on a long-term increase of $\delta^{18}O$ as the bottom cooled during the Ice Age.

Accurate Dates Required on Deep-Sea Cores

In order to ferret out Milankovitch oscillations from deep-sea cores, accurate dates are required for the cores. Otherwise, how would the scientists know that $\delta^{18}O$ in foraminifera shells cycles every 100,000 years? This introduces many new problems that will not be discussed here. There are numerous references in the creationist literature on the problems of Evolutionary-Uniformitarian dating methods, some of which will be mentioned below. Researchers today often just assume the Milankovitch mechanism and use the mechanism to date the deep-sea cores (Paillard, 2001, p. 329).

Deep-sea cores are generally dated by index microfossils, uranium series disequilibrium, and paleomagnetic stratigraphy (Oard, 1984b, 1985). Index fossil dating has depended upon first or last appearances of various microfossils. The microfossil dating for the ice age period has a limited number of these changes and the dating is rough (Shackleton, 1975, p. 9). First appearances and extinctions of organisms is a simplistic concept and based on the assumption of macroevolution. Such changes may be ecological or biological, and other cores in other regions may show a different pattern (Loubere, 1982). Besides, the oceanographer needs to know the dates of all these biostratigraphic events in order to know exactly when an organism first appears or totally disappears from the earth. This is where radiometric and paleomagnetic dating techniques enter into the picture. But these dating methods in general have many problems that are not generally discussed (Oard, 1984b, 1985; Morris, 1994; Woodmorappe, 1999; Vardiman, Snelling, and Chaffin, 2000).

I believe that the whole dating enterprise consists of one huge reinforcement syndrome (Oard, 1997a, pp. 11–17) or circular reasoning process, often subconscious, in which dating methods and other data sets, such as the Milankovitch mechanism, are manipulated into a "consistent" whole. Many examples of the reinforcement syndrome are revealed in the geological literature. It was once assumed that four ice ages occurred in the Pleistocene. Practically all data sets for 60 years *verified* the four-ice-age model. That model is now obsolete, replaced by the Milankovitch mechanism that postulates around 30 ice ages. At one time, geologists saw a worldwide Permian "ice age," but now that supposed pre-Pleistocene ice age is seen only in the Southern Hemisphere.

Marvin Lubenow (1992, pp. 247–266) shows from the literature how six supposedly independent fossil and radiometric dating systems all converged to say that Richard Leakey's skull 1470 was 2.6 to 2.9 million years old. However, the paleoanthropologists felt that the skull was too modern looking to be that old. So, the skull was "redated" and found to be only 1.6 to 1.8 million years old. The interesting aspect of this controversy is that most of these dating methods ended up "agreeing" with the new date. It is obvious that dating methods are subjective and *not* independent:

> The study of the ten-year controversy in the dating of the KBS Tuff is tremendously revealing. Whereas the public is led to believe that these dating methods are highly objective and accurate, the scientific literature itself reveals that they are highly subjective. There is no question that rock samples are often manipulated to give the desired results" (Lubenow, 1992, p. 264).

I believe the same situation has operated with deep-sea cores to manipulate dates to agree with the Milankovitch mechanism (Oard, 1984b, 1985).

Chapter 10

WILD ICE-CORE TEMPERATURE INTERPRETATIONS

An examination of any deep ice core profile will reveal that during the Ice Age and even earlier the oxygen isotope ratio fluctuated considerably and became more stable after the Ice Age. These fluctuations are especially prominent for the Greenland Ice Sheet and can represent as much as 50 meters of ice (see figures 2.5 through 2.8). Evolutionary-Uniformitarian scientists believe that these oscillations are a measure of extreme temperature fluctuations.

Wild Climatic Interpretations within the Evolutionary-Uniformitarian Paradigm

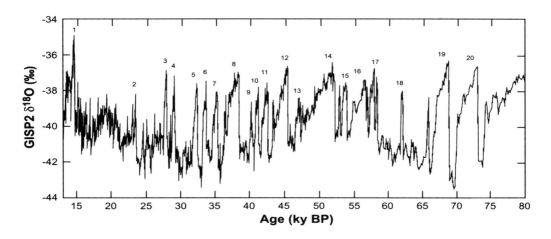

Figure 10.1   Plot of oxygen isotope fluctuation during the Ice Age in the GISP2 core. The numbers refer to Dansgaard-Oeschger interstadial events (from Schulz, 2002).

Figure 10.1 shows a time plot for the Ice Age period within the Evolutionary-Uniformitarian timescale. The higher $\delta^{18}O$ values are considered warmer interstadials and the lower $\delta^{18}O$ are believed to be colder stadials within the Ice Age. Recently, glaciologists have come to believe these $\delta^{18}O$ oscillations represent a temperature shift about double what they previously believed (Johnsen et al., 1995a; Cuffey et al., 1995; Jouzel et al., 1997; Cuffey and Clow, 1997; Jouzel, 1999). They are especially concerned with the rate of change in the $\delta^{18}O$, which appears so fast that it would correspond to catastrophic temperature changes. Other parameters, such as dust and various chemicals correlated to $\delta^{18}O$, also fluctuate at the same time, sometimes even more wildly than $\delta^{18}O$. These other parameters indicate that the change can occur in one to three years!

> These millennial-scale events represent quite large climate deviations: probably 20°C in central Greenland. . . .The events often begin or end rapidly: changes equal to most of the glacial-interglacial differences commonly occur over decades, and some indicators, more sensitive to shifts in the pattern of atmospheric circulation, change in as little as 1-3 years (Hammer et al., 1997, p. 26,315).

This quote may or may not mean that the temperature changed by 20°C in one to three years. Regardless, temperatures are believed to have changed 20°C within decades, and the deviation lasted a millennium or more. According to the interpretation of the $\delta^{18}O$ swings within the Evolutionary-Uniformitarian paradigm, back and forth millennial-scale monstrous climate changes occurred during the ice age. It took about half a century for scientists to finally believe that such rapid, abrupt climate shifts were possible:

> In the 1950s, a few scientists found evidence that some of the great climate shifts in the past had taken only a few thousand years. During the 1960s and 1970s, other lines of research made it plausible that the global climate could shift radically within a few hundred years. In the 1980s and 1990s, further studies reduced the scale to the span of a single century. Today, there is evidence that severe change can take less than a decade (Weart, 2003, p. 30).

Such belief in radical climate change took time to settle in the minds of evolutionary scientists because, "The actual history shows that even the best scientific data are never that definitive. People can see only what they find believable" (Weart, 2003, p. 36).

These Greenland ice core changes are believed to represent climate changes not only around the North Atlantic Ocean but also across the earth. Therefore, the oscillations should be observed in other climate records as well. It is interesting that before GRIP and GISP2 were drilled such oscillations were *rarely if ever seen* in such records for the midlatitudes. Ever since the GRIP results were published, however, researchers "discovered" rapid oscillations in many records from land and sea (Bond et al., 1993; Lehman, 1993; Kerr, 1993; Labeyrie, 2000; Sarnthein et al., 2000; Alley, 2000, p. 169). Such rapid ice age fluctuations are now found across the world, including the tropics (Allen et al., 1999; Werner et al., 2000b; Sirocko, 2003; Pahnke et al., 2003). However, the millennial scale fluctuations in Greenland ice cores and other climatic records are not found in Antarctic cores and do not correlate with cycles in the Antarctic ice cores (Jouzel et al., 2003, p. 2; Wunsch, 2003), a circumstance which seems strange, if these changes were global. Some scientists still remain skeptical of such millennial scale abrupt climatic changes (Wunsch, 2003).

Because of such radical climate changes, earth scientists have been desperately searching for a mechanism that can cause millennial scale temperature changes with a rapid onset in years to decades. Some scientists lean towards the idea that fluctuations in the Laurentide and Fennoscandian Ice Sheets at regular intervals discharged an enormous amount of icebergs into the North Atlantic Ocean. The icebergs rapidly changed the heat flux over the oceans, cooled the atmospheric temperatures, and caused what are called the *Heinrich events,* based on ice rafted debris found in sediment cores (Fronval et al., 1995). The ice core oscillations have been formally named Dansgaard-Oeschger events after two well-known leaders in their study. The average period of Dansgaard-Oescher events, which includes much variability, is 1,470 years within the Evolutionary-Uniformitarian dating system (Schulz, 2002). Every once in awhile, stronger Dansgaard-Oeschger events produce the Heinrich layers found on the North Atlantic bottom.

Other investigators believe the cause of the ice core oscillations is a change in the North Atlantic thermohaline circulation (Labeyrie, 2000; Broecker, 1994, 1997, 2000). The release of excess water to the ocean surface of the northern Atlantic from melting ice sheets stops the northward flowing Gulf Stream and results in cooler temperatures for the adjacent continents and Greenland (Rahmstorf, 1995). After awhile the ocean switches modes, and the current starts up again to cause the warm cycle. This system of transporting warm ocean water into the northern North Atlantic where it cools and sinks only to spread south as intermediate-depth cooler waters is called the *oceanic conveyor* or *superconveyer belt*. This belt is responsible for a significant fraction of higher latitude atmospheric heating. Ocean models have been employed to model these oscillations with supposed success, but the models are artificial (Rind et al., 2001). The physics of oceanographic models is not that well developed, although they are improving; and the initial conditions and parameterizations of complex variables make the models come up with any desired result. Broecker (1994) states:

> The second question has to do with the suitability of the ocean models used to generate changes in the mode of thermohaline circulation. Anyone who has pondered their architecture is aware that the results depend heavily on the assumptions made with regard to the surface boundary conditions. The strengths of the conveyor and anticonveyor circulation cells that jockey for dominance in the models' [sic] Atlantic are dictated by the density contrast between surface waters in the two polar regions. Because of this, the modelers can easily alter the nature of the response to forcing.

This same tweaking of models to produce desired results was also noted by Boyle and Weaver (1994, p. 42).

A simple change from one physically unrealistic model parameterization to another perhaps slightly less unrealistic parameterizion caused sweeping changes in the behaviour of the model. This model tweaking and other reasons is probably why some earth scientists shy away from the switching conveyor belt hypothesis for causing dramatic climatic fluctuations (Rind et al., 2001; Schulz, 2002).

The Younger Dryas Cold Plunge

One of the ice age climatic oscillations is worthy of note. This is the Younger Dryas (YD) event. Just as the ice age was coming to a close and the oxygen isotope ratio was increasing, suddenly the ratio and presumably global temperatures plunged to near glacial conditions. Within the Evolutionary-Uniformitarian timescale, the YD is supposed to have lasted about 1,000 to 1,500 years. A simplified chart of the Younger Dryas is shown in figure 10.2. The YD has been detected all across the Northern Hemisphere in a variety of paleoclimatic records (Jansen and Veum, 1990; Smith et al., 1997). It has been reported in New Zealand (Denton and Hendy, 1994) but is questionable elsewhere in the Southern Hemisphere (Rodbell, 2000). It is even represented in Antarctic ice cores by the Antarctic Cold Reversal (ACR) (Jouzel et al., 1995; Mayewski et al., 1996). However, the ACR is much weaker; and the timing between the YD and ACR seems to be $180°$ out of phase, with the ACR preceding the YD by about 1,500 years in the Evolutionary-Uniformitarian timescale (Mulvaney et al., 2000; Stenni et al., 2001).

The onset and termination of the YD is believed to have occurred in a matter of years to a few decades according to the Evolutionary-Uniformitarian model (Dansgaard, White, and Johnsen, 1989; Mayewski et al., 1993a; Taylor et al., 1997b). The oxygen isotope shift in the Greenland ice cores is now believed to represent a cooling of about $15°C$ (Cuffey et al., 1995; Severinghaus et al., 1998). The cause of the global Younger Dryas cold fluctuation is still unknown (Alley et

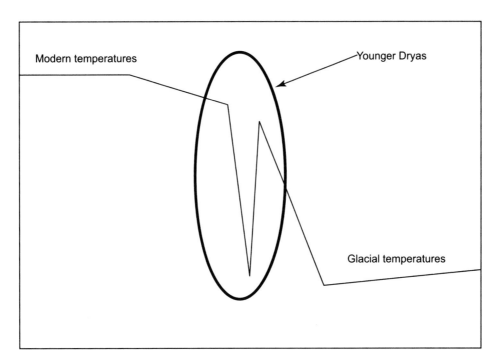

Figure 10.2   Simplified chart of δ¹⁸O and temperature from the Ice Age to today emphasizing the Younger Dryas (Vardiman, personal communication).

al., 1993), as are the causes for the other climatic oscillations. More realistic atmospheric and oceanographic models fail to produce such a temperature change for the Younger Dryas due to a complete shutdown of the North Atlantic conveyor belt (Rind et al., 2001).

Eemian Climate Oscillations

The Eemian represents the previous supposed interglacial within the European multiple-ice-age classification. It is called *stage 5e* within the deep-sea core classification scheme. Stage 5e is represented by a 100-meter section at the bottom of the core (figure 10.3). It is interesting that the wild Ice Age fluctuations continued downward into the previous "interglacial." The interglacial oscillations came as a total surprise (Monastersky, 1993; Nielsen, 1993, p. 31) and have been interpreted as catastrophic climate change within the previous "interglacial" period (Greenland Ice-Core Project (GRIP) Members, 1993; Johnsen et al., 1992a, 1995b, 1997; Dansgaard et al., 1993). Such radical temperature changes within an interglacial has fueled the idea that global warming may trigger a future rapid 10°C or more temperature drop in the *present* climate, at least in the North Atlantic region. I will briefly comment on this point in the next section.

Although such changes had never been noted before in other paleoclimatic records for this time, suddenly researchers discovered such oscillations in these other records as well (Pzedakis, Bennett, and Magri, 1994; Fronval and Jansen, 1996). For instance, abrupt climate changes for the last "interglacial" were "discovered" in deep-sea cores (Thouveny et al., 1994; Haflidason et al., 1995) and pollen records (Field, Huntley, and Müller, 1994). It looks like the reinforcement syndrome is alive and well within the so-called historical sciences (Oard, 1995, 1997, pp. 11–17). However, not all the reports are consistent. McManus et al. (1994) failed to find Eemian climate oscillations in two North Atlantic deep-sea cores.

126

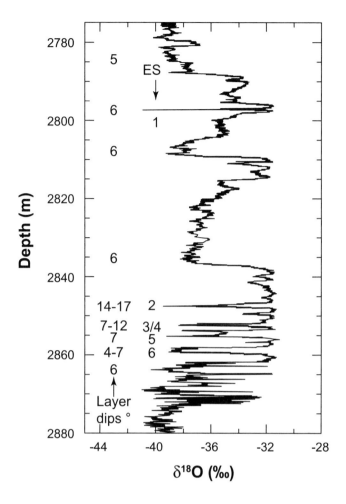

Figure 10.3 The stretched out Eemian portion, stage 5e, of the GRIP core (after Johnsen et al., 1997, p. 26,405).

However, the American team that drilled the GISP2 core disputed the climatic significance of the interglacial oscillations in the GRIP core, claiming instead that the oscillations represent mixing of ice at the bottom of the ice sheet due to glacial flow over rough terrain (Grootes et al., 1993; Alley et al., 1997b; Lehman, 1997; Dahl-Jensen et al., 1997). This conclusion was based on folding with inclined layers up to 20° and evidence of deformation processes several hundred meters above the bottom, which was a surprise to many workers (Alley et al., 1997b, p. 26,819). They did not expect such terrain effects so high up in the ice core. Some deep-sea core records continue to support a stable interglacial climate, while others do not (Keigwin et al., 1994; Adkins et al., 1997). Since skepticism of interglacial oscillations came out, some of the original claims of Eemian oscillations in other climatic records are now seen as "questionable" (Lehman, 1997).

However, the distortions in the bottom 200 meters of the GRIP and GISP2 cores may not be significant enough, so that the conclusion of flow disturbance can be questioned. Furthermore, Meese et al. (1997) counted what they believed are annual layers below 2,800 meters to 3,030 meters. They likely would not have performed this very tedious task if they believed the layers were disturbed. Besides, the layers could not be very disturbed if they were able to count dust bands. The European researchers that drilled the GRIP core have generally held to their original

127

interpretation since much evidence seems to support their position (Johnsen et al., 1995b, 1997). However, since the late 1990s, these researchers have been persuaded by the interpretations of the GISP2 core that such might not be the case. In fact, testing whether the bottom 200 meters has been deformed was the main reason a new Greenland ice core was drilled at North GRIP, Greenland (Dahl-Jensen et al., 2002; North Greenland Ice Core Project Members, 2004).

Wild Ice Core Oscillations Used to Fuel Global Warming Debate

As stated above, wild ice core fluctuations have given vent to hysterical rhetoric on how greenhouse warming may shift the climate to another "state" that results in a huge temperature drop (Taylor, 1999; Pearce, 1994, 2002; Alley, 2000, pp. 169–179; Alley, 2004). Broecker (1997, p. 1588) warns:

> Through the record kept in Greenland ice, a disturbing characteristic of the Earth's climate system has been revealed, that is, its capability to undergo abrupt switches to very different states of operation. I say "disturbing" because there is surely a possibility that the ongoing buildup of greenhouse gases might trigger yet another of these ocean reorganizations and thereby the associated large atmospheric changes. Should this occur when 11 to 16 billion people occupy our planet, it could lead to widespread starvation.

It is interesting that the fluctuations in the previous interglacial have especially fueled this concern, since an ice age is suppose to be cold anyway:

> Isotope and chemical analyses of the GRIP ice core from Summit, central Greenland, reveal that climate in Greenland during the last interglacial period was characterized by a series of severe cold periods, which began extremely rapidly and lasted from decades to centuries. As the last interglacial seems to have been slightly warmer than the present one, its unstable climate raises questions about the effects of future global warming (Greenland Ice-Core Project (GRIP) Members, 1993, p. 203).

Even a global ocean model postulated that if more freshwater (from precipitation and melting glaciers produced by a warmer climate) was added to the northern North Atlantic, the world could go into a rapid transition to a colder state (Weaver and Hughes, 1994). Of course, this model was highly idealized.

The greenhouse to ice age scare has been absorbed into the popular culture. William Calvin (1998, p. 47) threatens in the *Atlantic Monthly*: "But warming could lead, paradoxically, to drastic cooling—a catastrophe that could threaten the survival of civilization." Elizabeth Kolbert (2002) in *The New Yorker* follows suit with the same dire warning about the possible end of civilization. The movie *The Day After Tomorrow* dramatized such a greenhouse to icehouse rapid climatic shift, but in a matter of days not decades (Oard, 2004c).

The Interpretation of Large δ¹⁸O Fluctuations in the Creation-Flood Paradigm

Mainstream scientists are forced by the rapid $\delta^{18}O$ oscillations to postulate huge and rapid climate changes in the past. It has dramatically altered their view of climate change:

> The demonstration that natural climate variability during the last glacial cycle shifted rapidly between remarkable extremes has dramatically revised the understanding of climate change (Rohling, Mayewski, and Challenor, 2003, p. 257).

But, the origin of these changes is a major enigma:

> The origin of much of the variability in late Quaternary climate remains a major question in the understanding of processes of past and future climate change. The origin of major rapid, decadal climate change during the latest Quaternary remains an enigma (Sarnthein et al., 2000, p. 625).

How would such fluctuations be explained within the Creation-Flood model of the Ice Age?

The Creation-Flood Ice Age model postulates only one Ice Age before the stable post–Ice Age time. In this model, the supposed Eemian interglacial in the Evolutionary-Uniformitarian model would represent the earlier warmer part of the Ice Age. These wide "Eemian" $\delta^{18}O$ oscillations are likely *real climate oscillations*, just like in the colder part of the Ice Age, and not due to folds and distortions from ice movement over a rough bottom. In the GRIP core, the small size of the folds and the height above the bottom indicates just local distortion, not wholesale overturning of ice layers. The oscillations are also seen as evidence for the Creation-Flood paradigm and against the Evolutionary-Uniformitarian paradigm because the stable post-ice period (the Holocene) should be an analog for any interglacial, if interglacials really existed. Any interglacial period should have a *stable* climate, so in the Creation-Flood model the "Eemian" fluctuations occurred early in the Ice Age when temperatures were warmer (Oard, 1990).

As for the $\delta^{18}O$ fluctuations themselves, I would lean toward the Evolutionary-Uniformitarian view that they indeed represent climatic oscillations. Since so many other factors affect $\delta^{18}O$, I would attribute the fluctuations partly to temperature reinforced by other factors, such as greater snowfall during colder periods that would cause a lower $\delta^{18}O$ (see appendix 1). Since the thickness of ice represented by these fluctuations is up to around 50 meters, and it was assumed that a typical annual layer of ice in central Greenland would be about six meters thick in the Creation-Flood model (see chapter 3), I suggest that the oscillations represent *decadal* climatic fluctuations.

What would cause such decadal fluctuations? I suggest that the $\delta^{18}O$ fluctuations reflect variable volcanic dust and aerosol loads in the stratosphere, since volcanism suppresses both temperature

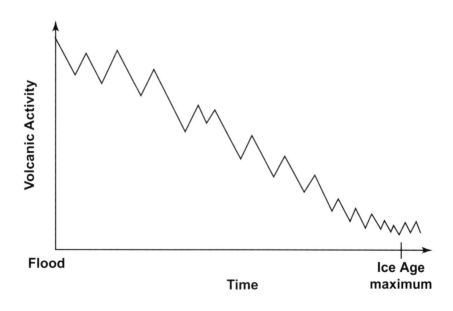

Figure 10.4   Postulated post-Flood volcanism up to glacial maximum (from Oard, 1990, p. 68).

and $\delta^{18}O$ (Stuiver, Grootes, and Braziunas, 1995). Figure 10.4 is a schematic representing the peaks and lulls in post-Flood volcanism between the end of the Flood and Ice Age maximum that I previously published (Oard, 1990, p. 68). When analyzing the heat balance equations for the ocean and atmosphere, I discovered that the amount of volcanic effluents in the upper atmosphere controlled the rate of ice sheet growth. During periods of strong volcanism, colder temperatures and greater snowfall with lower $\delta^{18}O$ would occur and vice versa during volcanic lulls:

> In other words, during periods of strong volcanism and reflection of solar radiation back to space, the cooling, over land, would be more intense. This, in turn, would cause colder, drier air to blow out over the warm ocean. As a result, ocean cooling would be more rapid, and the amount of moisture evaporated into the air would be higher. Consequently, ice sheet would grow rapidly, with higher volcanism. Conversely, they would develop more slowly, or even melt back at the margins, during volcanic lulls (Oard, 1990, p. 98).

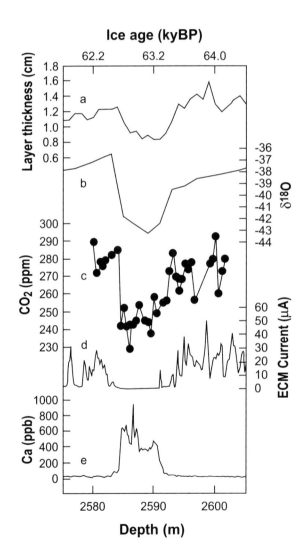

Figure 10.5 One $\delta^{18}O$ oscillation in the GISP2 core between 2580- and 2605-meter depths showing correlations with calcium (Ca) and CO_2 (from Smith et al., 1997, p. 26,579).

The oxygen isotope ratio during volcanic lulls would be higher. Such a climate change would be accompanied by greater wind speed, so that chemical deposition on the ice sheet likely would increase with colder temperatures. Thus, many variables would be correlated to $\delta^{18}O$ (figure 10.5).

It is especially interesting that $\delta^{18}O$ oscillations correlate with CO_2 in the Greenland ice cores (figure 10.5) (Staffelbach, Stauffer, and Oeschger, 1988; Smith et al., 1997). This suggests that CO_2 shifts of about 50 ppm occurred very rapidly, which is very difficult to perceive in the Evolutionary-Uniformitarian model (Dansgaard, 1987, p. 229). A number of hypotheses have been suggested, but no one seems to be sure of a solution. Dansgaard (1987, p. 229) suggested that intense deep-water formation could rapidly remove CO_2 from the atmosphere. This would go along with stronger winds and increased atmospheric circulation during cold phases of the Ice Age in the Creation-Flood model. However, other scientists disagree with Dansgaard, and they are probably correct.

Some scientists have observed that $\delta^{18}O$ and CO_2 are exactly in phase in the ice cores (figure 10.5), which should not be the case because of the lag in bubble close-off time (Staffelbach, Stauffer, and Oeschger, 1988; Wilson and Long, 1997). Therefore, they have suggested that the rapid CO_2 shifts are mainly due to chemical reactions *within* the ice, possible from dust and impurities that also correlate with $\delta^{18}O$ and CO_2 (Oeschger et al., 1985, 1988; Wolff et al., 1997; Anklin et al., 1997; Sowers et al., 1997; Wilson and Long, 1997; Stauffer et al., 1998). This possibility needs further exploration but is bolstered by the fact that such rapid fluctuations in CO_2 are not recorded in the Antarctic cores for the same supposed dates (Oeschger et al., 1988; Stauffer et al., 1998). Carbon dioxide equilibrates rapidly between hemispheres, so there should be no difference in atmospheric CO_2 for the same time, if indeed the timescale is the same on the two ice sheets. Antarctic ice has far less impurities than Greenland ice, which would support the chemical interpretation of CO_2 spikes in the Greenland cores during the Ice Age. If such rapid changes in CO_2 are chemically induced, this could have significant bearing on the interpretation of all Ice Age carbon dioxide measurements in ice cores.

As previously stated, other factors related to $\delta^{18}O$ and correlated to temperature could be partly responsible for such drastic $\delta^{18}O$ changes. One factor is sea ice (see appendix 1). Colder atmospheric temperatures would cause more sea ice. More sea ice would then cause more negative oxygen isotope ratios in the snow that falls on the Greenland Ice Sheet, and vice versa for less sea ice during warmer periods. The fluctuations in sea ice would occur late in the Ice Age because the warm ocean water early in the Ice Age needed to cool down. Increasing sea ice may be the main reason for the plunge in $\delta^{18}O$ during the Younger Dryas (Vardiman, 1997). So, the peaks and lulls in volcanism caused an oscillating climate during the Ice Age, which is reflected in $\delta^{18}O$ oscillations in the Greenland Ice Sheet. These $\delta^{18}O$ oscillations are probably due to both temperature and other variables that are discussed in appendix 1.

Another variable that could cause more negative $\delta^{18}O$ in ice cores during colder phases is increased meltwater pouring out over the ocean, as discussed in appendix 1. Such meltwater would have a low $\delta^{18}O$ and tend to float on the denser, salty ocean water. Evaporation from these meltwater spikes would likely cause lower $\delta^{18}O$ in the snow. Such a mechanism would be most applicable during the deglaciation phase of the Ice Age and could possibly explain the Younger Dryas $\delta^{18}O$ drop (Broecker et al., 1989; Rooth, 1990; Clark et al., 2001; Vardiman, personal communication). Such meltwater spikes would be aided by the catastrophic bursting of large pro-glacial lakes, such as glacial Lake Missoula (Oard, 2004a), at the edge of the ice sheet, or by possible gigantic subglacial floods (Shaw, 1996, 2002; Oard, 2004a, pp. 59-67).

Since the Antarctic Ice Sheet also built up during the Ice Age, both glacial/interglacial and millennial scale fluctuations within the Evolutionary-Uniformitarian model would be caused by volcanism-induced climate change. Since Antarctica would have been entirely surrounded by warm water during most of the Ice Age (see chapter 3), unlike the case with Greenland where continents break up and separate the oceans, some of the warmer oscillations would end up with quite high $\delta^{18}O$, even greater than the current post–Ice Age climate. The warmth of the surrounding oceans is also why the Antarctic equivalent of the Younger Dryas, the Antarctic Cold Reversal, is about one third the strength of the $\delta^{18}O$ oscillations in Greenland cores (see figure 2.11). Thus, the glacial/interglacial fluctuations and other smaller scale oscillations in the Antarctic ice cores would be correlated with the radical oscillations discovered in the Greenland cores in the Creation-Flood model.

Chapter 11

THE CREATION-FLOOD MODEL IS MORE LIKELY

The Creation-Flood model of the Ice Age and the origin and development of the Greenland and Antarctic Ice Sheets was presented in chapter 3 along with the Evolutionary-Uniformitarian model. Because of the assumptions of the latter model, namely the old age assumption, the ice sheets are dated as old. Glaciologists have constructed dating methods that give hundreds of thousands of years. The most scientific method is the counting of annual layers downward in the Greenland cores at the top of the ice sheet.

In this monograph, a critique of these dating methods was not only presented, but also an alternative model was developed, based on different assumptions. The main assumption is that the ice built up rapidly in a 700-year Ice Age and then slowed to the present rate we observe today. Thus, the counting of annual layers is accurate for the top of the Greenland ice cores but becomes more inaccurate with depth. The mainstream glaciologists end up counting subannual or storm layers with depth. Because of their assumptions, mainstream scientists have come to believe that the climate can quickly shift to a much colder or warmer climate; while in the Creation-Flood model such radical changes in oxygen isotope ratio represent differential volcanism during the Ice Age.

Thus, there are two models of viewing the Greenland and Antarctic Ice Sheets. The question now is whether the Creation-Flood model is superior to the Evolutionary-Uniformitarian model. Is there any way to test which model is better?

Ice Cores Generally Show One Ice Age

If there were about thirty ice ages over the past 2.5 million years, as believed by most Evolutionary-Uniformitarian scientists based on the astronomical theory of the ice age, one would expect to see evidence of glacial/interglacial oscillations near the bottom in areas where the bottom of the ice sheet is frozen to its bed. One indication that the Creation-Flood model is more likely is that Greenland ice cores show *only one Ice Age* followed by a post–Ice Age period. Multiple ice ages do not show up.

In the first ice core drilled at Camp Century, Dansgaard et al. (1969, p. 379) hoped that the thin annual layers in the bottom several meters would represent several previous glacial and interglacial periods that cycle every 100,000 years. Such hope failed to materialize. On the other hand, the bottom of the ice core could easily be disturbed due to its proximity to the bedrock. Evolutionary-Uniformitarian scientists have usually appealed to basal melting by geothermal heat or rapid flow out to sea for the missing ice ages. Since the ice at the bottom of the Camp Century core is well below freezing, retarding basal flow, Dansgaard et al. (1985, p. 73) rejected these alternative explanations, thus admitting that only one Ice Age shows up in the Camp Century core.

The GRIP and GISP2 cores were also expected to penetrate more than one glacial cycle near the bottom, but only one definite cycle was drilled with the very bottom ice thought to be disturbed (Yiou et al., 1997, p. 26,441) (see chapter 8). The bottom of the GRIP and GISP2 cores are well below freezing, so presumably no ice from previous ice ages should have been melted away, assuming steady state, of course. Since the ice at GRIP is at an ice divide, the ice should have moved straight down and not spread horizontally. Early ice flow models for the GRIP and GISP2 cores even predicted that the ice 100 meters above bedrock would be older than 200,000 years and that two glacial/interglacial cycles would show up in the ice above (Schøtt, Waddington, and Raymond, 1992). So, glacial/interglacial oscillations should be manifest at the bottom of these cores, if there really were more than one Ice Age. Obviously, these expectations did not pan out.

It is interesting that regardless of the way flow models stretch out the dating of the bottom of the ice cores, the ice cores still represent only a small portion of the millions of years assumed for the age of the ice sheets. Mainstream scientists would dearly love to find those missing hundreds of thousands or millions of years at the very bottom of the ice sheets, but the evidence is not there.

Remember these deductions are all within the Evolutionary-Uniformitarian model, assuming an equilibrium ice sheet for several million years. It is true that near the very bottom of the GRIP and GISP2 cores below the supposed interglacial interval there are large oscillations in $\delta^{18}O$ that some glaciologists claim are due to previous glacials and interglacials. However, these represent small vertical differences; and many glaciologists believe the oscillations are caused by bottom disturbances or superimposed ice, which is refrozen meltwater. Koerner and Fisher (2002) updated their idea that during the last "interglacial" most of the Greenland ice disappeared, except for some ice around central Greenland. If they are correct, all we know is that the Greenland Ice Sheet built up from low elevations in one Ice Age. The straightforward evidence from Greenland cores better supports the Creation-Flood model of the Ice Age.

The bottoms of the Greenland ice cores show higher $\delta^{18}O$ attributed to warmer temperatures that glaciologists attribute to an interglacial climate. In fact, the exceptionally high $\delta^{18}O$ at the very bottom of the GRIP core implies quite mild conditions for Greenland (Souchez, 1997). But such a pattern is expected in the Creation-Flood model in which the Ice Age begins with relatively mild winter temperatures, due to a warm ocean at the beginning, and cools to glacial maximum and deglaciation during a 700-year period. The fact that this "interglacial" interval shows $\delta^{18}O$ spikes similar to those observed in the Ice Age portion of the cores is more favorable to the Creation-Flood Ice Age model. Furthermore, such "interglacial" spikes do not mean that the present climate is unstable, since they were really part of the Ice Age (see chapter 10). Such possible "interglacial" spikes in $\delta^{18}O$ have forced Evolutionary-Uniformitarian scientists to claim that the present climate, possibly aided by global warming, can suddenly cool off around 15°C. This is a radical climatic deduction, and if these scientists ever get their way politically, it would likely be disastrous for the economies of the nations. Such abrupt cooling seems almost impossible in the present climate. The evidence of abrupt temperature changes in the Ice Age is more favorable to the Creation-Flood Ice Age model.

Antarctica on the other hand is simply dated by assuming the Milankovitch mechanism. The large $\delta^{18}O$ oscillations in the Vostok core are simply taken as four glacial/interglacial oscillations that cycle every 100,000 years according to the Milankovitch eccentricity cycle. Scientists also have claimed seven Milankovitch cycles in the new Dome C core with a date around 750,000 years (Pokar, 2003). Such dating is purely an assumption of the Evolutionary-Uniformitarian paradigm. In the Creation-Flood model, the claimed glacial/interglacial $\delta^{18}O$ oscillations in Antarctic cores are similar to Dansgaard-Oeschger fluctuations in the Greenland Ice Sheet. The large amplitude of $\delta^{18}O$ in the Antarctic cores likely was caused by the larger source of warmth from the larger ocean surrounding Antarctica. This is likely when one realizes that Dansgaard-Oeschger events are not found in Antarctic deep ice cores and that the Antarctic Cold Reversal (ACR) does not correspond to the Younger Dryas (YD). So, I conclude that the Antarctic ice core timescale is greatly stretched out and the claimed glacial/interglacial oscillations in long Antarctic cores are simply Dansgaard-Oeschger events in the Southern Hemisphere.

Surprise Broadening with Depth of Some Ice Core Variables

In the Creation-Flood Ice Age model, the annual layers are significantly thicker in the Ice Age portion of the cores with considerably less thinning of annual layers with depth. As stated in chapter 5, the longer period $\delta^{18}O$ oscillations that are claimed to be decadal oscillations are support for a thicker annual layer deeper in the Greenland ice cores (see figures 5.3, 5.6, and 5.7). Because the annual layers are thicker, one would expect that so-called reference horizons would broaden in the Evolutionary-Uniformitarian model the deeper in the ice sheet, because such horizons cover more supposed annual layers that are really subannual.

It is interesting in this regard that in the Evolutionary-Uniformitarian dating system the deeper 60 kyr ^{10}Be peak is broader than the 35 kyr peak. Beer et al. (1992, p. 143) state: "The ^{10}Be peak at 60 ka B.P. is smaller in amplitude and broader than the one at 35 ka B.P." This broadening is expected if the Creation-Flood model is true.

Such broadening with depth also shows up with volcanic spikes. For instance, volcanic spikes show an unexpected broadening with depth in the new Antarctic Dome C core:

> Additionally, concentration profiles across volcanic layers (chemical peaks) often imply that these events lasted longer than their likely atmospheric duration, even after accounting for mixing of surface snow. This suggests the existence of some form of soluble impurity transport within the ice, causing peak broadening (Barnes et al., 2003, pp. 1–2).

This "longer duration" or broadening with depth was analyzed for the top 350 meters of the core, which is the post–Ice Age section, but the broadening continued down into the Ice Age part of the core. Modern day volcanic spikes last up to three years. Based on DEP peaks in the Dome C core, Barnes et al. (2003, p. 6) found that at 1,650 meters volcanic peaks represented 20 years within the Evolutionary-Uniformitarian timescale.

There are 25 visible tephra layers, 1 to 24 millimeters thick, found in the Ice Age portion of the Dome Fuji core (Fujii et al., 1999). Because of the exaggerated thinning with depth in this core, the Evolutionary-Uniformitarian scientists were forced to conclude that some of these tephra layers represent a more or less continuous deposition of volcanic tephra from two to five years. Volcanic ash normally falls out of the stratosphere in around 1.5 years. Thus, they conclude that for the 5 years worth of tephra, the duration of the eruption is believed to have lasted greater than three years, which is rather long for a volcanic eruption.

Such broadening of volcanic peaks within the Evolutionary-Uniformitarian timescale is what would be expected in the Creation-Flood Ice Age model, while it is unacceptable in the Evolutionary-Uniformitarian model and thus must be explained by a subsidiary hypothesis. In the case of Dome C, Barnes et al. (2003) are looking for some kind of soluble impurity transport or diffusion within the solid ice. If they find such a viable mechanism (the current suggestion is speculative) what would it say about their annual layer dating methods using various chemicals?

Radio Echoes Indicate Little Movement of the Ice Sheets

One would expect that over millions of years the Greenland and Antarctic Ice Sheets would have moved considerably. If the ice is not frozen to the bed, the movement would look like that shown in figure 3.12 in which an ice molecule that starts from near the top of the ice sheet would move downward and laterally towards the edge of the ice sheet with time. If the ice is frozen to its bed, there would be a similar profile, except that the horizontal motion would be higher in the ice sheet with the bottom layer stagnant. Even ice near the centers of the ice sheets should have moved significantly toward the coast in the hundred or hundreds of thousands of years attributed for the ice sheets.

On the other hand, little movement of the ice sheet, especially in the interior, is expected in the Creation-Flood Ice Age model since there is little time for movement at the current rates observed today. It is likely that the ice sheets moved faster during the Ice Age, but this is not significant when one considers the size of the ice sheets and the short time of the Ice Age.

Scientists have been able to send radio echoes—radio or radar energy that is reflected off various layers—down through the ice (Robin, Evans, and Bailey, 1969; Gudmandsen, 1975; Paren and Robin, 1975; Nixdorf et al., 1999). The reflections are ubiquitous in the Antarctic and Greenland Ice Sheets (Robin, 1983d; Fahnestock et al., 2001).

There are several possible causes for radio echoes, but it is believed that the reflections represent isochronous sets of volcanic acid layers (Millar, 1981, 1982; Bogorodsky, Bentley, and Gudmandsen, 1985; Fujita and Mae, 1994; Jacobel and Hodge, 1995; Kanagaratnam et al., 2001). A recent model was compared to the GRIP DEP conductivity and shows that the echoes are likely caused by changes in ice conductivity (Miners et al., 2002). Since conductivity strongly correlates to impurities, the radio echoes are believed to be related to impurities:

> It is therefore clear that either sharp peaks (volcanic fallout) or transitions between bands (interstadials) of increased chemical variability are the main causes of the internal reflections in Greenland (Miners et al., 2002, p. 6–8).

The reflections do not represent reflections from one volcanic layer, since the average spacing of the radio echoes in the Greenland Ice Sheet is 41 meters. They probably represent reflections caused by multiple volcanic spikes (Jacobel and Hodge, 1995, p. 588; Siegert, Hindmarsh, and Hamilton, 2003, p. 114). Regardless of the exact cause, which is probably volcanic acid layers, the radio echoes represent *isochronous* layers.

The most interesting character of these radio echoes is that they indicate that there has been *little flow of the ice sheet*, which provides strong evidence for the Creation-Flood Ice Age model. Figure 11.1 shows two profiles from near the center of the Antarctic Ice Sheet near Dome B. Although ice sheet movement is very slow—1 to 4 m/yr, the ridges and troughs of the isochronous layers line up *nearly vertical*. The layers generally conform to the bedrock valleys and ridges with the amplitude decreasing upward and show the existence of bedrock lakes (Bogorodsky, Bentley, and Gudmandsen, 1985; Tobacco et al., 1998). Robin and Millar (1982, p. 290) state:

> Radio-echo layers are commonly observed to lie parallel to the ice surface in the upper part of the ice sheet and to become progressively aligned with the bedrock in the lower parts.

The straightforward interpretation of the radio echo images is that there has been little horizontal movement of the ice sheet. The ice in this area of Antarctica is supposed to be a few hundred thousand years old in the lower half of the ice. At 3 m/yr movement, which, based on figure 3.12, may be an underestimation in the lower levels, the lower to middle layers should have moved around 600 km in 200,000 years. The ice is *not* frozen to bedrock in this area of Antarctica, so the bottom ice should have flowed a long distance, since it is believed to be about one million years old (Pokar, 2003). Therefore, the troughs and ridges in the isochronous layers should not line up vertically or nearly vertically, but should be sheared off upward in the direction of flow.

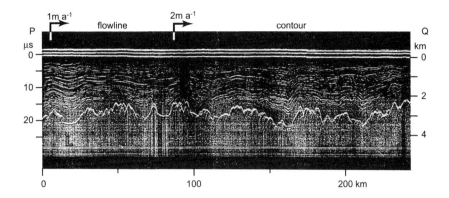

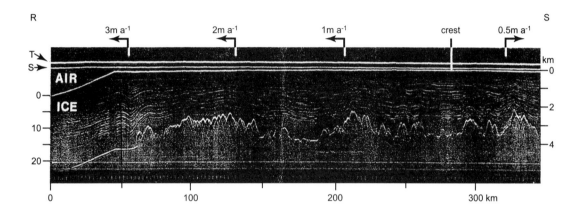

Figure 11.1   Radio echo profiles showing bedrock and internal layering near Dome B, central Antarctica (from Robin, Drewry, and Meldrum, 1977, plate 2).

The radio echo layers have the appearance of snow building up fairly evenly over mountains and valleys. If the ice sheets were as old as Evolutionary-Uniformitarian scientists claim, it seems that the valleys should have filled up with ice, due to downvalley flow, faster than the mountains were covered, so that the radio echoes in the top half of the ice sheet should not show the topography at the base of the ice sheet (see next section).

Another indication of little flow in the Antarctic Ice Sheet is that radio echoes from the deeper East Antarctic Ice Sheet towards the Transantarctic Mountains drape strongly over a 120-kilometer long hill that is higher than one kilometer (figure 11.2) (Siegert, Hindmarsh, and Hamilton, 2003). The flow is from the left to the right. The scientists expected that where the flow is forced over the subglacial hill on the upflow side that old ice would have uplifted to the surface. However, no old ice was found at this location on the surface; and, moreover, the isochronous lines do not show any separation between the layers or the vertical distance between the layers and the ice base (Siegert, Hindmarsh, and Hamilton, 2003, p. 120). This pattern makes no sense if the ice sheets have been flowing over this hill for many hundreds of thousands of years. The straightforward interpretation is that there has been little movement and that the ice accumulated evenly over the hill and the lower area to the south.

A similar pattern of radio echoes is observed in the Greenland Ice Sheet (Jacobel and Hodge, 1995). The troughs and ridges of the radio echoes line up nearly vertical in the interior of the ice

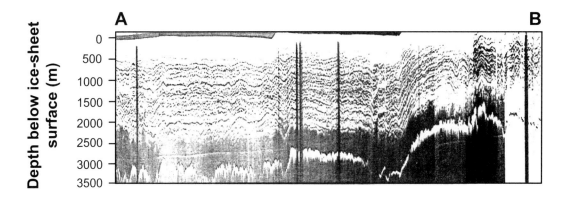

Figure 11.2 Radio echoes from near the center of the East Antarctic Ice Sheet towards the Transantarctic Mountains that drape over a 120-kilometer long hill that is higher than one kilometer (from Siegert, Hindmarsh, and Hamilton, 2003, p. 117). Note that because flow is from left to right, the scientists fully expected old ice to be forced upward to the surface on the stoss side of the hill. They were surprised to discover no "old" ice at the surface above this location.

sheet (Gogineni et al., 2001). It is interesting that the bottom layers do not appear to be deformed at scales larger than 20 meters at the location of the GRIP and GISP2 core sites:

> However, it does appear that the radar records can place some constraints on overturned folding near the bottom. The general pattern in all profiles is that the layers simply conform more and more closely to the bed topography as the bottom is approached. Nowhere do we see folding which grows steeper than the bed slopes below (Jacobel and Hodge, 1995, p. 589).

Such an observation favors the European interpretation of the "interglacial" $\delta^{18}O$ oscillations in the GRIP core. They represent real $\delta^{18}O$ oscillations and not overturned ice layers within several hundred meters of the bedrock. It also adds support for the Creation-Flood interpretation that these "interglacial" oscillations are really the early part of the Ice Age (see chapter 10).

Glaciologists have ignored the straightforward implications of vertical orientation of the troughs and ridges of the radio echo layers. They have generally incorporated such features into their flow models in such a way that the flow results in isochronous layers at similar depths in the ice sheet (see flow model for Dye 3 in figure 8.3). In other words, glaciologists are conforming the flow pattern to fit the isochronous layers (Bogorodsky, Bentley, and Gudmandsen, 1985, p. 164).

Bottom Topography Reflected in Ice Sheet Surface Topography

The troughs and ridges in the radio echoes caused by the bottom topography are even reflected at the *surface* of the ice sheet. Figure 11.3 shows 20-meter amplitude surface undulations that line up with bottom troughs and ridges, as represented by ice thickness, upstream from Dye 3 (Overgaard and Gundestrup, 1985). The pattern is offset upstream a few kilometers, indicating little flow, as expected in the Creation-Flood model.

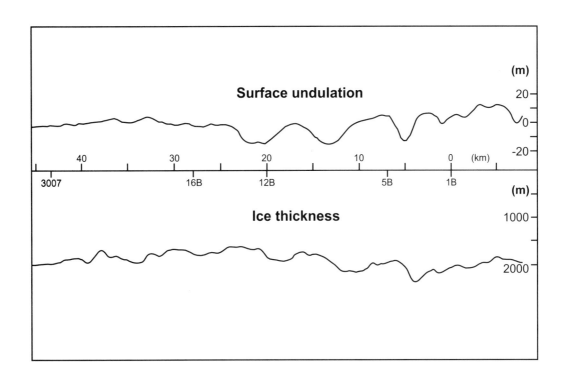

Figure 11.3 Ice sheet surface undulations correlated with ice thickness, which reflects bottom topography, downstream from Dye 3, Greenland. The offset appears to be two to three kilometers (from Overgaard and Gundestrup, 1985, p. 52).

The bottom topography of Antarctica also shows up at the surface of the ice sheet. Subglacial lakes, for instance, result in unusually flat areas on surface maps derived from radar altimetry (Young et al., 1982; Cudlip and McIntyre, 1987; Ridley, Cudlip, and Laxon, 1993). One large flat area on top of the Antarctic Ice Sheet corresponds to a large lake below:

> One distinct feature of particular interest, near the centre of the East Antarctic plateau, is a large flat region, 50 km x 185 km centred 150 km north-northwest of Vostok (78°28' S, 106°49' E). This region, which has previously been observed during radio-echo sounding (RES) flights and aerial surveys (Robin and others, 1977), is the surface expression of a large subglacial lake about 3940 m beneath the surface of the ice sheet (Ridley, Cudlip, and Laxon, 1993, p. 625).

There are sixty-four of these subglacial lakes below the ice sheet, and most are generally only several square kilometers in extent. In spite of the smaller size, most of these lakes still show up as flat areas on the ice sheet:

> Many [lakes] are also visible as unusually flat areas on surface maps derived from satellite radar altimetry (Cudlip and McIntyre 1987; Ridley et al. 1993), showing that subglacial lakes have a strong influence in the surface topography of the ice sheet (Vaughan et al., 1999b, p. 936).

A model of ice flow now claims that a flat surface is what is "expected" above a subglacial lake during ice flow (Pattyn, 2003). This situation is supposed to be like a standing wave in the atmosphere caused by a mountain range in which the wave pattern remains stationary but the wind flows through the pattern. This hypothesis may possibly work for the 14,000 km² area of subglacial Lake Vostok, but it can scarcely account for the same pattern over the much smaller subglacial lakes. Besides, in the grid model with low resolution, Lake Vostok was covered by only two grid points (Pattyn, 2003, p. 14)! How could two grid points cause a standing wave in the ice flow model?

If the ice had been flowing for several hundred thousand to over a million years, the surface expression of the lakes at the bottom of the ice sheet should be offset hundreds of kilometers downstream, even in the slow moving interior of the ice sheets. The lack of such offset is strong evidence for little ice sheet flow and favors the short timescale of the Creation-Flood Ice Age and ice sheet model.

Chapter 12

SUMMARY AND FUTURE RESEARCH

Summary

Since this monograph deals with the origin and development of the Greenland and Antarctic Ice sheets, information on their sizes, the climate, bedrock before and after glaciation, and internal properties of the firn snow and ice are presented in chapter 1.

The main variable for inferring the past climate, mainly temperature, comes from an analysis of the stable oxygen and deuterium isotope ratios down ice cores in the ice sheets. Based on stable isotope ratios, which can be caused by a number of physical processes as described in appendix 1, the Greenland Ice Sheet generally consists of a warm period at the very bottom, followed upward by the colder Ice Age, and then the post–Ice Age climate. The isotope pattern in Antarctica is different than the Greenland pattern and shows multiple large-amplitude changes over most of the core length, followed upward by a stable isotope pattern at the top, which is the post–Ice Age period. All this is described in chapter 2.

In chapter 3, the two main models for the origin and development of the ice sheets were briefly presented, since details of these models can be found in other publications. There is the mainstream Evolutionary-Uniformitarian model that essentially assumes the ice sheets have been in equilibrium for several million years or more. The contrasting Creation-Flood model postulates a time of rapid snowfall during the Ice Age, which started off relatively warm, followed by a quick transition to the present climate and the continued accumulation of snow in the present climate.

Since the models are so different, the dating of the cores by the Evolutionary-Uniformitarian methods was briefly described in chapter 4. These methods are annual layer counting, applied to the Greenland ice cores; glaciological flow models; reference horizons; and the Milankovitch mechanism.

Annual layer dating was analyzed in depth in chapters 5 to 7, since scientists claim that 110,000 or more annual layers have been counted down the GISP2 core, just like counting rings to determine the age of the tree. Chapter 5 is dedicated to the oxygen isotope method; chapter 6 analyzes what is called *visual stratigraphy;* and chapter 7 is devoted to annual layers picked up by various chemicals, especially nitric and sulfuric acid. Annual layers are fairly well defined in the top third of the Greenland ice cores, which represents only a few thousand years in both models. There are many problems associated with claimed "annual" layers in the middle and lower portions of the ice cores. Just the interpretation of the chemical data from source to ice is fraught with many difficulties, as outlined in appendix 2. It was shown that midway down the core, scientists begin counting more and more subannual layers, thinking that they are annual layers the deeper down the core they are found. These subannual layers can represent storms or weather cycles over numerous periods. The number of annual layers boils down to which model one assumes before he makes the count (Oard, 2003a).

The influence of the Evolutionary-Uniformitarian model is made manifest by the other three dating methods. Chapter 8 delves into glaciological flow models and references horizons in which old age is automatically built into the ice sheets. The flow model determines the first guess for the thickness of each annual layer. The models are tuned to certain references horizons, such as volcanic acidity spikes that are only significant for about 1,000 years, two beryllium-10 spikes, and various events in the multiple glacial/interglacial ice age scheme, including the Younger Dryas cold interval about 11,000 years ago and the warm interglacial about 100,000 years ago. Deep ice cores from the top of the Antarctic Ice Sheet are dated by such glacial reference horizons. This is how scientists can claim an age of over 400,000 years near the bottom of the Vostok core and 750,000 years for the lower portion of the new Dome C core. The Creation-Flood Ice Age model postulates significantly lower ice sheets during the Ice Age, especially for Greenland. The altimeter developed by analyzing ice core bubbles seems to contradict this model, but on closer inspection the interpretation of the data is equivocal.

One can legitimately ask how Evolutionary-Uniformitarian scientists know the dates for the events in the multiple ice age model by which they date the cores by reference horizons and flow modeling. It is because they *assume* the astronomical theory of the ice age or the Milankovitch mechanism that all paleoclimatic data tie together. The Milankovitch mechanism is supposedly proven by matching cycles of oxygen isotopes in deep-sea cores. This mechanism, the subject of chapter 9, not only assumes multiple ice ages, but also assumes that the ice ages have cycled every 100,000 years during the past 800,000 years. There are numerous problems associated with this mechanism and its use in analysis of deep-sea cores. The most significant problem is that the radiational changes of the 100,000-year eccentricity cycle are very weak. Deep-sea cores need first to be dated in order to compare cycles with the Milankovitch mechanism, and this brings up a whole new set of complications in dating methods. The reason why scientists can seemingly make all their data and dates "consistent" is attributed to the ubiquitous reinforcement syndrome.

Chapter 10 delves into a major shift in climatic thinking based on the Greenland ice cores from the top of the ice sheet. This shift relates to deductions made regarding abrupt shifts in climate, especially temperature, that supposedly occurred during the Ice Age and possible during the previous warmer "interglacial," a period that should be comparable to today. Such wild fluctuations, not seen before outside ice cores, are suddenly observed in many other paleoclimatic records such as deep-sea cores. Such fluctuations have given vent to the fear of a huge worldwide temperature drop caused by, of all things, global warming. This is an example of a wrong conclusion—abrupt climate swings—based on their faulty Evolutionary-Uniformitarian paradigm. On the other hand, the Creation-Flood model would simply interpret the abrupt changes in oxygen isotopes as caused by variable volcanic ash and aerosols during the Ice Age on a decadal timescale. Since the oscillations are confined to the Ice Age, the claimed interglacial oscillations in the Evolutionary-Uniformitarian model are really just Ice Age fluctuations in the early, warmer part of the Creation-Flood Ice Age model. Not only is the dating of Antarctic deep ice cores by the Milankovitch mechanism seen as a fictitious exercise, but also the claimed glacial/interglacial oscillations are likely the same, but with more amplitude, as the abrupt Ice Age changes in $\delta^{18}O$ in Greenland cores.

Of course, one can claim that it is one model against another, or one opinion opposed to another. However, there are several indications that the Creation-Flood model is the superior interpretation. Besides being a more rational interpretation of wild ice core fluctuations in $\delta^{18}O$ during the Ice Age, the Greenland ice cores generally show only one Ice Age, contrary to the expectations of mainstream scientists. Furthermore, the surprise broadening in the Evolutionary-

Uniformitarian timescale of volcanic and ^{10}Be spikes with depth is evidence for the Creation-Flood model. Especially significant is that troughs and ridges in isochronous radio echo data line up vertically with the bedrock topography, indicating little or no movement of the ice sheets. This supports the timescale of several thousand years for the buildup of these ice sheets and is contrary to the timescale in the Evolutionary-Uniformitarian model in which the ice half way down in the ice sheet should have moved several hundred kilometers.

Future Research

This monograph is comprehensive in that it analyzes many aspects of the Greenland and Antarctic ice cores. It is especially concerned with the chronology of the ice sheets as deduced from ice cores. However, as with any subject of research, there are more aspects to the subject than can be analyzed in one monograph. They have been left for further research. I will briefly list some future research topics.

1) The Milankovitch Mechanism and Quaternary Dating Methods

I only briefly touched on the Milankovitch mechanism, or the astronomical theory of ice ages, and Quaternary dating methods in chapter 9. These subjects may need a monograph or two in themselves because they relate to so many aspects of post-Flood chronology and climatology. They are so closely intertwined with many Quaternary paleoclimatic data sets that it would take much effort to unravel real data from interpretation of data. Many data sets and dating methods are correlated to the Milankovitch mechanism.

2) Ice Age Modeling

Climate models that include the atmosphere and the ocean have been developed at the National Center for Atmospheric Research. These models have become more sophisticated with further development. I believe they are approaching the accuracy we need to model the Ice Age and the many ramifications of that unique climate. (I may add that the models could also simulate conditions in the pre-Flood world as well as the Flood with appropriate initial and boundary conditions and possibly different relationships between variables.) Creationist can use such a model to simulate the buildup of the Greenland and Antarctic Ice Sheets, as well as the other ice sheets during the Ice Age that have since melted. The models should aid the creationist interpretation of many subsidiary Ice Age mysteries, such as the existence of pluvial lakes in currently dry areas, the wet Sahara Desert, the unique climate of mild winters and cool summers indicated by animals and plants during the Ice Age, and the climatic effects in Siberia that drew millions of woolly mammoths to that inhospitable land and their subsequent demise (Oard, 2004b).

Since the models have an ice subprogram, we can model the effect of the much faster deformation rate indicated by Ice Age ice (Reeh, 1985; Dahl-Jensen and Gundestrup, 1987; Fisher, 1987; Etheridge, 1989). We may be able to understand several mysterious phenomena within the Evolutionary-Uniformitarian model, such as the indication that the Laurentide Ice Sheet boundary was thin and probably surged.

Within the Evolutionary-Uniformitarian model, the ice age was forty to one hundred times dustier than now. However, their annual layers are much thinner. Thus, in the Creation-Flood Ice Age model with thicker annual layers, there would be much more dust, perhaps 1,000 or more times the current dust concentration. The latter model has the potential to account for the widespread, and sometimes thick, distribution of loess and generally stabilized sand dunes in the midlatitudes. Such atmospheric dust also would have a significant climatic effect, which could be modeled with a detailed climatic model.

3) Temperature Profiles

One aspect left for future research is the meaning of borehole temperatures. Can the Creation-Flood model with its quick Ice Age and unique paleoclimate account for the temperature profile down the ice cores? This question needs to be addressed.

The Evolutionary-Uniformitarian model claims to have matched the Camp Century temperature profile down the core with their expected earth history (Robin, 1955; Weertman, 1968; Dansgaard and Johnson, 1969a,b; Philberth and Federer, 1971; Budd, 1983). However, the researchers had to adjust several parameters in their equations to get the fit relatively close, such as decreased precipitation in the past. So it is difficult to know how much circular reasoning went into the calculated temperature profile from their model.

It is of interest that early-predicted temperature profiles in the Antarctic Ice Sheet were much too cold lower in the ice sheet. Budd, Jenssen, and Radok (1971) estimated temperatures of $-20°C$ to $-30°C$ at the base of the ice sheet. However, the discovery of lakes and relatively warm basal temperatures in Antarctic ice cores has shown the expected temperature profile did not pan out (Oswald and Robin, 1973). Could it be that the warmer temperatures found low in the ice sheet are a result of warmer winters early in the Ice Age as suggested in the Creation-Flood model?

Glaciologists have concluded during the past decade that the temperature changed much more in the Greenland Ice Sheet for a given change in $\delta^{18}O$ (Johnsen et al., 1995a; Cuffey et al., 1995; Kerr, 1996; Jouzel et al., 1997; Cuffey and Clow, 1997; Jouzel, 1999). This topic was introduced in the last section of chapter 2. However, they assume a more or less constant elevation of the ice sheet and a long period of time. The Creation-Flood model is so much different that applying the physical principles should provide a different temperature profile. The approach to take would be a geophysical inverse problem in using the current borehole temperatures and extrapolating backwards in the Creation-Flood model to see if the model can explain the temperature observations. Maybe the analysis will yield unique insights to Ice Age temperatures.

4) Ice Age Environment

Many environmental variables in the form of carbon dioxide, methane, and other chemicals have been measured in deep-sea cores. Many of these variables are correlated to oxygen and deuterium isotope ratios. It would be good to understand what all these relationships mean. If these variables can be plugged into the shorter Creation-Flood timescale, they may yield insights into environmental conditions just after the Flood that no longer exist today. This monograph only briefly touches on some of these issues; they need further development. For instance, there is the question of carbon dioxide and climate and its relationship to the carbon cycle. Some Evolutionary-Uniformitarian scientists believe that carbon dioxide is the amplifying factor in the Milankovitch mechanism that causes huge climate and environmental change (Cuffey and Vimeux, 2001). Is this true? How accurate are the CO_2 measurements in ice cores (Jaworowski, Segalstad, and Ono, 1992)? What can they tell about the paleoclimate?

Another area for future research is the biological implication of MSA in ice cores. Since MSA is a measure of biological productivity of the ocean surface, it is a possible measure of past productivity. Would the thicker annual layers in the Creation-Flood Ice Age model support much greater ocean plankton productivity during the Ice Age? Such deductions could also go a long way in determining how fast planktonic organisms accumulated on the bottom of the ocean after the Flood.

I have said little about the variable, called the *deuterium excess (d),* that links $\delta^{18}O$ to δD in equation 2.3. The deuterium excess varies, depending upon a number of variables that may be able to tell us more about the Ice Age climate. In particular, the deuterium excess can provide an estimate of the air temperature, relative humidity, wind speed at the source of evaporation, and the amount of sea ice near the ice sheet (Petit et al., 1991; Ciais et al., 1995; Armengaud et al., 1998; Vimeux et al., 1999, 2001a,b; Cavanaugh and Cuffey, 2002). However, it is also related to the supersaturation history and the kinetic effect in clouds (Fisher, 1991) (see appendix 1 for an explanation of the kinetic effect). The deuterium excess is also related to the kinetic effect of the initial evaporation, which needs further understanding in an Ice Age climate.

5) Antarctic Meteorites

It is well known that meteorites are concentrated on some areas of the Antarctic Ice Sheet, especially stagnant ice zones of the Allan Hills and Yamota Mountains nunataks (Cassidy, Olsen, and Yanai, 1977; Harvey et al., 1998; Wadhwa, 2004). The meteorites are found on what are called *blue ice areas* in which net melting is greater than the net accumulation (Bintanja, 1999). We need to know what the meaning of such a concentration of meteorites is.

Variables Determining the Oxygen Isotope Ratio

In chapter 2, the interpretation of the oxygen isotopes in terms of surface temperature (equation 2.4) was used to infer the past climate. However, it is known that the oxygen isotope ratio of the snow deposited on the Greenland and Antarctic Ice Sheets is determined by many other variables:

> Like any other time series of proxy data, including the deep sea foraminifera records, the δ profiles along ice cores are influenced by many parameters, for example the summer to winter precipitation ratio, and the mean condensation temperature in precipitating clouds (Dansgaard et al., 1985, p. 71).

These variables will be examined in this appendix.

The Physics of the Oxygen Isotope Ratio

Equation 2.4 in chapter 2 is a statistical relationship. What we really need to understand is the physics of evaporation and condensation processes that determines the final oxygen isotope ratio of the snow that falls on the ice sheets.

There are four physical mechanisms that determine the oxygen isotope ratio of the ice in the cores (table A1.1). The first variable is the oxygen isotope ratio of the seawater. This ratio determines the initial oxygen isotope ratio of the evaporated vapor. Seawater today has a $\delta^{18}O$ of zero by definition. However, this is an average for all oceans; locally and regionally $\delta^{18}O$ can vary significantly depending upon a number of factors (see listing after first variable in table A1.1). One factor is that $\delta^{18}O$ will vary depending upon the amount of ice on the land. Ice has a fairly low oxygen isotope ratio. The ice during the ice age is believed to have a $\delta^{18}O$ value of −30‰ (Dansgaard and Tauber, 1969). The water for the ice was evaporated from the ocean, causing the ocean to have a more positive $\delta^{18}O$. Therefore, the more ice on the land compared to today, the greater the oxygen isotope ratio of sea water, and the less ice on land than today the lower the ratio from today. If there were no ice on land, a condition we will consider for the beginning of the Ice Age in the Creation-Flood model, the ratio for the oceans would be about −0.7‰. At glacial maximum, it would be about 0.5‰ in the Creation-Flood model and about 1.1‰ in the Evolutionary-Uniformitarian model (Paillard, 2001, p. 329). Thus, the average oxygen isotope ratio of the vapor immediately above the ocean will vary by about 1.2‰ from the start of glaciation to maximum in the Creation-Flood model and 1.8‰ in the Evolutionary-Uniformitarian model from the time before the buildup of the Antarctic Ice Sheet to the time of glacial maximum in their last ice age.

The oxygen isotope ratio of the surface seawater also depends upon the mixing of low oxygen isotope meltwater into the ocean. When ice sheets and ice caps melt, such as during deglaciation, some of the low oxygen isotope water from melting ice sheets is returned to the sea. This water of course is mixed with runoff from the particular watersheds that would have a different oxygen iso-

Table A1.1 Physical variables or mechanisms of evaporation and condensation that determine the stable isotope ratios in ice cores.

tope ratio than the melted ice and which can vary locally and seasonally (Rohling and Bigg, 1998). High latitude rivers especially have low oxygen isotope ratios (Strain and Tan, 1993; Schmidt, 1998). Regardless, such runoff into the ocean would possess a much more negative oxygen isotope ratio than the ocean. Since fresh water tends to float on denser salt water, the surface water will end up with a lower $\delta^{18}O$. Vapor that evaporates from this seawater would also have a more negative $\delta^{18}O$. The vapor would be more negative the closer it was to the river deltas. Werner et al. (2000b) ran a climate simulation for a small meltwater spike that spread into the northern Atlantic Ocean from rivers. They discovered the oxygen isotope ratio of the vapor in the region decreased as much as 2‰ because of the lower $\delta^{18}O$ of the ocean surface. It is conceivable that the oxygen isotope ratio could decrease significantly more than 2‰ after a catastrophic discharge from a large Ice Age lake, such as glacial Lake Missoula (Oard, 2004a), that spilled a large volume of fresh water out onto the ocean. There is also the possibility that large subglacial floods occurred that dumped much more water into the ocean than did glacial Lake Missoula (Shaw, 1996, 2002).

A third factor that would affect the oxygen isotope ratio of the surface seawater is the ratio of precipitation to evaporation (table A1.1), which is generally related to the salinity (Rostek et al., 1993; Rohling and Bigg, 1998). The greater the precipitation over the evaporation, the less saline and the lower the oxygen isotope ratio of the surface water. Strong evaporation in the subtropical oceans has a $\delta^{18}O$ of seawater that is 0.5 to 1.5‰ greater than VSMOW, while mid-to-high latitude oceans with greater precipitation have $\delta^{18}O$ −0.5 to −1.0‰ less than VSMOW (Schmidt, 1998). So the vapor evaporated from the ocean at higher latitudes would have a lower $\delta^{18}O$.

A fourth factor that would tend to freshen and lower the oxygen isotope ratio of the sea surface is the discharge and melting of icebergs with low $\delta^{18}O$. Melting icebergs would act just like the input of fresh water from a melting ice sheet.

The formation of sea ice, a fifth factor, causes the water just below the ice to decrease its $\delta^{18}O$ (Strain and Tan, 1993; Rohling and Bigg, 1998). This is because the formation of sea ice preferentially favors an increase in ^{18}O in the ice with a reciprocal increase in ^{16}O of the water. However, there is no evaporation from an ocean covered with sea ice, and the water below the ice would tend to sink due to its increased salinity following the formation of sea ice. The formation and melting of sea ice could potentially be significant for the oxygen isotope ratio of seawater and evaporated water.

The second physical mechanism that determines the oxygen isotope ratio of the vapor is the temperature of the phase change (table A1.1). The temperature dependence has been worked out experimentally and tabulated in the form of what are called *fractionation factors* (Dansgaard, 1964) (table A1.2). Newer values are only slightly greater than those originally used by Dansgaard (Lorius and Johnsen, 1983, p. 48). This temperature relationship is based on the ratios of the vapor pressure of the lighter isotope divided by the vapor pressure of the heavier isotope. In the case of evaporation from the ocean, it is the sea surface temperature (SST) that determines the fractionation factor. For example, referring to table A1.2 at room temperatures, the fractionation factor for oxygen isotopes is 1.0091, while that for deuterium and hydrogen is 1.079 (Dansgaard, 1964, p. 438). If water had a temperature of 20°C and an oxygen isotope ratio of −20‰, then the vapor would be −29‰. The fractionation factors for negative temperatures are listed in table A1.2 mainly because the condensation process often occurs in supercooled clouds, in which the temperature can fall as cold as −20°C or colder before condensation begins. If water condenses at a temperature of −20°C and an oxygen isotope ratio of −20‰, the supercooled vapor would have a $\delta^{18}O$ of −6.5‰. One can see in table A1.2 that as the temperature of the ocean cools, the oxygen isotope ratio of the evaporating vapor progressively becomes more negative. At a temperature of 30°C and a $\delta^{18}O$ of zero, the fractionation factor would be about 1.008 so that the vapor would have an oxygen isotope ratio of about −8‰. At 0°C and a $\delta^{18}O$ of zero, the fractionation factor is 1.0111, and thus $\delta^{18}O$ would be −11‰. The rate of change is about 1‰ /10°C.

t °C	α_D	α_{18}
100	1.029	1.0033
80	1.037	1.0045
60	1.046	1.0058
40	1.060	1.0074
20	1.079	1.0091
0	1.106	1.0111
−10	1.123	1.0123
−20	1.146	1.0135

Table A1.2 Fractionation factors for the deuterium (α_D) and oxygen (α_{18}) isotopes related to temperature (from Dansgaard, 1964, p. 438).

However, the above fractionation factors were determined under assumed equilibrium or Rayleigh conditions (Fisher, 1992). This means that the temperature of the phases undergoing the phase change is the same, the phase change proceeds very slowly, and the two phases are immediately separated. The relative humidity in such a process is high. Nature is not so simple; the Rayleigh condition is an ideal and not likely in the real world (Jouzel and Merlivat, 1984, p. 11,749; Jouzel et al., 2000). This brings us to the third physical mechanism that has been little applied in theory. This is the kinetic effect.

The kinetic effect is difficult to understand and calculate (Dansgaard, 1964). It is based on the different molecular weights of the isotopes. The heavier isotopes diffuse in water or air slower than the lighter isotopes do; they have a lower diffusivity (Gedzelman and Arnold, 1994, p. 10,455). So, when evaporation is rapid in non-Rayleigh conditions, the lighter isotopes of water move faster to the evaporating surface, causing more of the lighter isotopes to pass into the vapor phase. Dansgaard (1964) explains the kinetic effect as an additional fractionation factor. Dansgaard (1964, p. 449) states from experiments in which dry air passes rapidly over water that the kinetic effect will cause a 200% increase in the fractionation factor for oxygen isotopes while only a 15% increase in the fractionation factor for hydrogen isotopes. So, the kinetic effect for the oxygen isotope ratio is much more significant (Lorius et al., 1989). This means that with water at room temperature, the vapor would have a $\delta^{18}O$ of −9‰ in equilibrium while −28‰ for the extreme conditions in the experiment. From this experiment, it appears that a more negative oxygen isotope ratio is favored by cooler, drier air blowing rapidly over warm water. These conditions cause rapid evaporation (Bunker, 1976) and as a result greater kinetic fractionation and lower oxygen isotope ratio of the vapor. There is also a kinetic effect when vapor turns directly to snow caused by the faster diffusion of the lighter isotopes in air (Ciais and Jouzel, 1994). The kinetic effect will cause the oxygen isotope ratio of the falling snow to be more negative than expected. Furthermore, the oxygen isotope ratio of the falling snow, unlike rain, does not become more positive due to exchange with vapor on its downward trajectory (Gedzelman and Lawrence, 1982; Jouzel and Merlivat, 1984, p. 11,750). Therefore, under some circumstances, the kinetic factor can have a large impact on the oxygen isotope ratio. Fast evaporation and the formation of snow favor significantly more negative oxygen isotope ratios.

I might add that it is mainly this difference between kinetic factors for δD and $\delta^{18}O$ that causes the differences in the deuterium excess d in equation 2.3 of chapter 2. The more the evaporation process is out of equilibrium, the greater is the deuterium excess. So the deuterium excess is not only a non-equilibrium indicator but also a measure of the rate of evaporation (Dansgaard, 1964, p. 450). Therefore, the deuterium excess depends upon the sea surface temperature, the relative humidity of the air, the wind speed in the moisture source area, and other climatological variables (Merlivat and Jouzel, 1979; Fisher, 1991; Petit et al., 1991; Ciais and Jouzel, 1994; Ciais et al., 1995; Armengaud et al., 1998; Vimeux et al., 1999, 2001a,b; Kavanaugh and Cuffey, 2002).

A fourth and last physical variable in table A1.1 is the number of condensation cycles the vapor has passed through. This determines the final oxygen isotope ratio of the vapor that is condensing to snow that falls on the ice sheet. This variable was discussed in chapter 2 and is shown in figure 2.2 (Dansgaard, 1961, p. 54; Robin, 1983a). This variable can especially have an impact if the source of the vapor was from as far away as the tropics to subtropics. In this case, the vapor would have had time to go through more condensation cycles and hence will become progressively more negative upon reaching the ice sheets. This variable is considered the most significant by glaciologists for determining the $\delta^{18}O$ of the snow that ends up as ice in ice cores. In fact, some researchers have stated the primary control of the oxygen isotope ratio in ice cores is the temperature difference between the source and the ice core site, which is a crude measure of the number of condensation cycles of the vapor (Werner, Heimann, and Hoffmann, 2001). Thus, vapor originating from polar oceans and falling on the ice sheet would be transported a shorter distance with fewer condensation cycles; and hence based on this factor alone, the snow would have a more positive oxygen isotope ratio than vapor transported from lower latitude.

Statistical Relationships

The physics determining the oxygen isotope ratio of the snow falling on the ice sheets is complicated and difficult to measure. It is much more practical to use statistical relationships in deriving climate information from oxygen isotope measurements in ice cores. Thus, a number of statistical relationships between the oxygen isotope ratio and other variables have been worked out (table A1.3). These correlations are second-order relationships; they depend upon the action of the physical variables.

1.	Surface temperature (positive)
2.	Condensation temperature (positive)
3.	Latitude (negative)
4.	Altitude (negative)
5.	Precipitation (positive)

Table A1.3   Statistical relationships with the oxygen isotope ratio and whether the correlation is positive or negative.

Surface air temperature, the most widely used correlation with the oxygen isotope ratio, is a statistical relationship. It is not directly related to the physics of fractionation. Surface temperature correlates well (see figure 2.4) because the physics involved in producing such negative oxygen isotope ratios on the ice sheet is proportional to the surface temperature. There is a relatively close correspondence, as represented by equation 2.4 in chapter 2. Because of the many complications, it is a wonder that equation 2.4 works out so well for most areas. However, this does not mean the relationship holds that well for the past, in particular during the Ice Age.

There are some areas where a different equation with a more random distribution and a lower correlation coefficient occurs. One area is the Antarctic Ice Sheet, where a number of factors conspire to make the relationship between oxygen isotopes and surface temperatures more chaotic (Koerner and Russell, 1979, p. 1,420). For instance, Schlosser (1999) found a fair amount of variability in the relationship between mean $\delta^{18}O$ in Antarctic snow at Neumayer and mean annual temperature, mainly because of the seasonal variability of snow accumulation. The oxygen isotope ratio is related to precipitation, which occurs mainly in the warmest air on the ice sheets (Bradley, 1985, p. 132). It has been observed in Antarctica that snow events have a high $\delta^{18}O$ in the warmer air, but the ratio drops 10-12‰ as the air cools, which is generally about 7°C within a day (Osada, 1994, p. 229). This is the reason why monthly surface temperature and oxygen isotope ratios do not correlate well at a station (Schlosser, 1999, p. 464).

The second statistical relationship discussed is the condensation temperature of the vapor. The colder the condensation temperature, the lower the oxygen isotope ratio based on equation 2.4

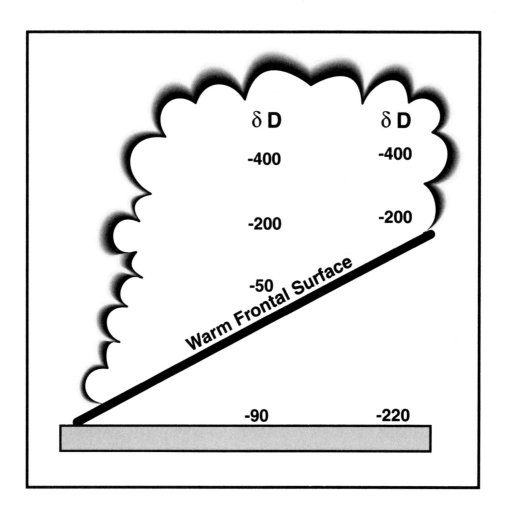

Figure A1.1 The relationship between the deuterium isotope ratio and condensation temperatures in stratiform clouds in which temperature cools upward. The values on the surfaces are the deuterium isotope ratios of the precipitation from various locations under the warm front (after Gedzelman, and Arnold, 1994, p. 10,456).

(figure A1.1) (Dansgaard, 1964; Werner et al., 2000a, p. 725). This is no small relationship. Lorius et al. (1979, p. 646) state that a 3°C change in condensation temperature would result in a 3.3‰ change in $\delta^{18}O$ over Antarctica. There is a monotonic decrease in the percentage of heavy isotopes in precipitation forming from vapor remaining in a given air parcel as it rises and condensation takes place (Gedzelman, Rosenbaum, and Lawrence, 1989, p. 1638). Of course, the oxygen isotope ratio at the particular condensation temperature also depends upon the previous evaporation/condensation cycles of the vapor. The condensation temperature is nearly impossible to measure. Generally, scientists infer a condensation temperature from the measured mean surface temperature, but this relationship can be way off. Bradley (1985, p. 132) states:

> In effect, they assume that mean condensation temperature and mean annual temperature vary in parallel. Why this should be so is hard to understand; most snowfall on polar ice sheets results from a small number of synoptic events occurring on only a fraction of days per year (generally <25%) so *mean annual* temperature,

152

which is greatly influenced by strong surface inversions in dry winter months, should have little in common with $\delta^{18}O$ values in the ice cores.

The top of the Antarctic Ice Sheet is one of those areas where the inferred condensation temperature based on the surface temperature can be way off. Inversions are very strong over Antarctica in winter, generally about 20°C, but usually disappear in summer (Ciais et al., 1995). So, most of the time, the condensation temperature above the inversion is much different than the surface temperature. For the Antarctic Ice Sheet, the oxygen isotope ratio in an ice core is correlated to the surface temperature and not the more accurate condensation temperature (Robin, 1977, p. 152). The poor correlation could especially be a problem during a climate change, such as in a glacial climate, in which the vapor likely would have condensed at a different temperature than expected from today's climate, or the inversion was weak, or there were more stratus clouds. So, using today's climate to infer surface or condensation temperatures from oxygen isotopes could be way off during the Ice Age.

A third and fourth statistical relationship is the inverse correlation of the oxygen isotope ratio with altitude and latitude (Ambach et al., 1968; Bowen and Wilkinson, 2002). Figure A1.2 shows a plot of oxygen isotopes for various latitudes and altitudes. A number of regression equations, similar to equation 2.4 in chapter 2, have been derived from these statistical relationships. In most cases the correlation is similar to that of surface temperature, since temperatures decrease with latitude and altitude. The statistical relationships have many exceptions, however. Figure 2.3 shows a plot of the mean annual oxygen isotope ratio in the Northern Hemisphere. One can see that there would be a different north-south equation between the ocean and the continents.

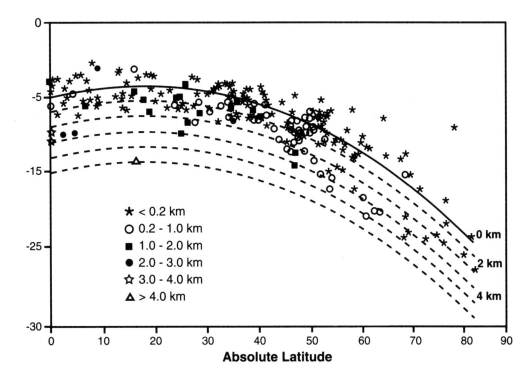

Figure A1.2   The oxygen isotope ratio for meteoric precipitation plotted against station latitude at various altitudes, as given by the symbols in the bottom left corner. Solid line at the top is the best-fit polynomial for low altitude stations while the dotted lines are model lines for altitudes of 1 to 5 kilometers (after Bowen and Wilkinson, 2002, p. 316).

There is a positive correlation of the oxygen isotope ratio with precipitation (Alley and Bender, 1998), the fifth statistical relationship, but this is more of a relationship with temperature, since cooler air is drier. In order to derive the net accumulation, it is assumed that the oxygen isotope ratio of the snow is proportional to the saturation vapor pressure above the inversion that normally occurs over the ice sheets (Lorius et al., 1985). This statistical relationship suggests that significantly less precipitation occurs for lower oxygen isotope ratios. This is why glaciologists infer that the snowfall was much less on the Greenland and Antarctic Ice Sheets during the ice age (Alley and Bender, 1998). However, there are exceptions, such as some Holocene data sets that show no correlation between accumulation and temperature (Reeh et al., 1978; Kapsner et al., 1995, p. 53).

Other Significant Variables

Quite a number of other variables can potentially affect the oxygen isotope ratio. Some of these may become significant during the Ice Age. These variables are listed in table A1.4.

The first variable discussed is the continental effect. It has been observed that the farther from

1. Continental effect (negative)

2. Sea ice effect (negative)

3. Seasonal proportion of precipitation (more winter precipitation, the more negative $\delta^{18}O$)

4. Changing source of moisture (the lower the latitude, the lower $\delta^{18}O$)

5. Amount effect (negative)

6. Blowing and drifting snow (variable)

7. Meltwater percolation (variable)

8. Development of hoar frost (variable)

9. Dust (positive)

Table A1.4   Other significant variables related to the $\delta^{18}O$ and whether the correlation is positive or negative.

the source of evaporation, namely the ocean, the more negative the oxygen isotope ratio in the precipitation (Kato, 1978; Koerner, 1979; Siegenthaler and Oeschger, 1980; Gat and Matsui, 1991; Njitchoua et al., 1999). This relationship for the western half of the United States can be seen on figure 2.3 in chapter 2. The continental effect also causes $\delta^{18}O$ of precipitation to become more negative going eastward in Europe (Rozanski, Sonntag, and Münnich, 1982). Figure A1.3 shows a plot of $\delta^{18}O$ with distance from the moisture source. This is the reason why the average oxygen isotope ratio varies from −9‰ along the coast of the Pacific Northwest to −17‰ downwind in Montana at the same latitude (Gibson et al., 2002). The continental effect especially depends on the number of condensation cycles as the vapor passed from the ocean to the continental interior. Other more minor factors in the continental effect are evaporation from water bodies and evapotranspiration from vegetation with different oxygen isotope ratios that mix with the far-transported vapor. Oxygen isotope ratios from interior water bodies tend to be more negative than those from oceanic sources at the same temperature; and since about one-third of the continental precipitation originates from inland water sources, the precipitation would have a more negative $\delta^{18}O$ (Koster, de Valpine, and Jouzel, 1993).

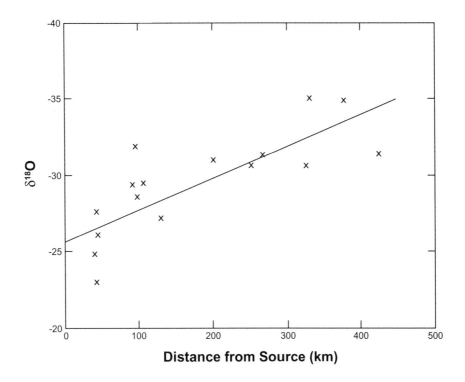

Figure A1.3 $\delta^{18}O$ with distance from moisture source in the eastern Queen Elizabeth Islands for the period August 1973 to May/June 1974 (after Koerner, 1979, p. 38).

A related variable to the continental effect is the extent of sea ice (figure A1.4). If the evaporating vapor came from the edge of the sea ice, extensive sea ice would result in a lower isotope ratio the farther inland. The reason for this is because there would be more condensation events as the vapor traveled inland (Bromwich and Weaver, 1983; Robin and Johnsen, 1983; Fisher and Alt, 1985). This is the basis of Vardiman's (1997) explanation for the Younger Dryas cold interval due to more extensive sea ice during late glaciation.

A third variable is the seasonal proportion of precipitation. Since summer precipitation has a higher $\delta^{18}O$ than winter precipitation, a change in the seasonal proportion will change the mean annual $\delta^{18}O$. For instance, if 50% of the precipitation falls during the warm half of the year and 50% during the cool half of the year, then the oxygen isotope ratio would be an average between the two. But if, due to some climate change, only 25% of the precipitation occurred in winter and 75% occurred during summer, then the average oxygen isotope ratio for the year would become more positive with no change in the annual temperature. Such a seasonal change could easily occur in changing from the Ice Age to the present climate (Robin, 1983b; Krinner, Genthon, and Jouzel, 1997; Schlosser, 1999; Werner et al., 2000b). If the proportion of precipitation that falls in a season changes due to climate change, then so will the oxygen isotope ratio (Steig, Grootes, and Stuiver, 1994).

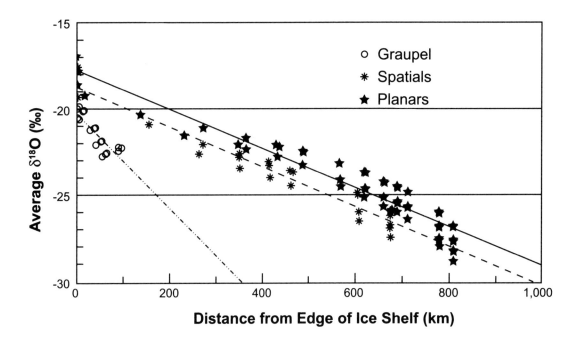

Figure A1.4 Dispersion of δ¹⁸O versus distance from the edge of an ice shelf (from Vardiman, 2001, p. 66).

A fourth variable is a change in source area due to a climate change or a change in the atmospheric circulation (Kapsner et al., 1995; Hendricks, DePaulo, and Cohen, 2000). It has been noted that the oxygen isotope ratio in the snow that falls on the ice sheet can vary considerably depending upon where the vapor originated. The vapor source for present snow for the top of the Greenland and Antarctic Ice Sheets is believed to originate in the subtropics based on the deuterium excess (Johnsen and White, 1989; Petit et al., 1991). However, other researchers find a more variable source. Based on a general circulation climate model of the atmosphere with a water isotope tracer built into the water cycle, Werner, Heimann, and Hoffmann (2001) determined that 15% of the vapor that ends up as snow at Summit, Greenland, originates from the polar seas; this vapor has an oxygen isotope ratio of −19.8‰. Ten percent of the vapor comes from the tropical Indopacific; by the time this vapor reaches the top of Greenland it has an oxygen isotope ratio of −46.6‰. Seventy-five percent of the moisture originated from various other sources; the sources from the polar seas and the Indopacific are the extremes. If the source ratios change during a climate change, then so would the annual oxygen isotope ratio. For instance, if more water came from the Indopacific than from polar regions, the average oxygen isotope ratio would become more negative. Charles et al. (1994, 1995) believe a change in moisture source is a significant variable in explaining the poor relationship between δ¹⁸O and temperature in the glacial part of the Greenland cores. Jouzel et al. (1996, p. 516) state that numerical models show for Antarctica that vapor originating from the tropics would have an oxygen isotope ratio about 12‰ less than that from vapor originating from the Antarctic Ocean. However, Werner, Heimann, and Hoffmann (2001) found no change in source area between the present climate and the glacial climate, but this was assuming the Evolutionary-Uniformitarian model. In the post-Flood Ice Age model, discussed in chapter 3, the source areas may have changed drastically compared to the present climate.

One well-known variable is the amount effect, the fifth variable listed in table A1.4. It has been noted, especially during warm season precipitation in low and midlatitudes, that the greater the rainfall the less the oxygen isotope ratio (Dansgaard, 1964, pp. 445-446; Gedzelman and Arnold, 1994; Njitchoua et al., 1999). The amount effect is related to several factors, including recycled moisture with lower oxygen isotope ratio (Gat and Matsui, 1991), less isotopic fractionation from evaporating rain in the atmosphere during heavy rain (Friedman, Machta, and Soller, 1962; Ehhalt et al., 1963; Stewart, 1975), and colder condensation temperatures higher in the cloud.

A sixth variable is wind scouring. Strong winds can remove and redeposit a part of a storm layer or a seasonal layer and affect the oxygen isotope ratio that is eventually recorded in ice as the snow is progressively buried deeper (Koerner and Russell, 1979; Fujii and Ohata, 1982; Fisher et al., 1983; Alley, 1988, p. 283; Schlosser, 1999; Vaughan et al., 1999a, p. 326; van der Veen et al., 1999). Wind scouring adds noise to the oxygen isotope record in relatively heavy accumulation areas, such as on the Greenland Ice Sheet. Ice pit studies indicate that the seasonal difference in oxygen isotope ratios is still generally preserved. Snow that falls at the South Pole has a $\delta^{18}O$ of $-44\text{\textperthousand}$ in summer and $-58\text{\textperthousand}$ in winter (Aldaz and Deutsch, 1967). However, in light accumulation areas, strong winds can remove an entire year of snow from an area. At Vostok, significant oscillations in $\delta^{18}O$ and snow accumulation are related to drift of snow accumulation waves at various temporal and spatial scales (Ekaykin et al., 2002). I think it is even conceivable that several years of record in very light accumulation areas can be removed. Strong winds occur with storms, of course, but they also occur in generally fair weather along the slopes of the ice sheets. These latter winds are katabatic winds that are caused by the radiational cooling and densification of the air just above the ice sheet and blow down a glacier or ice sheet (see chapter 1). Because of occasional strong winds and light accumulation, oxygen isotope ratios are not used for seasonal dating on top of Antarctica or within interior Antarctic cores.

Katabatic winds are common on the slopes of the Greenland and Antarctic Ice Sheets. These winds produce sastrugi, small-scale dunes or features of high relief on the snow surface, and larger-scale low-amplitude snow dunes. Just recently, extensive megadunes with amplitudes of 2-4 meters and wavelengths of 2-5 kilometers that move slowly by katabatic winds have been discovered on the Antarctic Ice Sheet (Fahnestock, et al., 2000; Frezzotti, Gandolfi, and Urbini, 2002). These megadunes significantly alter snow deposition processes and can significantly affect oxygen isotope ratios. They are observed near some of the ice core sites, which are normally at an ice divide where katabatic winds are light or nonexistent. This is one reason why scientists drill at the top of the ice sheets. However, snow dunes may have occurred in the past at a particular site, especially during the Ice Age.

A seventh variable that results in much noise in ice cores is the effect of meltwater that disturbs the oxygen isotope record (Koerner, Paterson, and Krouse, 1973; Koerner, 1997), as well as other ice core variables. Meltwater is especially a problem on ice caps in the Queen Elizabeth Islands where a fair amount of meltwater forms each year. Okuyama et al. (2003, p. 1) state in regard to these ice caps in northeast Canada: "However, the recognition of a climatic signal from other proxies such as oxygen isotopes ($\delta^{18}O$) and chemical compositions is strongly disturbed by summer melting." It can also be a problem for the Greenland and Antarctic Ice Sheets at lower elevations and in the past when the ice sheet was lower or temperatures warmer. Meltwater forms at the surface of the ice sheet and will percolate downward and refreeze (Pfeffer and Humphrey, 1996), mixing up the oxygen isotope signals in that interval. Especially problematic is that researchers have paid little attention to the impact of meltwater, since very little meltwater forms today at ice core sites and researchers assume the present is the key to the past. If there was more meltwater in the past, ice core misinterpretation can result (Koerner, 1997). On the other hand, in a 122-meter firn and ice core Pahjola et al. (2002) claim only a smoothing of the annual layers of oxygen isotopes from a heavy-accumulation, relatively mild ice cap in Svalbard. This ice cap averages 25% melting of the annual layer each year with a maximum of 50% observed during the study. Such high melting with a small effect on the oxygen isotope ratios seems incongruous. This deduction is reinforced when more oxygen isotope cycles were discovered than the number of postulated years.

The eighth variable listed in table A1.4 is the development of hoar frost. In the snow layers, mass losses and mass gains will cause a change in the oxygen isotope ratios due to evaporation and condensation fractionation (Sommerfeld, Judy, and Friedman, 1991). Generally, layers in which more ice is being deposited from the vapor, or liquid if there is melted snow, become a little more enriched in ^{18}O at the expense of the liquid or vapor phase (Epstein, Sharp, and Gow, 1965; Whillans and Grootes, 1985, p. 3,914; Nakawo et al., 1993).

The last variable is atmospheric dust that was especially high during glacial periods. Dust could raise the oxygen isotope ratio of snow by causing less cloud supercooling and hence condensation at warmer temperatures (Kapsner et al., 1995). This variable has been little evaluated.

There are four main physical variables that result in at least five statistical relationships. Furthermore, at least nine other processes, which change the physical variables, can result in different $\delta^{18}O$ values in ice cores. Since hardly any of these variables can be measured accurately (hence the statistical relationships), a large amount of uncertainty enters into the interpretation of $\delta^{18}O$ down ice cores. Such uncertainty is especially problematic during the Ice Age, even in the Evolutionary-Uniformitarian model. If we substitute the Creation-Flood model for the Evolutionary-Uniformitarian model, one can see that there are more possible ways to interpret $\delta^{18}O$ in ice cores.

THE MANY VARIABLES AFFECTING CHEMICALS FROM SOURCE TO ICE

Before a scientist can analyze the chemical and gaseous species down an ice core, he needs to have at least a general quantitative understanding of the many variables involved. The glaciologists must have some idea of the source or sources of the chemical species, source strength, atmospheric circulation pattern to the ice sheet, transport strength, the transfer behavior from atmosphere to snow, and post-depositional changes (Delmas and Legrand, 1989; Pearman et al., 1989; White et al., 1989; Shaw, 1989; Whitlow, Mayewski, and Dibb, 1992, p. 2045; Fuhrer et al., 1993, p. 1,873; Wolff, 1996). These variables are shown in table A2.1.

1.	Source or sources
2.	Source strength
3.	Atmospheric circulation pattern to the ice sheet
4.	Transport strength
5.	Transfer behavior from atmosphere to snow
6.	Post-depositional changes

Table A2.1. Main variables affecting a chemical species before incorporation into the Greenland and Antarctic Ice Sheets.

A scientist not only needs this quantitative information from the present but also must have at least a general understanding of these variables for past climates:

> Quantification of such effects on the deposition of aerosols and water-reactive trace gases is a prerequisite for reliable comparison of chemical long-term ice core records from different climatological regions on the Greenland ice sheet as well as between different climatic states in the past" (Fischer, Wagenbach, and Kipfstuhl, 1998, p. 21,927).

Furthermore, all these variables are expected to have changed in past climates:

> The sources, transports, reactions, and sinks of the various gases and aerosols were different in past climates with respect to the system we presently know (Delmas, 1992, p. 13).

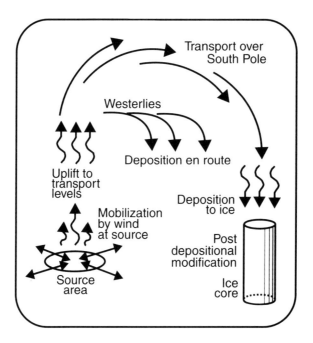

Figure A2.1   Processes affecting the concentration of dust measured in ice cores. Similar processes with more variables affect other chemical species (after Fuhrer, Wolff, and Johnsen, 1999).

Figure A2.1 is a schematic illustrating some of the processes involved before chemical species are locked in the ice.

The Sources and Their Strengths

There are enumerable problems in tracing back the chemical species to their sources. The many sources of chemicals include arid and semi-arid areas for dust, the ocean for sea salt species, volcanic eruptions, lightning, biomass burning, and stratospheric chemical reactions. Furthermore, instead of just one source for a particular chemical species, there can be multiple sources (Clausen and Langway, 1989, p. 227; Delmas and Legrand, 1989, p. 329). Sources may be large or small. A scientist must understand how these sources and their strengths change during a climate change such as an ice age.

The Transport Problem

Those chemical species that originate at the surface must first be mobilized by the wind. Once in the atmosphere, the impurities will spread out and can have a large spatial variability due to the atmospheric circulation and the short residence time of most compounds making up the impurities (Hansson, 1995). This is probably the reason for the large spatial variability in snow pit data from inland West Antarctica (Kreutz and Mayewski, 1999; Reusch et al., 1999). The subject of atmospheric chemistry during the transport process is very complex (Crutzen and Brühl, 1989).

Each one of these variables has present-day complications of its own, including non-linear reactions with other chemical species and environmental variables (Wagenbach et al., 1998a). The precipitation between the source and the ice sheet is an important variable: the more precipitation, the cleaner the atmosphere will be, and vice versa. Transport changes during climate change can dramatically alter the amount of pollutants deposited on the ice sheet:

> At the present time, back trajectories show that air arriving in Greenland can originate from North America, the Atlantic, or the Arctic basin—any change in the proportion of storm tracks coming from each direction could significantly alter the delivery of pollutants to Greenland, even if the source strengths remained constant (Wolff, 1996, p. 4).

One can see that any circulation change would alter the chemical species in an ice core.

The sources and atmospheric transport paths are not well known in the present world, not to mention during the time of the Ice Age when these variables would have been different (Delmas, 1992, p. 13). Shaw (1989, p. 13) grouses:

> We have to understand more about the physics, physical chemistry, and production of submicron-sized, mechanically generated particles if we are to be able to "read" the climate record from aerosols locked up in the polar ice sheets.

Deposition in the Surface Snow

Once the gas or aerosol reaches the atmosphere above the ice sheet, it must be deposited in the snow on top of the ice sheet. The relationship between the atmospheric chemical species and its deposition on the snow is called a *transfer function*. In general, the atmospheric aerosol is qualitatively, but not quantitatively, recorded in the top of the snow (Legrand and Mayewski, 1997, p. 227). There are three processes of deposition from the atmosphere into the surface snow: (1) wet deposition; (2) dry deposition; and (3) fog deposition, although fog deposition can be considered a type of wet deposition (Bergin et al., 1994).

Wet deposition occurs during precipitation, while dry deposition is the transport of particulate and gaseous contaminants from the atmosphere onto surfaces in the absence of precipitation. These are complicated mechanisms that are poorly understood (Davidson, 1989; Bergin et al., 1994, p. 3,207; Fischer, Wagenbach, and Kipfstuhl, 1998, p. 21,927; Dibb and Jaffrezo, 1997). Davidson (1989, p. 29, 30) reminds us:

> Because the complexities of deposition are only poorly understood, ice core data can merely provide rough estimates of airborne contaminant levels in previous times. . . . For example, the diversity of particle sizes and composition in the atmosphere may not be accurately reflected by characteristics of microparticles in glaciers. . . .Because of these problems, interpretation of ice core data is not always straightforward.

Wet deposition dominates deposition on Greenland and coastal Antarctica where fog also contributes (Delmas, 1992, p. 4; Bergin et al., 1994; Wolff et al., 1998).

Dry deposition is the main mode of particle and gaseous deposition on top of the Antarctic Ice Sheet since precipitation is so light. Dry deposition occurs as particles adhere to the surface, react chemically with the surface snow, or stick to firn grains as the aerosol is filtered through the upper part of the firn due to the wind pumping effect (Davidson, 1989; Legrand and Mayewski, 1997, p. 227; Wolff et al., 1998). Of course, the reverse process occurs in which particles are re-suspended into the atmosphere or vapors are reemitted. The rates of dry deposition are not well known (White et al., 1989, p. 92).

Fog has been found to carry more impurities than snow by factors of 4.7 for sulphate and 1.7 for sodium (Wolff et al., 1998, p. 11,062). So, fog that is reported regularly from at least coastal sites of Antarctica can be significant in depositing chemicals onto the snow surface. Fog may also contribute as much as one third of the species during the snowy summer season on Greenland (Legrand and Mayewski, 1997, p. 227).

The contributions of all three transfer functions on the ice sheets are poorly known. In general, the greater the snow accumulation, the fewer the impurities deposited on the ice sheets (Legrand and Mayewski, 1997, p. 227). Moreover, glaciologists must also know how the climate, especially the amount of precipitation, changed in the past in order to understand the species transfer from the atmosphere to the top of the snow:

> Thus changes in past snow accumulation rates in conjunction with changes in meteorological conditions could lead to a variable dilution of the dry flux, hence modulating concentrations in ice, even if atmospheric concentrations remained unchanged. An accurate interpretation of ice core data therefore requires knowledge of the mean snow accumulation rate over the past as well as the relative contributions of dry processes to the total deposition of impurities (Legrand and Mayewski, 1997, p. 227).

This knowledge seems impossible. A climate change may cause less precipitation and, therefore, less wet deposition, but dry and fog deposition would partly compensate for less wet deposition. This complicates the past transfer functions, which researchers simply assume are the same as the present poorly-known transfer functions (Steffensen, Clausen, and Christensen, 1996).

The time of deposition is not the exact age of the chemical species in the ice because of the lag between deposition and bubble close-off (Schwander, Stauffer, and Sigg, 1988; Schwander, 1989; Sowers et al., 1992; Schwander et al., 1997). Today, this lag is about 200 years on the Greenland Ice Sheet and 1,500 years on the top of the Antarctic Ice Sheet. During the ice age, according to the Evolutionary-Uniformitarian model, the much lower accumulations caused the age difference to be about 1,400 years on the Greenland Ice Sheet (Schwander et al., 1997) and around 3,000 years on top of the low accumulation Antarctic Ice Sheet (Delmas, 1992, p. 3).

In the Creation-Flood Ice Age model, precipitation is much greater during the Ice Age. One would expect much less dry deposition and much more wet deposition. Furthermore, the lag between snowfall and bubble close-off would be much less than today. Thus, the incorporation of chemicals into the snow and ice would be much different than what Evolutionary-Uniformitarian scientists expect. We would expect that during the Ice Age there would have been little lag between chemical species deposition and final incorporation in the ice.

Post-Depositional Changes

One would think that once the surface snow is buried, there would be no more change in the aerosols and gases as the snow piles up year-by-year and finally turns to ice. Unfortunately, this is not the case. Vapor is transported through the porous snow and firn and can carry aerosols and gases that are either transported out of the snow and into the atmosphere or react with chemicals in the snow or firn. For instance, the formation of depth hoar in which ice is vaporized and redeposited elsewhere can change the chemical concentration in the top layer by a factor of two (Alley et al., 1990; Aoki et al., 1998). The problem is especially significant for gases and for those particulates for which a gas phase species also exists (White et al., 1989). Chloride, fluoride, nitrate, and methanesulfonic acid (MSA) ions greatly diminish downward in the top few meters of snow, mainly in low accumulation areas on the Antarctic Ice Sheet due to gaseous diffusion upward (Mulvaney, Wagenbach, and Wolff, 1998; Wagnon, Delmas, and Legrand, 1999; Wolff et al., 2002). MSA is the end product of the oxidation of gaseous dimethylsulfide (DMS) given off to the atmosphere by marine phytoplankton (see chapter 7). The reason these ions diminish in the top of the firn is that these species, first deposited in the particulate form, change into a gaseous phase and are expelled from the top of the ice sheet. For instance, at the low accumulation site of Dome C, Antarctica, nitrate from nitric acid deposition was measured at 500 parts per billion (ppb) in fresh snow, but it decreased to 15 ppb within the top meter (Röthlisberger *et al.*, 2000). Such changes, though not as dramatic as at other core sites (Mulvaney, Wagenbach, and Wolff, 1998), are nevertheless significant. These ions also undergo serious loss resulting from deposition of volcanic acids. In some cases, high sulfuric acid concentrations due to volcanism displaced nitrate in ice cores (Röthlisberger et al., 2000, p. 20,566). Therefore, some of the chemical species undergo major concentration changes at the top of the ice sheet and before the firn is transformed into ice. Such post-depositional changes can be measured and taken into account in the present climate, but what about in past climates? Such post-depositional changes would be quite different if the snowfall was much heavier, as in the Creation-Flood Ice Age model.

Another factor to consider is that melt layers especially absorb CO_2 and acids (Hammer, 1982, pp. 128-129; Clausen and Langway, 1989). The melt water can also redistribute gases and particles in the firn. Melt layers are rare on top of the present Greenland and Antarctic Ice Sheets. For this reason, the effect of melt layers is insignificant today and ignored for the past as a result of the uniformitarian assumption. However, there probably would be a fair amount of summer melting in the Creation-Flood Ice Age model, which would change the distribution of CO_2 and acids from what is expected today. Sublimation, primarily during summer, has the potential to increase and/or decrease the concentration of some species (White et al., 1989, pp. 89–90). The amount of sublimation is also expected to have been different during the Ice Age.

Another interesting post-depositional change is worthy of note. It is well known that MSA has a strong seasonal contrast with a maximum in summer due to greater photosynthesis of marine plankton. Such seasonal differences are recorded in the very top of the Antarctic Ice Sheet. However, the pattern of summer maximum and winter minimum, defined by either the oxygen or deuterium isotope ratio, *shifts 180°* several years after deposition during the Antarctic summer (Mulvaney et al., 1992; Legrand and Pasteur, 1998; Pasteur and Mulvaney, 2000). This strange shift is believed to result from *anomalous diffusion* caused by chemical and temperature gradients in which MSA diffuses downward but keeps its cyclicity (Rempel, Wettlaufer, and Waddington, 2002).

Glossary

aerosol. Very small particles in the air.

air hydrate or clathrate. A crystalline molecular complex formed from the mixture of water and atmospheric gases at high pressure.

chemical species. The various chemicals and dust incorporated into the ice sheets.

computer parametizations. The physic relationship of a process used in a computer model.

Dansgaard-Oeschger events. Abrupt changes in $\delta^{18}O$ in ice cores during the Ice Age. The last event is called the *Younger Dryas* and occurred during deglaciation. These events are now found in many other paleoclimatic records including deep-sea cores.

debris flow. A moving mass of rock fragments of all sizes within a finer-grained matrix.

debrite. The deposit laid down by a debris flow.

deconvolution of oxygen isotopes. The excercise of a computer deriving what is believed to be the original oxygen isotope curve for when the sequence first fell as snow on the top of the ice sheet. The exercise is based on several assumptions, such as the assumed annual layer thickness.

DEP. An acronym for the dielectric profiling method that is applied down an ice core as an alternating current (ac) method. It picks up not only ice core acidity, but also some of the bases as well.

depth hoar. Low-density firn or snow containing large, faceted, often cup-shaped ice crystals. Depth hoar is connected with the rapid crystallization of below-surface vapor accompanied by strong vertical temperature gradients..

depth hoar complex. A repeating sequence of low-density depth hoar layers and higher density wind crust or wind slab layers.

deuterium excess. The constant left over in the relationship between the oxygen isotope and the deuterium isotope ratios in equation 2.3. It is related to climatic conditions at the source of the moisture and cloud processes.

diamictite. A lithified rock with no genetic connotations composed of rocks of various sizes mixed within a finer-grained matrix.

dimethylsulfide (DMS). A sulfur compound given off be certain phytoplankton.

eccentricity. A measure of the ellipticity of the earth's orbit about the sun with zero being a perfect circle and one being a straight line. The current eccentricity of the earth is 0.017 in which the sun is three million miles closer to the earth at perihelion on January 3 than it is at aphelion on July 4.

ECM. An acronym for electrical conductivity method, an electrical measurement technique used to determine the acidity profile in an ice core.

Eemian. The previous supposed interglacial in the European classification of the Evolutionary-Uniformitarian ice age model.

firn snow. Old snow that has survived at least one summer melt season. Firn is transitional between snow and glacier ice.

fjord. A long, narrow arm of the sea in a U-shaped, steep-walled, and deep valley that is found along a mountainous coast.

foraminifera. A small plankton marine animal that secretes a series of calcium carbonate chambered tests or round shells.

fractionation. The result of a process, such as a phase change, whereby an isotope with a different molecular weight or vapor pressure is favored over other isotopes of the same molecule.

glaciomarine diamict. Unconsolidated debris that is composed of rocks of all sizes mixed into a fine-grained matrix and that was deposited by a glacier or ice sheet moving out into a marine environment.

Heinrich event. An especially strong Dansgaard-Oeschger event that results in partial collapse of the eastern Laurentide Ice Sheet and ends up discharging abundant icebergs across the North Atlantic.

Holocene (Recent) Epoch. Last and still continuing portion of the Quaternary Period. It began 10,000 years ago at the end of the "last" ice age within the Evolutionary-Uniformitarian model.

ice stratigraphy. A visual or non-visual layering observed in an ice core. The visual layers can consist of depth hoar complexes, cloudy dust bands, and melt layers.

ice stream. A linear area on a glacier or ice sheet that is moving much faster than the average.

interglacial. A period of warmer temperatures and diminished ice sheets which occurrs between glacial periods.

interstadial. A relatively brief warmer interval with a glacial period.

isostatic subsidence and rebound. The sinking or rising of the earth's crust due to the addition or removal, respectively, of a load, such as glacial ice.

katabatic wind. A wind (caused by the radiational cooling and densification of the air just above the ice sheet) that blows down a glacier or ice sheet.

kinetic effect. A process that favors the lightest isotopes during a phase change.

loess. A blanket deposit of wind-blown silt.

LLS. An acronym for laser light scattering. The LLS technique uses a laser beam to measure variations in dust concentrations in an ice core.

methanesulfonic acid (CH_3SO_3H) or MSA. An acidic end product of the oxidation of gaseous dimethylsulfide (DMS) given off to the atmosphere by certain marine phytoplankton.

non-sea-salt component. The component of the chemical species that remains after subtracting the presumed amount derived from sea salt. This is accomplished by using the ratio with respect to Na^+ and subtracting from the bulk chemical species measured in the ice core.

nunatak. An isolated peak of bedrock that projects above the surface of a glacier.

oxygen isotope ratio. The ratio of stable oxygen isotopes, $^{16}O/^{18}O$, in various materials, such as seawater, glacier ice, and fossil shells.

paleosol. A buried soil.

perihelion. The near approach of the earth to the sun in its orbit.

phytoplankton. Microscopic marine plants, such as diatoms, floating near the surface of the ocean.

Pleistocene. The period of geological time roughly two million years ago to about 10 thousand years ago according to the Evolutionary-Uniformitarian model.

pluvial lakes. Lakes that occurred in semi-arid or arid climates when precipitation was higher or evaporation less than today.

precession of the equinox. The rotation of the orbital ellipse of the earth around the sun.

sastrugi. Dunes or features of high relief on the snow surface.

SMOW. An acronym that stands for standard mean ocean water, which is used as a standard upon with oxygen isotope ratios are compared.

stadial. A relatively brief colder interval within a glacial period.

striated pavement. A scratched or grooved bedrock surface. The striations could have been made by a glacier, landslide, or other process.

superimposed ice. Ice at the bottom of glacier or ice sheet that is formed by the freezing on of basal melt-water or water from a subglacial lake.

thermohaline circulation. The circulation of the ocean due to pressure changes causing differences in water temperature and salt density.

till. Debris left behind by a glacier and composed of rocks of various sizes and shapes mixed into a fine-grained matrix.

tillite. A consolidated till or diamictite generated from a glacier or ice sheet.

transfer function or equation. A statistical relationship or equation relating variables from two systems.

turbidite. The deposit laid down by a turbidity current.

turbidity current. A mass flow with fewer rocks and more water within the moving mass than that found in a debris flow.

uniformitarianism. The principle that processes similar to those observed today are responsible for the rocks and fossils.

varve. A sedimentary lamina or sequence of laminae deposited in a body of water within one year's time.

wind crust. A higher-density, finer-grained accumulation caused by moderate to strong winds.

wind pumping. The movement of air in firn snow on top of a glacier or ice sheet. This movement is caused by differences in wind speed in the air with time above the glacier.

Younger Dryas. A sudden, abrupt cold period during the warming after the Ice Age. This is the last Dansgaard-Oeschger event.

References

Adkins, J. F., E. A. Boyle, L. Keigwin, and E. Cortijo, 1997: Variability of the North Atlantic thermohaline circulation during the last interglacial period. *Nature, 390*, 154–156.

Ageta, Y., et al., 1998: Deep ice-core drilling at Dome Fuji and glaciological studies in east Dronning Maud Land, Antarctica. *Annals of Glaciology, 27*, 333–337.

Aldaz, L., and S. Deutsch, 1967: On a relationship between air temperature and oxygen isotope ratio of snow and firn in the South Pole region. *Earth and Planetary Science Letters, 3*, 267–274.

Allen, J. R. M., et al., 1999: Rapid environmental changes in southern Europe during the last glacial period. *Nature, 400*, 740–743.

Alley, R. B., 1988: Concerning the deposition and diagenesis of strata in polar firn. *Journal of Glaciology, 34* (118), 283–290.

——, 2000: *The Two-Mile Time Machine.* Princeton University Press, 240 pp.

——, 2004: Abrupt climate change. *Scientific American, 291* (5), 62–69.

——, and D. R. Bentley, 1988: Ice-core analysis on the Siple Coast of West Antarctica. *Annals of Glaciology, 11*, 1–7.

——, and B. R. Koci, 1988: Ice-core analysis at Site A, Greenland: Preliminary results. *Annals of Glaciology, 10*, 1–4.

——, and S. Anandakrishnan, 1995: Variations in melt-layer frequency in the GISP2 ice core: Implications for Holocene summer temperatures in central Greenland. *Annals of Glaciology, 21*, 64–70.

——, and G. A. Woods, 1996: Impurity influence on normal grain growth in the GISP2 ice core, Greenland. *Journal of Glaciology, 42* (141), 255–260.

——, and M. L. Bender, 1998: Greenland ice cores: Frozen in time. *Scientific American, 278* (2), 80–85.

——, E. S. Saltzman, K. M. Cuffey, and J. J. Fitzpatrick, 1990: Summertime formation of depth hoar in central Greenland. *Geophysical Research Letters, 17* (12), 2393–2396.

——, et al., 1993: Abrupt increase in Greenland snow accumulation at the end of the Younger Dryas event. *Nature, 362*, 527–529.

——, A. J. Gow, S. J. Johnsen, J. Kipfstuhl, D. A. Meese, and Th. Thorsteinsson, 1995: Comparison of deep ice cores. *Nature, 373*, 393–394.

——, et al., 1997a: Visual-stratigraphic dating of the GISP2 ice core: Basis, reproducibility, and application. *Journal of Geophysical Research, 102* (C12), 26 367–26 381.

——, A. J. Gow, D. A. Meese, J. J. Fitzpatrick, E. D. Waddington, and J. F. Bolzan, 1997b: Grain-scale processes, folding, and stratigraphic disturbance in the GISP2 ice core. *Journal of Geophysical Research, 102* (C12), 26 819–26 830.

Alt, D., 2001: *Glacial Lake Missoula and Its Humongous Floods.* Mountain Press Publishing Company, 199 pp.

Ambach, W., W. Dansgaard, H. Eisner, and J. Møller, 1968: The altitude effect on the isotopic composition of precipitation and glacier ice in the Alps. *Tellus,* **20,** 597–600.

Anandakrishnan, S., J. J. Fitzpatrick, R. B. Alley, A. J. Gow, and D. A. Meese, 1994: Shear-wave detection of asymmetric c-axis fabrics in the GISP2 ice core, Greenland. *Journal of Glaciology,* **40** (136), 491–496.

Anderson, I., 1986: A glimpse of the green hills of Antarctica. *New Scientist,* **111** (1515), 22.

Anklin, M., J. Schwander, B. Stauffer, J. Tschumi, A. Fuchs, J. M. Barnola, and D. Raynaud, 1997: CO_2 record between 40 and 8 kyr B.P. from the Greenland Ice Core Project ice core. *Journal of Geophysical Research,* **102** (C12), 26 539–26 545.

Aoki, S., et al., 1998: Preliminary investigation of palaeoclimate signals recorded in the ice core from Dome Fuji station, east Dronning Maud Land, Antarctica. *Annals of Glaciology,* **27,** 338–342.

Aristarain, A. J., R. J. Delmas, and M. Briat, 1982: Snow chemistry on James Ross Island (Antarctic Peninsula). *Journal of Geophysical Research,* **87** (C13), 11 004–11 012.

Armengaud, A., R. D. Koster, J. Jouzel, and P. Ciais, 1998: Deuterium excess in Greenland snow: Analysis with simple and complex models. *Journal of Geophysical Research,* **103** (D8), 8947–8953.

Azuma, N., Y. Wang, K. Mori, H. Narita, T. Hondoh, H. Shoji, and O. Watanabe, 1999: Textures and fabrics in the Dome F (Antarctica) ice core. *Annals of Glaciology,* **29,** 163–168.

Bales, R. C., J. R. McConnell, E. Mosley-Thompson, and B. Csatho, 2001: Accumulation over the Greenland Ice Sheet from historical and recent records. *Journal of Geophysical Research,* **106** (D4), 33 813–33 825.

Bamber, J. L., and P. Huybrechts, 1996: Geometric boundary conditions for modeling the velocity field of the Antarctic Ice Sheet. *Annals of Glaciology* **23,** 364–373.

——, R. J. Hardy, P. Huybrechts, and I. Joughin, 2000: A comparison of balance velocities, measured velocities and thermomechanically modeled velocities for the Greenland Ice Sheet. *Annals of Glaciology,* **30,** 211–216.

——, R. L. Layberry, and S. P. Gogineni, 2001: A new ice thickness and bed set for the Greenland Ice Sheet 1. Measurements, data reduction, and errors. *Journal of Geophysical Research,* **106** (D24), 33 773–33 780.

Barker, P. F., P. J. Barrett, A. K. Cooper, and P. Huybrechts, 1999: Antarctic glacial history from numerical models and continental margin sediments. *Palaeogeography, Palaeoclimatology, Palaeoecology*, **150,** 247–267.

Barnes, P. R. F., E. W. Wolff, H. M. Mader, R. Udisti, E. Castellano, and R. Röthlisberger, 2003: Evolution of chemical peak shapes in the Dome C, Antarctica, ice core. *Journal of Geophysical Research,* **108** (D3), 4126, doi:10.1029/2002JD002538.

Barrett, P., 2003: Cooling a continent. *Nature,* **421,** 221–223.

Barrett, P. J., C. J. Adams, W. C. McIntosh, C. C. Swisher III, and G. S. Wilson, 1992: Geochronological evidence supporting Antarctic deglaciation three million years ago. *Nature,* **359,** 816–818.

Basile, I., F. E. Grousset, M. Revel, J. R. Petit, P. E. Biscaye, and N. I. Barkov, 1997: Patagonian origin of glacial dust deposited in East Antarctica (Vostok and Dome C) during glacial stages 2, 4 and 6. *Earth and Planetary Science Letters,* **146,** 573–589.

——, J. R. Petit, S. Touron, F. E. Grousset, and N. Barkov, 2001: Volcanic layers in Antarctic (Vostok) ice cores: Source identification and atmospheric implications. *Journal of Geophysical Research,* **106** (D23), 31 915–31 931.

Bates, R. L., and J. A. Jackson, Eds., 1984: *Dictionary of Geological Terms.* 3rd ed. Anchor Press/Doubleday, 571 pp.

Bates, T. S., B. K. Lamb, A. Guenther, J. Dignon, and R. E. Stoiber, 1992: Sulfur emissions to the atmosphere from natural sources. *Journal of Atmospheric Chemistry,* **14,** 315–337.

Baumgartner, S., J. Beer, M. Suter, B. Dittrich-Hannen, H. -A. Synal, P. W. Kubik, C. Hammer, and S. Johnsen, 1997: Chlorine 36 fallout in the Summit Greenland Ice Core Project ice core. *Journal of Geophysical Research,* **102** (C12), 26 659–26 662.

——, J. Beer, J. Masarik, B. Wagner, L. Meynadier, and H. -A. Synal, 1998: Geomagnetic modulation of the ^{36}Cl flux in the GRIP ice core, Greenland. *Science,* **279,** 1330–1332.

Beer, J., et al., 1983: Temporal ^{10}Be variations in ice. *Radiocarbon,* **25** (2), 269–278.

——, et al., 1985: ^{10}Be variations in polar ice cores. *Greenland Ice Core: Geophysics, Geochemistry, and the Environment,* Geophysical Monograph, No. 33, American Geophysical Union, 66–70.

——, U. Siegenthaler, G. Bonani, R. C. Finkel, H. Oeschger, M. Suter, and W. Wölfli, 1988: Information on past solar activity and geomagnetism from ^{10}Be in the Camp Century ice core. *Nature,* **331,** 675–679.

——, S. J. Johnsen, G. Bonani, R. C. Finkel, C. C. Langway, H. Oeschger, B. Stauffer, M. Suter, and W. Woelfli, 1992: ^{10}Be peaks as time marker in polar ice cores. *The Last Deglaciation: Absolute and Radiocarbon Chronologies,* E. Bard and W. S. Broecker, Eds., Springer-Verlag, 41–153.

Beget, J. E., 1986: Modeling the influence of till rheology on the flow and profile of the Lake Michigan Lobe, southern Laurentide Ice Sheet, U.S.A. *Journal of Glaciology,* **32** (111), 235–241.

Beget, J., 1987: Low profile of the northwest Laurentide Ice Sheet. *Arctic and Alpine Research,* **19,** 81–88.

Bender, M., L. D. Labeyrie, D. Raynaud, and C. Lorius, 1985: Isotopic composition of atmospheric O_2 in ice linked with deglaciation and global primary productivity. *Nature,* **318,** 349–352.

——, T. Sowers, and L. Labeyrie, 1994: The Dole effect and its variations during the last 130,000 years as measured in the Vostok ice core. *Global Biogeochemical Cycles,* **8** (3), 363–376.

——, T. Sowers, M. -L. Dickson, J. Orchardo, P. Grootes, P. A. Mayewski, and D. A. Meese, 1994: Climate correlations between Greenland and Antarctica during the past 100,000 years. *Nature,* **372,** 663–666.

Bentley, M. J., and J. B. Anderson, 1998: Glacial and marine geological evidence for the ice sheet configuration in the Weddell Sea—Antarctica Peninsula region during the last glacial maximum. *Antarctic Science,* **10** (3), 309–325.

Berger, A., 1977a: Support for the astronomical theory of climate change. *Nature,* **269,** 44–45.

——, 1977b: Long-term variation of the earth's orbital elements. *Celestial Mechanics,* **15,** 53–74.

——, 1978: Long-period variations of daily insolation and Quaternary climate changes. *Journal of Atmospheric Science,* **35,** 2362–2367.

Bergin, M. H., J. L. Jaffrezo, C. I. Davidson, R. Caldow, and J. Dibb, 1994: Fluxes of chemical species to the Greenland Ice Sheet at Summit by fog and dry deposition. *Geochimica et Cosmochimica Acta,* **58** (15), 3207–3215.

Berresheim, H., and F. L. Eisele, 1998: Sulfur chemistry in the Antarctic troposphere experiment: An overview of project SCATE. *Journal of Geophysical Research,* **103** (D1), 1619–1627.

——, J. W. Huey, R. P. Thorn, F. L. Eisele, D. J. Tanner, and A. Jefferson, 1998: Measurements of dimethyl sulfide, dimethyl sulfoxide, dimethyl sulfone, and aerosol ions at Palmer Station, Antarctica. *Journal of Geophysical Research,* **103** (D1), 1629–1637.

Bintanja, R., 1999: On the glaciological, meteorological, and climatological significance of Antarctic blue ice areas. *Reviews of Geophysics,* **37** (3), 337–359.

Biscaye, P. E., F. E. Grousset, M. Revel, S. Van der Gaast, G. A. Zielinski, A. Vaars, and G. Kukla, 1997: Asian provenance of glacial dust (stage 2) in the Greenland Ice Sheet Project 2 ice core, Summit, Greenland. *Journal of Geophysical Research,* **102** (C12), 26 765–26 781.

Bloom, A. L., 1971: Glacial-eustatic and isostatic controls of sea level. *The Late Cenozoic Glacial Ages*, K. K. Turekian, Ed., Yale University Press, 355–379.

Bloomberg, R., 1989: WW II planes to be deiced. *Engineering Report*, March 9.

Bogorodsky, V. V., C. R. Bentley, and P. E. Gudmandsen, 1985: *Radioglaciology*. D. Reidel Publishing Co., 254 pp.

Bolzan, J. F., and M. Strobel, 1994: Accumulation-rate variations around Summit, Greenland. *Journal of Glaciology,* **40** (134), 56–66.

Bond, G., W. Broecker, S. Johnsen, J. McManus, L. Labeyrie, J. Jouzel, and G. Bonani, 1993: Correlations between climate records from North Atlantic sediments and Greenland ice. *Nature,* **365**, 143–147.

Bottenheim, J. W., and L. A. Barrie, 1996: Chemical reactions in the polar troposphere relevant to C, S, and N compounds. *Chemical Exchange Between the Atmosphere and Polar Snow*, E. W. Wolff and R. C. Bales, Eds. NATO ASI Series 1, Global Environmental Change, Vol. 43, Springer-Verlag, 201–224.

Bowen, G. J., and B. Wilkinson, 2002: Spatial distribution of $\delta^{18}O$ in meteoric precipitation. *Geology,* **30** (4), 315–318.

Boyle, E. A., 1997: Cool tropical temperatures shift the global $\delta^{18}O$-T relationship: An explanation for the ice core $\delta^{18}O$–borehole thermometry conflict? *Geophysical Research Letters,* **24** (3), 273–276.

Boyle, E., and A. Weaver, 1994: Conveying past climates. *Nature,* **372**, 41–42.

Bradley, R. S., 1985: *Quaternary Paleoclimatology—Methods of Paleoclimatic Reconstruction.* Allen and Unwin, 472 pp.

Broecker, W. S., 1994: An unstable superconveyor. *Nature,* **367**, 414–415.

——, 1997: Thermohaline circulation, the Achilles heel of our climate system: Will man-made CO_2 upset the current balance? *Science,* **278**, 1582–1588.

——, 2000: Abrupt climate change: Causal constraints provided by the paleoclimate record. *Earth-Science Reviews,* **51**, 137–154.

——, J. P. Kennett, B. P. Flower, J.T. Teller, S. Trumbore, G. Bonani, and W. Wolfli, 1989: Routing of meltwater from the Laurentide Ice Sheet during the Younger Dryas cold episode. *Nature,* **341**, 318–321.

Bromwich, D. H., 1988: Snowfall in high southern latitudes. *Reviews of Geophysics,* **26** (1), 149–168.

——, and C. J. Weaver, 1983: Latitudinal displacement from main moisture source controls ^{18}O of snow in coastal Antarctica. *Nature,* **301**, 145–147.

Brooks, E. J., S. Harder, J. Severinghaus, E. J. Steig, and C. M. Sucher, 2000: On the origin and timing of rapid changes in atmospheric methane during the last glacial period. *Global Biogeochemical Cycles,* **14** (2), 559–572.

Budd, W. F., 1983: Summary and conclusions. *The Climatic Record in Polar Ice Sheets*, G. de Q. Robin, Ed., Cambridge University Press, 177–179.

——, D. Jenssen, and U. Radok, 1971: Derived physical characteristics of the Antarctic ice sheet. University of Melbourne Meteorology Department Publication 18, 117–126.

——, et al., 1989: Group report how can an ice core chronology be established? *The Environmental Record in Glaciers and Ice Sheets*, H. Oeschger and C. C. Langway, Jr., Eds., John Wiley & Sons, 177–192.

Bunker, A. F., 1976: Computations of surface energy flux and annual air-sea interaction cycles of the North Atlantic Ocean. *Monthly Weather Review,* **104**, 1122–1140.

Burckle, L. H., and N. Potter, Jr., 1996: Pliocene-Pleistocene diatoms in Paleozoic and Mesozoic sedimentary and igneous rocks from Antarctica: A Sirius problem solved. *Geology,* **24**, 235–238.

Calvin, W. H., 1998: The great climate flip-flop. *Atlantic Monthly,* **281** (1), 47–64.

Canals, M., R. Urgeles, and A. M. Calafat, 2000: Deep sea-floor evidence of past ice streams off the Antarctic Peninsula. *Geology,* **28**, 31–34.

——, et al., 2003: Uncovering the footprint of former ice streams off Antarctica. *EOS,* **84** (11), 97, 102–103.

Cassidy, W. A., E. Olsen, and K. Yanai, 1977: Antarctica: A deep-freeze storehouse for meteorites. *Science,* **198**, 727–731.

Castelnau, O., Th. Thorsteinsson, J. Kipfstuhl, P. Duval, and G. R. Canova, 1996: Modelling fabric development along the GRIP ice core, central Greenland. *Annals of Glaciology,* **23**, 194–201.

Chappellaz, J., T. Blunier, S. Kints, A. Dällenbach, J. M. Barnola, J. Schwander, D. Raynaud, and B. Stauffer, 1997: Changes in the atmospheric CH_4 gradient between Greenland and Antarctica during the Holocene. *Journal of Geophysical Research,* **102** (D13), 15 987–15 997.

Charles, C. D., D. Rind, J. Jouzel, R. D. Koster, and R. G. Fairbanks, 1994: Glacial-interglacial changes in moisture sources for Greenland: Influences on the ice core record of climate. *Science,* **263**, 508–511.

——, D. Rind, J. Jouzel, R. D. Koster, and R. G. Fairbanks, 1995: Seasonal precipitation timing and ice core records. *Science,* **269**, 247–248.

Charlesworth, J, K., 1957: *The Quaternary Era.* Edward Arnold, 1700 pp.

Chylek, P., B. Johnson, P. A. Damiano, K. C. Taylor, and P. Clement, 1995: Biomass burning record and black carbon in the GISP2 ice core. *Geophysical Research Letters,* **22** (2), 89–92.

Ciais, P., and J. Jouzel, 1994: Deuterium and oxygen 18 in precipitation: Isotopic model, including mixed cloud processes. *Journal of Geophysical Research,* **99** (D8), 16 793–16 803.

Ciais, P., J. W. C. White, J. Jouzel, and J. R. Petit, 1995: The origin of present-day Antarctic precipitation from surface snow deuterium excess data. *Journal of Geophysical Research,* **100** (D9), 18 917–18 927.

Clark, P. U., S. J. Marshall, G. K. C. Clarke, S. W. Hostetler, J. M. Licciardi, and J. T. Teller, 2001: Freshwater forcing of abrupt climate change during the last glaciation. *Science,* **293**, 283–287.

Clausen, H. B., and C. C. Langway, Jr., 1989: The ionic deposits in polar ice cores. *The Environmental Record in Glaciers and Ice Sheets*, H. Oeschger and C. C. Langway, Jr., Eds., John Wiley & Sons, 225–247.

——, C. U. Hammer, C. S. Hvidberg, D. Dahl-Jensen, J. P. Steffensen, J. Kipfstuhl, and M. Legrand, M., 1997: A comparison of the volcanic records over the past 4000 years from the Greenland Ice Core Project and Dye 3 Greenland ice cores. *Journal of Geophysical Research,* **102** (C12), 26 707–26 723.

Clayton, L., J. T. Teller, and J. W. Attig, 1985: Surging of the southwestern part of the Laurentide Ice Sheet. *Boreas,* **14**, 235–241.

Colbeck, S. C., 1989: Snow-crystal growth with varying surface temperatures and radiation penetration. *Journal of Glaciology,* **35** (119), 23–29.

——, 1991: The layered character of snow covers. *Reviews of Geophysics,* **29** (1), 81–96.

Cole-Dai, J., E. Mosley-Thompson, S. P. Wight, and L. G. Thompson, 2000: A 4100-year record of explosive volcanism from an East Antarctica ice core. *Journal of Geophysical Research,* **105** (D19), 24 431–24 441.

Coplen, T. B., 1995: Discontinuance of SMOW and PDB. *Nature,* **375**, 285.

——, C. Kendall, and J. Hopple, 1983: Comparison of stable isotope reference samples. *Nature,* **302**, 236–238.

Craig, H., and L. Gordon, 1965: Deuterium and oxygen 18 variations in the ocean and marine atmosphere. *Stable Isotopes in Oceanographic Studies and Paleotemperatures*, E. Tongiorgi, Ed., Laboratorio Geologia Nucleare, 1–122.

Crowell, J. C., 1999: Pre-Mesozoic ice ages: Their bearing on understanding the climate system. Geological Society of America Memoir 192, 112 pp.

Crowley, T. J., and S. K. Baum, 1995: Is the Greenland Ice Sheet bistable? *Paleoceanography,* **10**, 357–363.

Crutzen, P. J., and C. Brühl, 1989: The impact of observed changes in atmospheric composition on global atmospheric chemistry and climate. *The Environmental Record in Glaciers and Ice Sheets,* H. Oeschger and C. C. Langway, Jr., Eds., John Wiley & Sons, 249–266.

Cudlip, W., and N. F. McIntyre, 1987: Seasat altimeter observations of an Antarctic "lake." *Annals of Glaciology,* **9**, 55–59.

Cuffey, K. M., and G. D. Clow, 1997: Temperature, accumulation, and ice sheet elevation in central Greenland through the last deglacial transition. *Journal of Geophysical Research,* **102** (C12), 26 383–26 396.

——, and S. J. Marshall, 2000: Substantial contribution to sea-level rise during the last interglacial from the Greenland Ice Sheet. *Nature,* **404**, 591–594.

——, and F. Vimeux, 2001: Covariation of carbon dioxide and temperature from the Vostok ice core after deuterium-excess correction. *Nature,* **412**, 523–527.

——, G. D. Clow, R. B. Alley, M. Stuiver, E. D. Waddington, and R. W. Saltus, 1995: Large Arctic temperature change at the Wisconsin-Holocene glacial transition. *Science,* **270**, 455–458.

Curran, M. A. J., T. D. van Ommen, and V. Morgan, 1998: Seasonal characteristics of the major ions in the high-accumulation Dome Summit South ice core, Law Dome, Antarctica. *Annals of Glaciology,* **27**, 385–390.

——, T. D. van Ommen, V. I. Morgan, K. L. Phillips, and A. S. Palmer, 2003: Ice core evidence for Antarctic sea ice decline since the 1950s. *Science,* **302**, 1203–1206.

Dahl-Jensen, D., and N. S. Gundestrup, 1987: Constitutive properties of ice at Dye 3, Greenland. *The Physical Basis of Ice Sheet Modelling,* IAHS Publication 170, 31–43.

——, T. Thorsteinsson, R. Alley, and H. Shoji, 1997: Flow properties of the ice from the Greenland Ice Core Project ice core: The reason for folds? *Journal of Geophysical Research,* **102** (C12), 26 831–26 840.

——, N. S. Gundestrup, H. Miller, O. Watanabe, S. J. Johnsen, J. P. Steffensen, H. B. Clausen, A. Svensson, and L. B. Larsen, 2002: The NorthGRIP deep drilling programme. *Annals of Glaciology,* **35**, 1–4.

Dansgaard, W., 1961: The isotopic composition of natural waters with special reference to the Greenland ice cap. *Meddelelser Om Grønland,* **165** (2), 1–120.

——, 1964: Stable isotopes in precipitation. *Tellus,* **16** (4), 436–468.

——, 1987: The core evidence of abrupt climatic changes. *Abrupt Climate Change: Evidence and Implications,* W. H. Berger and L. D. Labeyrie, Eds., D. Reidel Publishing Co., 223–233.

——, and H. Tauber, 1969: Glacial oxygen-18 content and Pleistocene ocean temperatures. *Science,* **166**, 499–502.

——, and S. J. Johnsen, 1969a: A flow model and a time scale for the ice core from Camp Century, Greenland. *Journal of Glaciology,* **8** (53), 215–223.

——, and ——, 1969b: Comment on paper by J. Wertman, 'Comparison between measured and theoretical temperature profiles of the Camp Century, Greenland, borehole.' *Journal of Geophysical Research,* **74** (4), 1109–1110.

——, and H. Oeschger, 1989: Past environmental long-term records from the Arctic. *The Environmental Record in Glaciers and Ice Sheets,* H. Oeschger and C. C. Langway, Jr., Eds., John Wiley & Sons, 287–318.

——, S. J. Johnsen, J. Moller, and C. C. Langway, Jr., 1969: One thousand centuries of climatic record from Camp Century on the Greenland Ice Sheet. *Science,* **166,** 377–381.

——, S. J. Johnsen, H. B. Clausen, and C. C. Langway, Jr., 1970: Ice cores and paleoclimatology. *Radiocarbon Variations and Absolute Chronology,* Proceedings of the Twelfth Nobel Symposium, John Wiley & Sons, 337–351.

——, ——, ——, and ——, 1971: *The Late Cenozoic Glacial Ages,* K. K. Turekian, Ed., Yale University Press, 37–56.

——, S. J. Johnsen, H. B. Clausen, and N. Gundestrup, 1973: Stable isotope glaciology. *Meddelelser Om Grønland,* **197** (2), 1–53.

——, H. B. Clausen, N. Gundestrup, C. U. Hammer, S. J. Johnsen, P. M. Kristinsdottir, and N. Reeh, 1982: A new Greenland deep ice core. *Science,* **218,** 1273–1277.

——, S. J. Johnsen, H. B. Clausen, D. Dahl-Jensen, N. Gundestrup, and C. U. Hammer, 1984: North Atlantic climatic oscillations revealed by deep Greenland ice cores. *Climate Processes and Climate Sensitivity, Geophysical Monograph,* No. 29, American Geophysical Union, 288–298.

——, H. B. Clausen, N. Gundestrup, S. J. Johnsen, and C. Rygner, 1985: Dating and climatic interpretation of two deep Greenland ice cores. *Greenland Ice Core: Geophysics, Geochemistry, and the Environment, Geophysical Monograph,* No. 33, American Geophysical Union, 71–76.

——, J. W. C. White, and S. J. Johnsen, 1989: The abrupt termination of the younger Dryas climate event. *Nature,* **339,** 532–534.

——, et al., 1993: Evidence for general instability of past climate from a 250-kyr ice-core record. *Nature,* **364,** 218–220.

Davidson, C. I., 1989: Mechanisms of wet and dry deposition of atmospheric contaminants to snow surfaces. *The Environmental Record in Glaciers and Ice Sheets,* H. Oeschger and C. C. Langway, Jr., Eds., John Wiley & Sons, 29–51.

De Angelis, M., and M. Legrand, 1994: Origins and variations of fluoride in Greenland precipitation. *Journal of Geophysical Research,* **99** (D1), 1157–1172.

——, J. P. Steffensen, M. Legrand, H. Clausen, and C. Hammer, 1997: Primary aerosol (sea salt and soil dust) deposited in Greenland ice during the last climatic cycle: Comparison with east Antarctic records. *Journal of Geophysical Research,* **102** (C12), 26 681–26 698.

DeConto, R. M., and D. Pollard, 2003: Rapid Cenozoic glaciation of Antarctica induced by declining atmospheric CO_2. *Nature,* **421,** 245–249.

Delmas, R. J., 1992: Environmental information from ice cores. *Reviews of Geophysics,* **30** (1), 1–21.

——, and M. Legrand, 1989: Long-term changes in the concentrations of major chemical compounds (soluble and insoluble) along deep ice cores. *The Environmental Record in Glaciers and Ice Sheets,* H. Oeschger and C. C. Langway, Jr., Eds., John Wiley & Sons, 319–341.

——, M. Legrand, A. J. Aristarain, and F. Zanolini, 1985: Volcanic deposits in Antarctic snow and ice. *Journal of Geophysical Research,* **90** (D7), 12 901–12 920.

Delmonte, B., J. R. Petit, and V. Maggi, 2002: Glacial to Holocene implications of the new 27000-year dust record from the EPICA Dome C (East Antarctica) ice core. *Climate Dynamics,* **18,** 647–660.

Delmotte, M., D. Raynaud, V. Morgan, and J. Jouzel, 1999: Climatic and glaciological information inferred from air-content measurements of a Law Dome (East Antarctica) ice core. *Journal of Glaciology,* **45** (150), 255–262.

Denton, G. H., and C. H. Hendy, 1994: Younger Dryas age advance of Franz Josef Glacier in the Southern Alps of New Zealand. *Science,* **264,** 1 434–1 437.

Dibb, J. E., and J. L. Jaffrezo, 1997: Air-snow exchange investigations at Summit, Greenland: An overview. *Journal of Geophysical Research,* **102** (C12), 26 795–26 807.

Domack, E., A. Leventer, R. Gilbert, S. Brachfeld, S. Ishman, A. Camerlenghi, K. Gavahan, D. Carlson, and A. Barkoukis, 2001: Cruise reveals history of Holocene Larsen Ice Shelf. *EOS,* **82** (2), 13, 16, 17.

Dott, Jr., R. H., and R. L. Batten, 1976: *Evolution of the Earth.* 2nd ed. McGraw-Hill, 504 pp.

Drewry, D. J., Ed., 1983: *Antarctica: Glaciological and Geophysical Folio.* Scott Polar Research Institute, University of Cambridge.

Duplessy, J. C., 1978: Isotopic studies. *Climatic Change,* J. Gribbin, Ed., Cambridge University Press, 46–67.

Duval, P., and C. Lorius, 1980: Crystal size and climatic record down to the last ice age from Antarctic ice. *Earth and Planetary Science Letters,* **48**, 59–64.

Ehhalt, D., K. Knott, J. F. Nagel, and J. C. Vogel, 1963: Deuterium and oxygen 18 in rain water. *Journal of Geophysical Research,* **68** (13), 3 775–3 780.

Ehrmann, W. U., M. J. Hambrey, J. G. Baldauf, J. Barron, B. Larsen, A. MacKensen, S. W. Wise, Jr., and J. C. Zackos, J.C., 1992: History of Antarctic glaciation: An Indian Ocean perspective. *Synthesis of Results from Scientific Drilling in the Indian Ocean, Geophysical Monograph,* No. 70, American Geophysical Union, 423–446.

Ekaykin, A. A., V. Ya. Lipenkov, N. I. Barkov, J. R. Petit, V. Masson-Delmotte, 2002: Spatial and temporal variability in isotope composition of recent snow in the vicinity of Vostok station, Antarctica: Implications for ice-core record interpretation. *Annals of Glaciology,* **35**, 181–186.

EPICA Community Members, 2004: Eight glacial cycles from an Antarctic ice core. *Nature,* **429**, 623–628.

Emiliani, C., 1966: Isotopic temperatures. *Science,* **154**, 851–857.

Epstein, S., 1959: The variations of the O^{18}/O^{16} ratio in nature and some geologic implications. *Researchers in Geochemistry,* Vol.1, P. H. Abelson, Ed., John Wiley & Sons, 217–240.

——, and R. P. Sharp, 1959: Oxygen-isotope variations in the Malaspina and Saskatchewan glaciers. *Journal of Geology,* **67**, 88–102.

——, R. P. Sharp, and A. J. Gow, 1965: Six-year record of oxygen and hydrogen isotope variations in South Pole firn. *Journal of Geophysical Research,* **70** (8), 1 809–1 814.

——, ——, and ——, 1970: Antarctic Ice Sheet: Stable isotope analysis of Byrd station cores and interhemispheric climatic implications. *Science,* **168**, 1 570–1 572.

Etheridge, D. M., 1989: Dynamics of the Law Dome ice cap, Antarctica, as found from bore-hole measurements. *Annals of Glaciology,* **12**, 46–50.

Fahnestock, M. A., T. A. Scambos, C. A. Shuman, R. J. Arthern, D. P. Winebrenner, and R. Kwok, 2000: Snow megadune fields on the East Antarctic Plateau: Extreme atmospheric-ice interaction. *Geophysical Research Letters,* **27** (22), 3 719–3 722.

Fahnestock, M., W. Abdalati, S. Luo, and S. Gogineni, 2001: Internal layer tracing and age-depth-accumulation relationships for the northern Greenland ice sheet. *Journal of Geophysical Research,* **106** (D24), 33 789–33 797.

Field, M. H., B. Huntley, and H. Müller, 1994: Eemian climate fluctuations observed in a European pollen record. *Nature,* **371**, 779–783.

Finkel, R. C., and K. Nishiizumi, 1997: Beryllium 10 concentrations in the Greenland Ice Sheet Project 2 ice core from 3-40 ka. *Journal of Geophysical Research,* **102** (C12), 26 699–26 706.

Fisher, D. A., 1987: Enhanced flow of Wisconsin ice related to solid conductivity through strain history and recrystallization. *The Physical Basis of Ice Sheet Modelling,* IAHS Publication 170, 45–51.

——, 1991: Remarks on the deuterium excess in precipitation in cold regions. *Tellus,* **43B**, 401–407.

——, 1992: Stable isotope simulations using a regional stable isotope model coupled to a zonally averaged global model. *Cold Regions Science and Technology*, **21**, 61–77.

——, and B. T. Alt, 1985: A global oxygen isotope model—semi-empirical, zonally averaged. *Annals of Glaciology*, **7**, 117–124.

——, and R. M. Koerner, 1986: On the special rheological properties of ancient microparticle-laden Northern Hemisphere ice as derived from bore-hole and core measurements. *Journal of Glaciology*, **32** (112), 501–510.

——, R. M. Koerner, W. S. B. Paterson, W. Dansgaard, N. Gundestrup, and N. Reeh, 1983: Effect of wind scouring on climatic records from ice-core oxygen-isotope profiles. *Nature*, **301**, 205–209.

Fischer, H., 2001: Imprint of large-scale atmospheric transport patterns on sea-salt records in northern Greenland ice cores. *Journal of Geophysical Research*, **106** (D20), 23 977–23 984.

——, D. Wagenbach, and J. Kipfstuhl, 1998: Sulfate and nitrate firn concentrations on the Greenland Ice Sheet 1. Large scale geographical deposition changes. *Journal of Geophysical Research*, **103** (D17), 21 927–21 934.

——, M. Wahlen, J. Smith, D. Mastroianni, and B. Deck, 1999: Ice core records of atmospheric CO_2 around the last three glacial terminations. *Science*, **283**, 1 712–1 714.

Fodor, R. V., 1982: Frozen earth: Explaining the ice ages. *Weatherwise*, **35** (3), 109–114.

Frezzotti, M., S. Gandolfi, and S. Urbini, 2002: Snow megadunes in Antarctica: Sedimentary structure and genesis. *Journal of Geophysical Research*, **107** (D18), 1–12.

Friedman, I., L. Machta, and R. Soller, 1962: Water-vapor exchange between a water droplet and its environment. *Journal of Geophysical Research*, **67** (7), 2 761–2 766.

Friedmann, A., J. C. Moore, T. Thorsteinsson, J. Kipfstuhl, and H. Fischer, 1995: A 1200 year record of accumulation from northern Greenland. *Annals of Glaciology*, **21**, 19–25.

Froggatt, P. C., C. S. Nelson, L. Carter, G. Griggs, and K. P. Black, 1986: An exceptionally large late Quaternary eruption from New Zealand. *Nature*, **319**, 578–582.

Fronval, T., and E. Jansen, 1996: Rapid changes in ocean circulation and heat flux in the Nordic seas during the last interglacial period. *Nature*, **383**, 806–810.

——, E. Jansen, J. Bloemendal, and S. Johnsen, 1995: Oceanic evidence for coherent fluctuations in Fennoscandian and Laurentide Ice Sheets on millennium timescales. *Nature*, **374**, 443–446.

Fuhrer, K., A. Neftel, M. Anklin, and V. Maggi, 1993: Continuous measurements of hydrogen peroxide, formaldehyde, calcium and ammonium concentrations along the new GRIP core from Summit, central Greenland. *Atmospheric Environment*, **27A** (12), 1 873–1 880.

——, E. W. Wolff, and S. J. Johnsen, 1999: Timescales for dust variability in the Greenland Ice Core Project (GRIP) ice core in the last 100,000 years. *Journal of Geophysical Research*, **104** (D24), 31 043–31 052.

Fujii, Y., and T. Ohata, 1982: Possible causes of the variation in microparticle concentration in an ice core from Mizuho Station, Antarctica. *Annals of Glaciology*, **3**, 107–112.

——, M. Kohno, H. Motoyama, S. Matoba, O. Watanabe, S. Fujita, N. Azuma, T. Kikuchi, T. Fukuoka, and T. Suzuki, 1999: Tephra layers in the Dome Fuji (Antarctica) deep ice core. *Annals of Glaciology*, **29**, 126–130.

Fujita, S., and S. Mae, 1994: Causes and nature of ice-sheet radio-echo internal reflections estimated from the dielectric properties of ice. *Annals of Glaciology*, **20**, 80–86.

——, N. Azuma, H. Motoyama, T. Kameda, H. Narita, Y. Fujii, and O. Watanabe, 2002a: Electrical measurements on the 2503 m Dome F Antarctic ice core. *Annals of Glaciology*, **35**, 313–320.

——, N. Azuma, H. Motoyama, T. Kameda, H. Narita, S. Matoba, M. Igarashi, M. Kohno, Y. Fujii, and O. Watanabe, 2002b: Linear and non-linear relations between the high-frequency-limit conductivity, AC-

ECM signals and ECM signals of Dome F Antarctic ice core from a laboratory experiment. *Annals of Glaciology,* **35**, 321–328.

Gat, J. R., and E. Matsui, 1991: Atmospheric water balance in the Amazon Basin: An isotopic evapotranspiration model. *Journal of Geophysical Research,* **96** (D7), 13 179–13 188.

Gedzelman, S. D., and J. R. Lawrence, 1982: The isotopic composition of cyclonic precipitation. *Journal of Applied Meteorology,* **21**:1385–1404.

——, and R. Arnold, 1994: Modeling the isotopic composition of precipitation. *Journal of Geophysical Research,* **99** (D5), 10 455–10 471.

——, J. M. Rosenbaum, and J. R. Lawrence, 1989: The megalopolitan snowstorm of 11-12 February 1938: Isotopic composition of the snow. *Journal of the Atmospheric Sciences,* **46** (12), 1637–1649.

Gibson, J. A. E., R. C. Garrick, H. R. Burton, and A. R. McTaggart, 1990: Dimethylsulfide and the alga *Phaeocystis pouchetii* in Antarctic coastal waters. *Marine Biology,* **104**, 339–346.

Gibson, J. J., et al., 2002: Isotopic studies in large river basins: A new global research focus. *EOS,* **83** (52), 613, 616, 617.

Gogineni, S., et al., 2001: Coherent radar ice thickness measurements over the Greenland ice sheet. *Journal of Geophysical Research,* **106** (D24), 33 761–33 772.

Goktas, F., H. Fischer, H. Oerter, R. Weller, S. Sommer, and H. Miller, H., 2002: A glacio-chemical characterization of the new EPICA deep-drilling site on Amundsenisen, Dronning Maud Land, Antarctica. *Annals of Glaciology,* **35**, 347–354.

Gow, A. J., and T. Williamson, 1971: Volcanic ash in the Antarctic Ice Sheet and its possible climatic implications. *Earth and Planetary Science Letters,* **13**, 210–218.

——, and ——, 1976: Rheological implications of the internal structure and crystal fabrics of the West Antarctic Ice Sheet as revealed by deep core drilling at Byrd Station. *Geological Society of America Bulletin,* **87**, 1665–1677.

——, H. T. Ueda, and D. E. Garfield, 1968: Antarctic Ice Sheet: Preliminary results of first core hole to bedrock. *Science,* **161**, 1011–1013.

——, S. Epstein, and W. Sheehy, 1979: On the origin of stratified debris in ice cores from the bottom of the Antarctic Ice Sheet. *Journal of Glaciology,* **23** (89), 185–192.

——, D. A. Meese, R. B. Alley, J. J. Fitzpatrick, A. Anandakrishnan, G. A. Woods, and B. C. Elder, 1997: Physical and structural properties of the Greenland Ice Sheet Project 2 ice core: A review. *Journal of Geophysical Research,* **102** (C12), 26 559–26 575.

Greenland Ice-Core Project (GRIP) Members, 1993: Climate instability during the last interglacial period recorded in the GRIP ice core. *Nature,* **364**, 203–207.

Grönvold, K., N. Oskarsson, S. J. Johnsen, H. B. Clausen, C. U. Hammer, G. Bond, and E. Bard, 1995: Ash layers from Iceland in the Greenland GRIP ice core correlated with oceanic and land sediments. *Earth and Planetary Science Letters,* **135**, 149–155.

Grootes, P. M., and M. Stuiver, 1997: Oxygen 18/16 variability in Greenland snow and ice with 10^{-3}- to 10^5-year time resolution. *Journal of Geophysical Research,* **102** (C12), 26 455–26 470.

——, M. Stuiver, J. W. C. White, S. Johnsen, and J. Jouzel, 1993: Comparison of oxygen isotope records from the GISP2 and GRIP Greenland ice cores. *Nature,* **366**, 552–554.

Grossman, D., 2003: Drilling through ice in search of history. *The New York Times*, 22 July 2003, p. D2.

Grousset, F. E., P. E. Biscaye, M. Revel, J. R. Petit, K. Pye, S. Joussaume, and J. Jouzel, 1992: Antarctic (Dome C) ice-core dust at 18 k.y. B. P.: Isotopic constraints on origins. *Earth and Planetary Science Letters,* **111**, 175–182.

Gudmandsen, P., 1975: Layer echoes in polar ice sheets. *Journal of Glaciology,* **15** (73), 95–101.

178

Haflidason, H., H. P. Sejrup, D. K. Kristensen, and S. Johnsen, 1995: Coupled response of the late glacial climatic shifts of northwest Europe reflected in Greenland ice cores: Evidence from the northern North Sea. *Geology,* **23,** 1059–1062.

Hambrey, M. J., P. N. Webb, D. M. Harwood, and L. A. Krissek, 2003: Neogene glacial record from the Sirius Group of the Shackleton Glacier region, central Transantarctic Mountains. *Geological Society of America Bulletin,* **115,** 994–1015.

Hammer, C. U., 1977: Dust studies on Greenland ice cores. *Isotopes and Impurities in Snow and Ice,* IAHS Publication 118, 365–370.

——, 1980: Acidity of polar ice cores in relation to absolute dating, past volcanism, and radioechoes. *Journal of Glaciology,* **25** (93), 359–372.

——, 1982: The history of atmospheric composition as recorded in ice sheets. *Atmospheric Chemistry,* E. D. Goldberg, Ed., Springer-Verlag, 119–134.

——, 1983: Initial direct current in the buildup of space charges and the acidity of ice cores. *Journal of Physical Chemistry,* **87,** 4099–4103.

——, 1986: Frozen news on hot events. *Nature,* **322,** 778.

——, 1989: Dating by physical and chemical seasonal variations and reference horizons. *The Environmental Record in Glaciers and Ice Sheets,* H. Oeschger and C. C. Langway, Jr., Eds., John Wiley & Sons, 99–121.

——, H. B. Clausen, W. Dansgaard, N. Gundestrup, S. J. Johnsen, and R. Reeh, 1978: Dating of Greenland ice cores by flow models, isotopes, volcanic debris, and continental dust. *Journal of Glaciology,* **20** (82), 3–26.

——, H. B. Clausen, and W. Dansgaard, 1980: Greenland Ice Sheet evidence of post-glacial volcanism and its climatic impact. *Nature,* **288,** 230–235.

——, H. B. Clausen, and C. C. Langway, Jr., 1985: The Byrd ice core: Continuous acidity measurements and solid electrical conductivity measurements. *Annals of Glaciology,* **7,** 214.

——, ——, and ——, 1994: Electrical conductivity method (ECM) stratigraphic dating of the Byrd Station ice core, Antarctica. *Annals of Glaciology,* **20,** 115–120.

——, ——, and ——, 1997: 50,000 years of recorded global volcanism. *Climatic Change,* **35,** 1–15.

——, H. B. Clausen, W. Dansgaard, A. Neftel, P. Kristinsdottir, and E. Johnson, 1985: Continuous impurity analysis along the Dye 3 deep core. *Greenland Ice Core: Geophysics, Geochemistry, and the Environment, Geophysical Monograph,* No. 33, American Geophysical Union, 90–94.

——, H. B. Clausen, and H. Tauber, 1986: Ice-core dating of the Pleistocene/ Holocene boundary applied to a calibration of the ^{14}C time scale. *Radiocarbon,* **28** (2A), 284–291.

——, P. A. Mayewski, D. Peel, and M. Stuiver, 1997: Preface. *Journal of Geophysical Research,* **102** (C12), 26 315–26 316.

Hanna, E., P. Huybrechts, and T. L. Mote, 2002: Surface mass balance of the Greenland Ice Sheet from climate-analysis data and accumulation/runoff models. *Annals of Glaciology,* **35,** 67–72.

Hansson, M. E., 1995: Are changes in atmospheric cleansing responsible for observed variations of impurity concentrations in ice cores? *Annals of Glaciology,* **21,** 219–224.

Harwood, D. M., 1983: Diatoms from the Sirius Formation, Transantarctic Mountains. *Antarctic Journal of the United States,* **18** (5), 98–100.

——, 1985: Late Neogene climatic fluctuations in the southern high-latitudes: Implications of a warm Pliocene and deglaciated Antarctic continent. *Suid-Afrikaanse Tydskrif vir Wetenskap,* **81,** 239–241.

Harvey, R. P., N. W. Dunbar, W. C. McIntosh, R. P. Esser, K. Nishiizumi, S. Taylor, and M. W. Caffee, 1998: Meteoritic event recorded in Antarctic ice. *Geology,* **26,** 607–610.

Hays, J. D., J. Imbrie, and N. J. Shackleton, 1976: Variations in the earth's orbit: Pacemaker of the ice ages. *Science,* **194**, 1121–1132.

Hecht, A.D. et al., 1989: Group report long-term ice core records and global environmental changes. *The Environmental Record in Glaciers and Ice Sheets*, H. Oeschger and C. C. Langway, Jr., Eds., John Wiley & Sons, 379–388.

Hendricks, M. B., D. J. DePaolo, and R. C. Cohen, 2000: Space and time variations of $\delta^{18}O$ and δD in precipitation: Can palaeotemperature be estimated from ice cores? *Global Biogeochemical Cycles,* **14** (3), 851–861.

Herron, S., and C. C. Langway, Jr., 1979: The debris-laden ice at the bottom of the Greenland Ice Sheet. *Journal of Glaciology,* **23** (89), 193–207.

——, and C. C. Langway, Jr., 1987: Derivation of paleoelevations from total air content of two deep Greenland ice cores. *The Physical Basis of Ice Sheet Modelling,* IAHS Publication 170, 283–296.

Hogan, A., 1997: A synthesis of warm air advection to the South Polar Plateau. *Journal of Geophysical Research,* **102** (D12), 14 009–14 020.

Holmlund, P., and J.-O. Näslund, 1994: The glacially sculptured landscape in Dronning Maud Land, Antarctica, formed by wet-based mountain glaciation and not by the present ice sheet. *Boreas,* **23**, 139–148.

Hooyer, T. S., and N. R. Iverson, 2002: Flow mechanism of the Des Moines lobe of the Laurentide ice sheet. *Journal of Glaciology,* **48** (163), 575–586.

Hondoh, T., H. Shoji, O. Watanabe, A. N. Salamatin, and V. Ya. Lipenkov, 2002: Depth-age and temperature prediction at Dome Fuji station, East Antarctica. *Annals of Glaciology,* **35**, 384–389.

Huybrechts, P., 1994: Formation and disintegration of the Antarctic Ice Sheet. *Annals of Glaciology,* **20**, 336–363.

——, 1996: Basal temperature conditions of the Greenland Ice Sheet during the glacial cycles. *Annals of Glaciology,* **23**, 226–236.

——, D. Steinhage, F. Wilhelms, and J. Bamber, 2000: Balance velocity and measured properties of the Antarctic ice sheet from a new compilation of gridded data for modeling. *Annals of Glaciology,* **30**, 52–60.

Hvidberg, C. S., 2000: When Greenland ice melts. *Nature,* **404**, 551–552.

Iken, A., E. Echelmeyer, W. Harrison, and M. Funk, 1993: Mechanisms of fast flow in Jakobshavns Isbrae, West Greenland: Part I. Measurements of temperature and water level in deep boreholes. *Journal of Glaciology,* **39** (131), 15–25.

Imbrie, J., and K. P. Imbrie, 1979: *Ice Ages Solving the Mystery*. Enslow Publishers, 224 pp.

Indermühle, A., E. Monnin, B. Stauffer, and T. F. Stocker, 2000: Atmospheric CO_2 concentration from 60 to 20 kyr BP from Taylor Dome ice core, Antarctica. *Geophysical Research Letters,* **27** (5), 735–738.

Ito, T., 1989: Antarctic submicron aerosols and long-range transport of pollutants. *Ambio,* **18**, 34–41.

Ivey, J. P., D. M. Davies, V. Morgan, and G. P. Ayers, 1986: Methanesulphonate in Antarctic ice. *Tellus,* **38B**, 375–379.

Jacobel, R. W., and S. M. Hodge, 1995: Radar internal layers from the Greenland summit. *Geophysical Research Letters,* **22** (5), 587–590.

Jaffrezo, J. L., C. I. Davidson, M. Legrand, and J. E. Dibb, 1994: Sulfate and MSA in the air and snow on the Greenland Ice Sheet. *Journal of Geophysical Research,* **99** (D1), 1241–1253.

Jansen, E., and T. Veum, 1990: Evidence for two-step deglaciation and its impact on North Atlantic deep-water circulation. *Nature,* **343**, 612–616.

Jaworowski, Z., T. V. Segalstad, and N. Ono, 1992: Do glaciers tell a true atmospheric CO_2 story? *The Science of the Total Environment, 114*, 227–284.

Jenssen, D., 1983: Elevation and climatic changes from total gas content and stable isotopic measurements. *The Climatic Record in Polar Ice Sheets*, G. de Q. Robin, Ed., Cambridge University Press, 138–144.

——, and U. Radok, 1982: On the joint interpretation of total gas contents and stable isotope ratios in ice cores. *Annals of Glaciology, 3*, 152–155.

Johns, W. H., 1993: Tree rings again. *Creation Research Society Quarterly, 30* (3), 129–131.

Johnsen, S. J., 1977: Stable isotope homogenization of polar firn and ice. Isotopes and Impurities in Snow and Ice, IAHS Publication 118, 210–219.

——, and G. de Q. Robin, 1983: Diffusion of stable isotopes. *The Climatic Record in Polar Ice Sheets*, G. de Q. Robin, Ed., Cambridge University Press, 57–63.

——, and J. W. C. White, 1989: The origin of Arctic precipitation under present and glacial conditions. *Tellus, 41B*, 452–468.

——, and W. Dansgaard, 1992: On flow model dating of stable isotope records from Greenland ice cores. *The Last Deglaciation: Absolute and Radiocarbon Chronologies*, E. Bard and W. S. Broecker, Eds., Springer-Verlag, 13–24.

——, W. Dansgaard, H. B. Clausen, and C. C. Langway, Jr., 1972: Oxygen isotope profiles through the Antarctic and Greenland Ice Sheets. *Science, 235*, 429–434.

——, H. B. Clausen, W. Dansgaard, K. Fuhrer, N. Gundestrup, C. U. Hammer, P. Iversen, J. Jouzel, B. Stauffer, and J. P. Steffensen, 1992a: Irregular glacial interstadials recorded in a new Greenland ice core. *Nature, 359*, 311–313.

——, H. B. Clausen, W. Dansgaard, N. S. Gundestrup, M. Hansson, P. Jonsson, J. P. Steffensen, and A. E. Sveinbjørnsdottir, 1992b: A "deep" ice core from East Greenland. *Meddelelser om Grønland, Geoscience, 29*, 3–22.

——, D. Dahl-Jensen, W. Dansgaard, and N. Gundestrup, 1995a: Greenland palaeotemperatures derived from GRIP bore hole temperature and ice core isotope profiles. *Tellus, 47B*, 624–629.

——, H. B. Clausen, W. Dansgaard, N. S. Gundestrup, C. U. Hammer, and H. Tauber, 1995b: The Eem stable isotope record along the GRIP ice core and its interpretation. *Quaternary Research, 43*, 117–124.

——, et al., 1997: The $\delta^{18}O$ record along the Greenland Ice Core Project deep ice core and the problem of possible Eemian climatic instability. *Journal of Geophysical Research, 102* (C12), 26 397–26 410.

Joughin, I., M. Fahnestock, D. MacAyeal, J. L. Bamber, and P. Gogineni, 2001: Observations and analysis of ice flow in the largest Greenland ice stream. *Journal of Geophysical Research, 106* (D24), 34 021–34 034.

Jouzel, J., 1999: Calibrating the isotopic paleothermometer. *Science, 286*, 910–911.

——, and L. Merlivat, 1984: Deuterium and oxygen 18 in precipitation: Modeling of the isotopic effects during snow formation. *Journal of Geophysical Research, 89* (D7), 11 749–11 757.

——, J. R. Petit, and D. Raynaud, 1990: Palaeoclimatic information from ice cores: The Vostok records. *Transactions of the Royal Society of Edinburgh, 81*, 349–355.

——, C. Lorius, J. R. Petit, C. Genthon, N. I. Barkov, V. M. Kotllyakov, and V. M. Petrov, 1987: Vostok ice core: A continuous isotope temperature record over the last climatic cycle (160,000) years. *Nature, 329*, 403–408.

——, et al., 1993: Extending the Vostok ice-core record of palaeoclimate to the penultimate glacial period. *Nature, 364*, 407–412.

——, et al., 1995: The two-step shape and timing of the last deglaciation in Antarctica. *Climate Dynamics, 11*, 151–161.

——, et al., 1996: Climatic interpretation of the recently extended Vostok ice records. *Climate Dynamics,* **12**, 513–521.

——, et al., 1997: Validity of the temperature reconstruction from water isotopes in ice cores. *Journal of Geophysical Research,* **102** (C12), 26 471–26 487.

——, et al., 1999: More than 200 meters of lake ice above subglacial Lake Vostok, Antarctica. *Science,* **286**, 2138–2141.

——, G. Hoffmann, R. D. Koster, and V. Masson, 2000: Water isotopes in precipitation: Data/model comparison for present-day and past climates. *Quaternary Science Reviews,* **19**, 363–379.

——, et al., 2001: A new 27 ky high resolution East Antarctic climate record. *Geophysical Research Letters,* **28** (16), 3199–3202.

——, F. Vimeux, N. Caillon, G. Delaygue, G. Hoffmann, V. Masson-Delmotte, and F. Parrenin, 2003: Magnitude of isotope/temperature scaling for interpretation of central Antarctic ice cores. *Journal of Geophysical Research,* **108** (D12), 4361, doi:10.1029/2002JD002677.

Kameda, T., M. Nakawo, S. Mae, O. Watanabe, and R. Naruse, 1990: Thinning of the ice sheet estimated from total gas content of ice cores in Mizuho Plateau, East Antarctica. *Annals of Glaciology,* **14**, 131–135.

Kanagaratnam, P., S. P. Gogineni, N. Gundestrup, and L. Larsen, 2001: High-resolution radar mapping of internal layers at the North Greenland Ice Core Project. *Journal of Geophysical Research,* **106** (D24), 33 799–33 811.

Kapsner, W. R., R. B. Alley, C. A. Shuman, S. Anandakrishnan, and P. M. Grootes, 1995: Dominant influence of atmospheric circulation on snow accumulation in Greenland over the past 18,000 years. *Nature,* **373**, 52–54.

Karlöf, L., et al., 2000: A 1500 year record of accumulation at Amundsenisen western Dronning Maud Land, Antarctica, derived from electrical and radioactive measurements on a 120 m ice core. *Journal of Geophysical Research,* **105** (D10), 12 471–12 483.

Karlstrom, E. T., 2000: Fabric and origin of multiple diamictons within the pre-Illinoian Kennedy Drift east of Waterton-Glacier International Peace park, Alberta, Canada, and Montana, USA. *Geological Society of America Bulletin,* **112**, 1496–1506.

——, and R. W. Barendregt, 2001: Fabric, paleomagnetism, and interpretation of pre-Illinoian diamictons and paleosols on Cloudy Ridge and Milk River Ridge, Alberta and Montana. *Geographie Physique et Quaternaire,* **55** (2), 141–157.

Kato, K., 1978: Factors controlling oxygen isotopic composition of fallen snow in Antarctica. *Nature,* **272**, 46–48.

Kavanaugh, J. L., and K. M. Cuffey, 2002: Generalized view of source-region effects on δD and deuterium excess of ice-sheet precipitation. *Annals of Glaciology,* **35**, 111–117.

Keigwin, L. D., W. B. Curry, S. J. Lehman, S. Johnsen, 1994: The role of the deep ocean in North Atlantic climate change between 70 and 130 kyr ago. *Nature,* **371**, 323–326.

Kellogg, D. E., and T. B. Kellogg, 1996: Diatoms in South Pole ice: Implications for eolian contamination of Sirius Group deposits. *Geology,* **24**, 115–118.

Kennett, J., 1982: *Marine Geology.* Prentice-Hall, Englewood Cliffs, 813 pp.

Kerr, R. A., 1993: How ice age climate got the shakes. *Science,* **260**, 890–892.

——, 1996: Ice bubbles confirm big chill. *Science,* **272**, 1584–1585.

——, 1999: From eastern quakes to a warming's icy clues. *Science,* **283**, 28–29.

King, P. B., 1965: Tectonics in Quaternary time in middle North America. *The Quaternary of the United States,* H. E. Wright, Jr. and D. G. Frey, Eds., Princeton University Press, 831–870.

Klevberg, P., and M. J. Oard, 2005: Drifting interpretation of the Kennedy gravels. *Creation Research Society Quarterly,* **41**(4), 289-315.

——, M. J. Oard, and R. Bandy, 2003: Are paleosols really ancient soils? *Creation Research Society Quarterly,* **40** (3), 134–149.

——, R. Bandy, and M. J. Oard, 2005: Investigation of several alleged paleosols in the Northern Rocky Mountains. *Creation Research Society Quarterly,* submitted.

Koch, P. L., J. C. Zachos, and D. L. Dettman, 1995: Stable isotope stratigraphy and paleoclimatology of the Paleogene Bighorn Basin (Wyoming, USA). *Palaeogeography, Palaeoclimatology, Palaeoecology,* **115**, 61–89.

Koerner, R. M., 1979: Accumulation, ablation, and oxygen isotope variations on the Queen Elizabeth Islands ice caps, Canada. *Journal of Glaciology,* **22** (86), 25–41.

——, 1989: Ice core evidence for extensive melting of the Greenland Ice Sheet in the last interglacial. *Science,* **244**, 964–967.

——, 1997: Some comments on climatic reconstructions from ice cores drilled in areas of high melt. *Journal of Glaciology,* **43** (143), 90–97.

——, and R. D. Russell, 1979: O variations in snow on the Devon Island ice cap, Northwest Territories, Canada. *Canadian Journal of Earth Sciences,* **16**, 1419–1427.

——, and D. A. Fisher, 2002: Ice-core evidence for widespread Arctic glacier retreat in the Last Interglacial and the early Holocene. *Annals of Glaciology,* **35**, 19–24.

——, W. S. B. Paterson, and H. R. Krouse, 1973: $\delta^{18}O$ profile in ice formed between the equilibrium and firn lines. *Nature,* **245**, 137–140.

Kolbert, E., 2002: Ice memory: Does a glacier hold the secret of how civilization began—and how it may end? *New Yorker,* January 7, 30–37.

Koster, R. D., D. P. de Valpine, and J. Jouzel, 1993: Continental water recycling and $H_2^{18}O$ concentrations. *Geophysical Research Letters,* **20** (20), 2215–2218.

Kotlyakov, V. M., C. Lorius, J. Palais, and D. Raynaud, 2001: Introduction to special section: Vostok. *Journal of Geophysical Research,* **106** (D23), 31 833–31 835.

Kreutz, K. J., and P. A. Mayewski, 1999: Spatial variability of Antarctic surface snow glaciochemistry: Implications for palaeoatmospheric circulation reconstructions. *Antarctic Science,* **11** (1), 105–118.

——, P. A. Mayewski, S. I. Whitlow, and M. S. Twickler, 1998: Limited migration of soluble ionic species in a Siple Dome, Antarctica, ice core. *Annals of Glaciology,* **27**, 371–377.

——, P. A. Mayewski, M. S. Twickler, S. I. Whitlow, J. W. C. White, C. A. Shuman, C. F. Raymond, H. Conway, and J. R. McConnell, 1999: Seasonal variations of glaciochemical, isotopic and stratigraphic properties in Siple dome (Antarctica) surface snow. *Annals of Glaciology,* **29**, 38–44.

Krinner, G., C. Genthon, and J. Jouzel, 1997: GCM analysis of local influences on ice core δ signals. *Geophysical Research Letters,* **24** (22), 2825–2828.

——, D. Raynaud, C. Doutriaux, and H. Dang, 2000: Simulations of the Last Glacial Maximum ice sheet surface climate: Implications for the interpretation of ice core air content. *Journal of Geophysical Research,* **105** (D2), 2059–2070.

Ktitarev, D., G. Gödert, and K. Hutter, 2002: Cellular automaton model for recrystallization, fabric, and texture development in polar ice. *Journal of Geophysical Research,* **107** (B8), EPM5.

Labeyrie, L., 2000: Glacial climate instability. *Science,* **290**, 1905–1907.

Lal, C., 1987: [10]Be in polar ice: Data reflect changes in cosmic ray flux or polar meteorology. *Geophysical Research Letters,* **14** (8), 785–788.

Lal, D., A. J. T. Jull, G. S. Burr, and D. J. Donahue, 1997: Measurements of in situ ^{14}C concentrations in Greenland Ice Sheet Project 2 ice covering a 17-kyr time span: Implications to ice flow dynamics. *Journal of Geophysical Research,* **102** (C12), 26 505–26 510.

Landais, A., et al., 2003: A tentative reconstruction of the last interglacial and glacial inception in Greenland based on new gas measurements in the Greenland Ice Core Project (GRIP) ice core. *Journal of Geophysical Research,* **108** (D18), 4563, doi:10.1029/2002JD003147.

Landwehr, J. M., and I. J. Winograd, 2001: Dating the Vostok ice core record by importing the Devils Hole chronology. *Journal of Geophysical Research,* **106** (D23), 31 853–31 861.

Langway, Jr., C. C., 1967: Stratigraphic analysis of a deep ice core from Greenland. U.S. Army Corps of Engineers, Cold Regions Research and Engineering Laboratory Research Report 77, 130 pp.

——, 1970: Stratigraphic analysis of a deep ice core from Greenland. Geological Society of America Special Paper 25, 186 pp.

——, K. Osada, H. B. Clausen, C. U. Hammer, H. Shoji, and A. Mitani, 1994: New chemical stratigraphy over the last millennium for Byrd Station, Antarctica. *Tellus,* **46B**, 40–51.

Larsen, H. C., A. D. Saunders, P. D. Clift, J. Beget, W. Wei, S. Spezzaferri, and ODP Leg 152 Scientific Party, 1994: Seven million years of glaciation in Greenland. *Science,* **264**, 952–955.

Layberry, R. L., and J. L. Bamber, 2001: A new ice thickness and bed data set for the Greenland Ice Sheet 2. Relationship between dynamics and basal topography. *Journal of Geophysical Research,* **106** (D24), 33 781–33 788.

Legrand, M., 1995: Sulphur-derived species in polar ice: A review. *Ice Core Studies of Global Biogeochemical Cycles,* R. J. Delmas, Ed., NATO ASI Series 1, Global Environmental Change, Vol. 30, Springer-Verlag, 91–119.

——, and C. Feniet-Saigne, 1991: Methanesulfonic acid in south polar snow layers: A record of strong El Nino? *Geophysical Research Letters,* **18** (2), 187–190.

——, and L. A. Barrie, 1996: Working group report—acidic gases. *Chemical Exchange Between the Atmosphere and Polar Snow,* E. W. Wolff and R. C. Bales, Eds., NATO ASI Series 1, Global Environmental Change, Vol. 43, Springer-Verlag, 647–652.

——, and P. Mayewski, 1997: Glaciochemistry of polar ice cores: A review. *Reviews of Geophysics,* **35** (3), 219–243.

——, and E. C. Pasteur, 1998: Methane sulfonic acid to non-sea-salt sulfate ratio in coastal Antarctic aerosol and surface snow. *Journal of Geophysical Research,* **103** (D9), 10 991–11 006.

——, M. De Angelis, T. Staffelbach, A. Neftel, and B. Stauffer, 1992: Large perturbations of ammonium and organic acids content in the Summit-Greenland ice core, finger print from forest fires? *Geophysical Research Letters,* **19** (5), 473–475.

——, C. Hammer, M. De Angelis, J. Savarino, R. Delmas, H. Clausen, and S. J. Johnsen, 1997: Sulfur-containing species (methanesulfonate and SO_4) over the last climatic cycle in the Greenland Ice Core Project (central Greenland) ice core. *Journal of Geophysical Research,* **102** (C12), 26 663–26 679.

——, E. Wolff, and D. Wagenbach, 1999: Antarctic aerosol and snowfall chemistry: Implications for deep Antarctic ice-core chemistry. *Annals of Glaciology,* **29**, 66–72.

Legrand, M. R., and R. J. Delmas, 1986: Relative contributions of tropospheric and stratospheric sources to nitrate in Antarctic snow. *Tellus,* **38B**, 236–249.

——, and ——, 1988a: Reply to C. M. Laird, E. J. Zeller and G. A. M. Dreschhoff. *Tellus,* **40B**, 237–240.

——, and ——, 1988b: Formation of HCl in the Antarctic atmosphere. *Journal of Geophysical Research,* **93** (D6), 7153–7168.

——, and S. Kirchner, 1990: Origins and variation of nitrate in South Polar precipitation. *Journal of Geophysical Research,* **95** (D4), 3493–3507.

Lehman, S., 1993: Ice sheets, wayward winds and sea change. *Nature,* **365,** 108–110.

——, 1997: Sudden end of an interglacial. *Nature,* **390,** 117–118.

Letréguilly, A., P. Huybrechts, and N. Reeh, 1991: Steady-state characteristics of the Greenland Ice Sheet under different climates. *Journal of Glaciology,* **37** (125), 149–157.

Li, S. -M., and L. A. Barrie, 1993: Biogenic sulfur aerosol in the Arctic troposphere: 1. Contributions to total sulfate. *Journal of Geophysical Research,* **98** (D11), 20 613–20 622.

——, L. A. Barrie, and A. Sirois, 1993: Biogenic sulfur aerosol in the Arctic troposphere: 2. Trends and seasonal variations. *Journal of Geophysical Research,* **98** (D11), 20 623–20 631.

Lidmar-Bergström, K., S. Olsson, and M. Olvmo, 1997: Palaeosurfaces and associated saprolites in southern Sweden. *Palaeosurfaces: Recognition, Reconstruction and Palaeoenvironmental Interpretation,* M. Widdowson, Ed., Geological Society of London Special Publication 120, 95–124.

Lipenkov, V. Ya., N. I. Barkov, P. Duval, and P. Pimienta, 1989: Crystalline texture of the 2083 m ice core at Vostok Station, Antarctica. *Journal of Glaciology,* **35** (121), 392–398.

Lipenkov, V., F. Candaudap, J. Ravoire, E. Dulac, and D. Raynaud, 1995: A new device for the measurement of air content in polar ice. *Journal of Glaciology,* **41** (138), 423–429.

Lorius, C., L. Merlivat, J. Jouzel, and M. Pourchet, 1979: A 30,000-yr isotope climatic record from Antarctic ice. *Nature,* **280,** 644–648.

——, J. Jouzel, C. Ritz, L. Merlivat, N. I. Barkov, Y. S. Korotkevich, and V. M. Kotlyakov, 1985: A 150,000-year climatic record from Antarctic ice. *Nature,* **316,** 591–596.

——, G. Raisbeck, J. Jouzel, and D. Raynaud, 1989: Long-term environmental records from Antarctic ice cores. *The Environmental Record in Glaciers and Ice Sheets,* H. Oeschger and C. C. Langway, Jr., Eds., John Wiley & Sons, 343-361.

——, J. Jouzel, and D. Raynaud, 1993: Glacials-interglacials in Vostok: Climate and greenhouse gases. *Global and Planetary Change,* **7,** 131–143.

Loubere, P., 1982: Plankton ecology and the paleoceanographic—climatic record. *Quaternary Research,* **17,** 314–324.

Lubenow, M. L., 1992: *Bones of Contention: A Creationist Assessment of Human Fossils.* Baker Book House, 296 pp.

MacAyeal, D., 1995: Challenging an ice-core paleothermometer. *Science,* **270,** 444–445.

Maccagnan, M., J. M. Barnola, R. Delmas, and P. Duval, 1981: Static electrical conductivity as an indicator of the sulfate content of polar ice cores. *Geophysical Research Letters,* **9** (9), 970–972.

Maggi, V., 1997: Mineralogy of atmospheric microparticles deposited along the Greenland Ice Core Project ice core. *Journal of Geophysical Research,* **102** (C12), 26 725–26 734.

Martinerie, P., D. Raynaud, D. Mazaudier, A. J. Gow, G. Holdsworth, V. Ya. Lipenkov, and N. W. Young, 1988: The relationship between total gas content of polar ice, atmospheric pressure and surface elevation (abstract). *Annals of Glaciology,* **11,** 203.

——, V. Ya. Lipenkov, and D. Raynaud, 1990: Correction of air-content measurements in polar ice for the effect of cut bubbles at the surface of the sample. *Journal of Glaciology,* **36** (124), 299–303.

——, D. Raynaud, D. M. Etheridge, J. M. Barnola, and D. Mazaudier, 1992: Physical and climatic parameters which influence the air content in polar ice. *Earth and Planetary Science Letters,* **112,** 1–13.

——, V. Y. Lipenkov, D. Raynaud, J. Chappellaz, N. I. Barkov, and C. Lorius, 1994: Air content paleo record in the Vostok ice core (Antarctica): A mixed record of climatic and glaciological parameters. *Journal of Geophysical Research,* **99** (D5), 10 565–10 576.

Masarik, J., and J. Beer, 1999: Simulation of particle fluxes and cosmogenic nuclide production in the Earth's atmosphere. *Journal of Geophysical Research,* **104** (D10), 12 099–12 111.

Mathews, W. H., 1974: Surface profiles of the Laurentide Ice Sheet in its marginal areas. *Journal of Glaciology,* **13** (67), 37–43.

Matsuoka, K., F. Furukawa, S. Fujita, H. Maeno, S. Uratsuka, R. Naruse, and O. Watanabe, 2003: Crystal orientation fabrics within the Antarctic ice sheet revealed by multipolarization plane and dual-frequency radar. *Journal of Geophysical Research,* **108** (B10), 2499, doi:10.1029/2003JB002425.

Mayewski, P. A., L. D. Meeker, S. Whitlow, M. S. Twickler, M. C. Morrison, R. B. Alley, P. Bloomfield, and K. Taylor, 1993a: The atmosphere during the Younger Dryas. *Science,* **261**, 195–197.

——, L. D. Meeker, M. C. Morrison, M. S. Twickler, S. I. Whitlow, K. K. Ferland, D. A. Meese, M. R. Legrand, and J. P. Steffensen, 1993b: Greenland ice core "signal" characteristics: An expanded view of climate change. *Journal of Geophysical Research,* **98** (D7), 12 839–12 847.

——, et al., 1996: Climate change during the last deglaciation in Antarctica. *Science,* **272**, 1636–1638.

——, L. D. Meeker, M. S. Twickler, S. Whitlow, Q. Yang, W. B. Lyons, and M. Prentice, 1997: Major features and forcing of high-latitude northern hemisphere atmospheric circulation using a 110,000-year-long glaciochemical series. *Journal of Geophysical Research,* **102** (C12), 26 345–26 366.

Mazaud, A., C. Laj, and M. Bender, 1994: A geomagnetic chronology for Antarctic ice accumulation. *Geophysical Research Letters,* **21** (5), 337–340.

McConnell, J. R., R. C. Bales, R. W. Stewart, A. M. Thompson, M. R. Albert, and R. Ramos, 1998: Physically based modeling of atmosphere-to-snow-to-firn transfer of H_2O_2 at South Pole. *Journal of Geophysical Research,* **103** (D9), 10 561–10 570.

——, E. Mosley-Thompson, D. H. Bromwich, R. C. Bales, and J. D. Kyne, 2000: Interannual variations of snow accumulation on the Greenland Ice Sheet (1985-1996): New observations versus model predictions. *Journal of Geophysical Research,* **105** (D3), 4039–4046.

McHargue, L. R., and P. E. Damon, 1991: The global Beryllium 10 cycle. *Reviews of Geophysics,* **29** (2), 141–158.

McManus, J. F., 2004: A great grand-daddy of ice cores. *Nature,* **429**, 611–612.

——, G. C. Bond, W. S. Broecker, S. Johnsen, L. Labeyrie, and S. Higgins, 1994: High-resolution climate records from the North Atlantic during the last interglacial. *Nature,* **371**, 326–329.

Meese, D. A., A. J. Gow, R. B. Alley, P. M. Grootes, P. A. Mayewski, M. Ram, K. C. Taylor, E. D. Waddington, G. A. Zielinski, and G. C. Bond, 1993: Counting down . . . the GISP2 depth/age scale. *EOS* Fall Meeting Supplement, **74** (43), 83.

——, D. A., R. B. Alley, A. J. Gow, P. Grootes, P. A. Mayewski, M. Ram, K. C. Taylor, E. D. Waddington, and G. Zielinski, 1994: Preliminary depth-age scale of the GISP2 ice core. U.S. Army Corps of Engineers, Cold Regions Research and Engineering Laboratory Special Report 94-1.

——, A. J. Gow, R. B. Alley, G. A. Zielinski, P. M. Grootes, M. Ram, K. C. Taylor, P. A. Mayewski, and J. F. Bolzan, 1997: The Greenland Ice Sheet Project 2 depth-age scale: Methods and results. *Journal of Geophysical Research,* **102** (C12), 26 411–26 423.

Merlivat, L., and J. Jouzel, 1979: Global climatic interpretation of the deuterium-oxygen 18 relationship for precipitation. *Journal of Geophysical Research,* **84** (C8), 5029–5033.

Millar, D. H. M., 1981: Radio-echo layering in polar ice sheets and past volcanic activity. *Nature,* **292**, 441–442.

——, 1982: Acidity levels in ice sheets from radio echo-soundings. *Annals of Glaciology,* **3**, 199–203.

Miller, S. L., 1969: Clathrate hydrates of air in Antarctic ice. *Science,* **165**, 489–490.

Miners, W. D., E. W. Wolff, J. C. Moore, R. Jacobel, and L. Hempel, 2002: Modeling the radio echo reflections inside the ice sheet at Summit, Greenland. *Journal of Geophysical Research,* **107** (B8), 2172, doi:10.1029/2001JB000535.

Minikin, A., M. Legrand, J. Hall, D. Wagenbach, C. Kleefeld, E. Wolff, E. C. Pasteur, and F. Ducroz, 1998: Sulfur-containing species (sulfate and methanesulfonate) in coastal Antarctic aerosol and precipitation. *Journal of Geophysical Research,* **103** (D9), 10 975–10 900.

Monmaney, T., 1994: Pat Epps' excellent adventure. *Forbes FYI,* March 14, 101–112.

Monastersky, R., 1993: Ancient ice reveals wild climate shifts. *Science News,* **144**, 36.

Moore, J. C., 1988: Dielectric variability of a 130 m Antarctic ice core: Implications for radar sounding. *Annals of Glaciology,* **11**, 95–99.

——, 1993: High-resolution dielectric profiling of ice cores. *Journal of Glaciology,* **39** (132), 245–248.

——, R. Mulvaney, and J. G. Paren, 1989: Dielectric stratigraphy of ice: A new technique for determining total ionic concentrations in polar ice cores. *Geophysical Research Letters,* **16** (10), 1177–1180.

——, E. W. Wolff, H. B. Clausen, and C. U. Hammer, 1992: The chemical basis for the electrical stratigraphy of ice. *Journal of Geophysical Research,* **97** (B2), 1887–1896.

Morgan, K., 2003: Fallen trees? Scotch pines emit nitrogen oxides into the air. *Science News,* **163**, 166.

Morgan, V. I., C. W. Wookey, J. Li, T. D. van Ommen, W. Skinner, and M. F. Fitzpatrick, 1997: Site information and initial results from deep ice drilling on Law Dome, Antarctica. *Journal of Glaciology,* **43** (143), 3–10.

Morris, Julie D., 1991: Applications of cosmogenic [10]Be to problems in the earth sciences. *Annual Review of Earth and Planetary Science,* **19**, 313–350.

Morris, John D., 1994: *The Young Earth.* Master Books, 207 pp.

Mulvaney, R., E. C. Pasteur, D. A. Peel, S. Saltzman, and P. -Y. Whung, 1992: The ratio of MSA to non-sea-salt sulphate in Antarctic Peninsula ice cores. *Tellus,* **44B**, 295–303.

——, D. Wagenbach, and E. W. Wolff, 1998: Postdepositional change in snowpack nitrate from observations of year-round near-surface snow in coastal Antarctica. *Journal of Geophysical Research,* **103** (D9) 11 021–11 031.

——, R. Röthlisberger, E. W. Wolff, S. Sommer, J. Schwander, M. A. Hutterli, and J. Jouzel, 2000: The transition from the last glacial period in inland and near-coastal Antarctica. *Geophysical Research Letters,* **27**, 2673–2676.

——, H. Oerter, A. D. Peel, W. Graf, C. Arrowsmith, E. C. Pasteur, B. Knight, G. C. Littot, and W. D. Miners, 2002: 1000 year ice-core records from Berkner Island, Antarctica. *Annals of Glaciology,* **35**, 45–51.

Muscheler, R., J. Beer, G. Wagner, and R. C. Finkel, 2000: Changes in deep-water formation during the Younger Dryas event inferred from [10]Be and ^{14}C records. *Nature,* **408**, 567–570.

Nakawo, M., S. Chiba, H. Satake, and S. Kinouchi, 1993: Isotopic fractionation during grain coarsening of wet snow. *Annals of Glaciology,* **18**, 129–134.

Naruse, R., 1979: Thinning of the ice sheet in Mizuho Plateau, East Antarctica. *Journal of Glaciology,* **24** (90), 45–52.

Neftel, A., M. Andrée, J. Schwander, and B. Stauffer, 1985: Measurements of a kind of dc-conductivity on cores from Dye 3. *Greenland Ice Core: Geophysics, Geochemistry, and the Environment, Geophysical Monograph,* No. 33, American Geophysical Union, 32–38.

Neftel, A., P. Jacob, and D. Klockow, 1986: Long-term record of H_2O_2 in polar ice cores. *Tellus,* **33B**, 262–270.

Nielsen, R. H., 1993: Chill warnings from Greenland. *New Scientist,* **139** (1888), 29–33.

Nixdorf, U., D, Steinhage, U. Meyer, L. Hempel, M. Jenett, P. Wachs, and H. Miller, 1999: The newly developed airborne radio-echo sounding system of the AWI as a glaciological tool. *Annals of Glaciology,* **29,** 231–238.

Njitchoua, R., L. Sigha-Nkamdjou, L. Dever, C. Marlin, D. Sighomnou, and P. Nia, 1999: Variations of the stable isotopic compositions of rainfall events from the Cameroon rain forest, Central Africa. *Journal of Hydrology,* **223,** 17–26.

North Greenland Ice Core Project Members, 2004: High-resolution record of Northern Hemisphere climate extending into the last interglacial period. *Nature,* **431,** 147–151.

Oard, M. J., 1984a: Ice ages: The mystery solved? Part I: The inadequacy of a uniformitarian ice age. *Creation Research Society Quarterly,* **21** (2), 66–76.

——, 1984b: Ice ages: The mystery solved? Part II: The manipulation of deep-sea cores. *Creation Research Society Quarterly,* **21** (3), 125–137.

——, 1985: Ice ages: The mystery solved? Part III: Paleomagnetic stratigraphy and data manipulation. *Creation Research Society Quarterly,* **21** (4), 170–181.

——, 1990: *An Ice Age Caused by the Genesis Flood.* Institute for Creation Research, 243 pp.

——, 1995: A tale of two Greenland ice cores. *Creation Ex Nihilo Technical Journal,* **9** (2), 135–136.

——, 1997a: *Ancient Ice Ages or Gigantic Submarine Landslides? Creation Research Society Monograph,* No. 6, Creation Research Society, 130 pp.

——, 1997b: Are pre-Pleistocene rhythmites caused by the Milankovitch mechanism? *Creation Ex Nihilo Technical Journal,* **11** (2), 126–128.

——, 1997c: Greenland ice cores indicate massive Ice Age volcanism. *Creation Ex Nihilo Technical Journal,* **11** (1), 9–10.

——, 2000: The extinction of the woolly mammoth: was it a quick freeze? *Creation Ex Nihilo Technical Journal,* **14** (3), 24–34.

——, 2001: Do Greenland ice cores show over one hundred thousand years of annual layers? *TJ,* **15** (3), 39–42.

——, 2003a: Are polar ice sheets only 4500 years old? Impact 361, *Acts & Facts* 32 (July), Institute for Creation Research.

——, 2003b: The 'cool-tropics paradox' in palaeoclimatology. *TJ,* **17** (1), 6–8.

——, 2004a: *The Missoula Flood Controversy and the Genesis Flood. Creation Research Society Monograph,* No. 13, Creation Research Society, 133 pp.

——, 2004b: *Frozen in Time: The Woolly Mammoth, the Ice Age, and the Bible.* Master Books, 216 pp.

——, 2004c: The Greenhouse warming hype of the move *The Day After Tomorrow.* Impact 373, *Acts & Facts* 33 (July), Institute for Creation Research.

——, cited 2005: New ice core records 120,000 years? [Available on line at http://www.answersingenesis. org/docs2003/0730ngrip.asp.]

Oeschger, H., 1985: The contribution of ice studies to the understanding of environmental processes. *Greenland Ice Core: Geophysics, Geochemistry, and the Environment, Geophysical Monograph,* No. 33, American Geophysical Union, 9–17.

——, J. Beer, U. Siegenthaler, B Stauffer, W. Dansgaard, and C. C. Langway, 1984: late glacial climate history from ice cores. *Climate Processes and Climate Sensitivity, Geophysical Monograph,* No. 29, American Geophysical Union, 299–306.

——, B. Stauffer, R. Finkel, and C. C. Langway, Jr., 1985: Variations of the CO_2 concentration of occluded air and of anions and dust in polar ice cores. *The Carbon Cycle and Atmospheric CO_2: Natural Variations Archean to Present, Geophysical Monograph*, No. 32, American Geophysical Union, 132–142.

——, A. Neftel, T. Staffelbach, and B. Stauffer, 1988: The dilemma of the rapid variations in CO_2 in Greenland ice cores. *Annals of Glaciology,* **10**, 215–216.

Oglesby, R. J., 1989: A GCM study of Antarctic glaciation. *Climate Dynamics,* **3**, 135–156.

Ohmura, A., and N. Reeh, 1991: New precipitation and accumulation maps for Greenland. *Journal of Glaciology,* **37** (25), 140–148.

Okuyama, J., H. Narita, T. Hondoh, and R. M. Koerner, 2003: Physical properties of the P96 ice core from Penny Ice Cap, Baffin Island, Canada, and derived climatic records. *Journal of Geophysical Research,* **108** (B2), 2090, doi:10.1029/2001JB001707.

Osada, K., 1994: Seasonal variations of major ionic concentration levels in drifting-snow samples obtained from east Dronning Maud Land, East Antarctica. *Annals of Glaciology,* **20**, 226–230.

Oswald, G. K. A., and G. de Q. Robin, 1973: Lakes beneath the Antarctic Ice Sheet. *Nature,* **245**, 251–254.

Overgaard, S., and N. S. Gundestrup, 1985: Bedrock topography of the Greenland Ice Sheet in the Dye 3 area. *Greenland Ice Core: Geophysics, Geochemistry, and the Environment, Geophysical Monograph*, No. 33, American Geophysical Union, 49–56.

Pahnke, K., R. Zahn, H. Elderfield, and M. Schulz, 2003: 340,000-year centennial-scale marine record of Southern Hemisphere climatic oscillation. *Science,* **301**, 948–952.

Paillard, D., 2001: Glacial cycles: Toward a new paradigm. *Reviews of Geophysics,* **39** (3), 325–346.

Palmer, A. S., T. D. van Ommen, M. A. J. Curran, V. Morgan, J. M. Souney, and P. A. Mayewski, 2001a: High-precision dating of volcanic events (A.D. 1301-1995) using ice cores from Law Dome, Antarctica. *Journal of Geophysical Research,* **106** (D22), 28 089–28 095.

——, T. D. van Ommen, M. A. J. Curran, and V. Morgan, 2001b: Ice-core evidence for a small solar-source of atmospheric nitrate. *Geophysical Research Letters,* **28** (10), 1953–1956.

Paren, J. G., and G. de Q. Robin, 1975: Internal reflections in polar ice sheets. *Journal of Glaciology,* **14** (71), 251–259.

Parish, T. R., and D. H. Bromwich, 1991: Continental-scale simulation of the Antarctic katabatic wind regime. *Journal of Climate,* **4**, 135–146.

——, and G. Wendler, 1991: The kabatatic wind regime at Adelie Land, Antarctica. *International Journal of Climatology,* **11**, 97–107.

Parrenin, F., J. Jouzel, C. Waelbroeck, D. Ritz, and J. M. Barnola, 2001: Dating the Vostok ice core by an inverse method. *Journal of Geophysical Research,* **106** (D23), 31 837–31 851.

Pasteur, E. C., and R. Mulvaney, 2000: Migration of methane sulfate in Antarctic firn and ice. *Journal of Geophysical Research,* **105** (D9), 11 525–11 534.

Paterson, W. S. B., 1981: *The Physics of Glaciers*. 2nd ed. Pergamon Press, 380 pp.

——, 1991: Why ice-age ice is sometimes "soft." *Cold Regions Science and Technology,* **20**, 75–98.

Paterson, W. S. B., and C. U. Hammer, 1987: Ice core and other glaciological data. *North America and Adjacent Oceans during the Last Deglaciation*, W. F. Ruddiman and H. E. Wright, Jr., Eds. Volume K-3, *The Geology of North America*, Geological Society of America, 91–109.

Pattyn, F., 2003: A new three-dimensional higher-order thermomechanical ice sheet model: Basic sensitivity, ice stream development, and ice flow across subglacial lakes. *Journal of Geophysical Research,* **108** (B8), 2382, doi:10.1029/2002JB002329.

Pearce, F., 1994: Will global warming plunge Europe into an ice age? *New Scientist,* **144** (1952), 20.

——, 2002: On the brink—the tiniest change can push the Earth's climate over the edge. *New Scientist,* **173** (2328), 18.

Pearman, G. I., et al., 1989: Group Report—what anthropogenic impacts are recorded in glaciers? *The Environmental Record in Glaciers and Ice Sheets*, H. Oeschger and C. C. Langway, Jr., Eds., John Wiley & Sons, 269–286.

Pearson, P. N., P. W. Ditchfield, J. Singano, K. G. Harcourt-Brown, C. J. Nicholas, R. K. Olsson, N. J. Shackleton, and M. A. Hall, 2001: Warm tropical sea surface temperatures in the Late Cretaceous and Eocene epochs. *Nature,* **413**, 481–487.

Peel, D. A., 1989: Trace metals and organic compounds in ice cores. *The Environmental Record in Glaciers and Ice Sheets*, H. Oeschger and C. C. Langway, Jr., Eds., John Wiley & Sons, 207–223.

——, 1995: Profiles of the past. *Nature,* **378**, 234–235.

Petit, J. R., J. W. C. White, N. W. Young, J. Jouzel, and Y. S. Korotkevich, 1991: Deuterium excess in recent Antarctic snow. *Journal of Geophysical Research,* **96** (D3), 5113–5122.

——, et al., 1997: Four climate cycles in Vostok ice core. *Nature,* **387**, 359–360.

——, et al., 1999: Climate and atmospheric history of the past 420,000 years from the Vostok ice core, Antarctica. *Nature,* **399**, 429–436.

Petrow, S., 1992: The lost squadron. *Life,* **15** (14), 60–68.

Pfeffer, W. T., and N. F. Humphrey, 1996: Determination of timing and location of water movement and ice-layer formation by temperature measurements in sub-freezing snow. *Journal of Glaciology,* **42** (141), 292–304.

Philberth, K., and B. Federer, 1971: On the temperature profile and the age profile in the central part of cold ice sheet. *Journal of Glaciology,* **10** (58), 3–14.

Pohjola, V. A., J. C. Moore, E. Isaksson, T. Jauhiainen, R. S. W. van de Wal, T. Martma, H. A. J. Meijer, and R. Vaikmäe, 2002: Effect of periodic melting on geochemical and isotopic signals in an ice core from Lomonosovfonna, Svalbard. *Journal of Geophysical Research,* **107** (D4), doi:10.1029/2000JD000149.

Pokar, M., 2003: Oldest ever ice core is a ticket to prehistory. *New Scientist,* **179** (2411), 20–21.

Pzedakis, P. C., K. D. Bennett, and D. Magri, 1994: Climate and the pollen record. *Nature,* **370**, 513.

Rahmstorf, S., 1995: Bifurcations of the Atlantic thermohaline circulation in response to changes in the hydrological cycle. *Nature,* **378**, 145–149.

Raisbeck, G. M., and F. Yiou, 1985: [10]Be in polar ice and atmospheres. *Annals of Glaciology,* **7**, 138–140.

——, F. Yiou, M. Fruneau, J. M. Loiseaux, M. Lieuvin, J. C. Ravel, and C. Lorius, 1981: Cosmogenic [10]Be concentrations in Antarctic ice during the past 30,000 years. *Nature,* **292**, 825–826.

——, F. Yiou, D. Bourles, C. Lorius, J. Jouzel, and N. I. Barkov, 1987: Evidence for two intervals of enhanced [10]Be deposition in Antarctic ice during the last glacial period. *Nature,* **326**, 273–277.

Ram, M., and M. Illing, 1994: Polar ice stratigraphy from laser-light scattering: Scattering from meltwater. *Journal of Glaciology,* **40** (136), 505–508.

——, and G. Koenig, 1997: Continuous dust concentration profile of pre-Holocene ice from the Greenland Ice Sheet Project 2 ice core: Dust stadials, interstadials, and the Eemian. *Journal of Geophysical Research,* **102** (C12), 26 641–26 648.

——, M. Illing, P. Weber, G. Koenig, and M. Kaplan, 1995: Polar ice stratigraphy from laser-light scattering: Scattering from ice. *Geophysical Research Letters,* **22** (24), 3525–3527.

Rampino, M. R., and S. Self, 1992: Volcanic winter and accelerated glaciation following the Toba super-eruption. *Nature,* **359**, 50–52.

——, and ——, 1993: Climate-volcanism feedback and the Toba eruption of ~74,000 years ago. *Quaternary Research,* **40**, 269–280.

Raynaud, D., 1983: Total gas content. *The Climatic Record in Polar Ice Sheets*, G. de Q. Robin, Ed., Cambridge University Press, 79–82.

——, and C. Lorius, 1973: Climatic implications of total gas content in ice at Camp Century. *Nature,* **243**, 283–284.

——, and C. Lorius, 1977: Total gas content in polar ice: Rheological and climatic implications. *Isotopes and Impurities in Snow and Ice,* IAHS Publication 118, 326–333.

——, and B. Lebel, 1979: Total gas content and surface elevation of polar ice sheets. *Nature,* **281**, 289–291.

——, and I. M. Whillans, 1982: Air content of the Byrd core and past changes in the West Antarctic Ice Sheet. *Annals of Glaciology,* **3**, 269–273.

——, C. Lorius, W. F. Budd, and N. W. Young, 1979: Ice flow along an I.A.G. P. flow line and interpretation of data from an ice core in Terre Adélie, Antarctica. *Journal of Glaciology,* **24** (90), 103–115.

——, R. Delmas, J. M. Ascencio, and M. Legrand, 1982: Gas extraction from polar ice cores: A critical issue for studying the evolution of atmospheric CO_2 and ice-sheet surface elevation. *Annals of Glaciology,* **3**, 265–268.

——, J. Chappellaz, C. Ritz, and P. Martinerie, 1997: Air content along the Greenland Ice Core Project core: A record of surface climatic parameters and elevation in central Greenland. *Journal of Geophysical Research,* **102** (C12), 26 607–26 613.

Reeh, N., 1985: Was the Greenland ice sheet thinner in the late Wisconsinan than now? *Nature,* **317**, 797–799.

——, 1989: Dating by ice flow modeling: A useful tool or an exercise in applied mathematics? *The Environmental Record in Glaciers and Ice Sheets*, H. Oeschger and C. C. Langway, Jr., Eds., John Wiley & Sons, 141–159.

——, H. B. Clausen, W. Dansgaard, N. Gundestrup, C. U. Hammer, and S. J. Johnsen, 1978: Secular trends of accumulation rates at three Greenland Stations. *Journal of Glaciology,* **20** (82), 27–30.

——, S. J. Johnsen, and D. Dahl-Jensen, 1985: Dating the Dye 3 deep ice core by flow model calculations. *Greenland Ice Core: Geophysics, Geochemistry, and the Environment, Geophysical Monograph*, No. 33, American Geophysical Union, Washington, D.C., 57–65.

——, H. Oerter, and H. H. Thomsen, 2002: Comparison between Greenland ice-margin and ice-core oxygen-18 records. *Annals of Glaciology,* **35**, 136–144.

Rempel, A. W., J. S. Wettlaufer, and E. D. Waddington, 2002: Anomalous diffusion of multiple impurity species: Predicted implications for the ice core climate records. *Journal of Geophysical Research,* **107** (B12), 2330, doi:10.1029/2002JB001857.

Reusch, D. B., P. A. Mayewski, S. I. Whitlow, I. I. Pittalwala, and M. S. Twickler, 1999: Spatial variability of climate and past atmospheric circulation patterns from central West Antarctic glaciochemistry. *Journal of Geophysical Research,* **104** (D6), 5985–6001.

Ridley, J. K., W. Cudlip, and S. W. Laxon, 1993: Identification of subglacial lakes using ERS-1 radar altimeter. *Journal of Glaciology,* **39** (133), 625–634.

Rind, D., P. deMenocal, G. Russell, S. Sheth, D. Collins, G. Schmidt, and J. Teller, 2001: Effects of glacial meltwater in the GISS coupled atmosphere-ocean model—1. North Atlantic Deep Water response. *Journal of Geophysical Research,* **106** (D21), 27 335–27 353.

Risbo, T., H. B. Clausen, and K. L. Rasmussen, 1981: Supernovae and nitrate in the Greenland Ice Sheet. *Nature,* **294**, 637–639.

Ritz, C., V. Rommelaere, and C. Dumas, 2001: Modeling the evolution of Antarctic ice sheet over the last 420,000 years: Implications for altitude changes in the Vostok region. *Journal of Geophysical Research,* **106** (D23), 31 943–31 964.

Robin, G. de Q., 1955: Ice movement and temperature distribution in glaciers and ice sheets. *Journal of Glaciology,* **2**, 523–532.

——, 1977: Ice cores and climatic change. *Philosophical Transactions of the Royal Society of London,* **280B**, 143–168.

——, 1983a: The climatic record from ice cores. *The Climatic Record in Polar Ice Sheets,* G. de Q. Robin, Ed., Cambridge University Press, 180–184.

——, 1983b: Isotopic-temperature (δ-θ) noise. *The Climatic Record in Polar Ice Sheets,* G. de Q. Robin, Ed., Cambridge University Press, 184–189.

——, 1983c: Profile data, inland Antarctica. *The Climatic Record in Polar Ice Sheets,* G. de Q. Robin, Ed., Cambridge University Press, 112–118.

——, 1983d: Radio-echo studies of internal layering of polar ice sheets. *The Climatic Record in Polar Ice Sheets,* G. de Q. Robin, Ed., Cambridge University Press, 89–93.

——, and D. H. M. Millar, 1982: Flow of ice sheets in the vicinity of subglacial peaks. *Annals of Glaciology,* **3**, 290–294.

——, and S. J. Johnsen, 1983: Atmospheric processes. *The Climatic Record in Polar Ice Sheets,* G. de Q. Robin, Ed., Cambridge University Press, 47–52.

——, S. Evans, and J. T. Bailey, 1969: Interpretation of radio echo sounding in polar ice sheets. *Philosophical Transactions of the Royal Society of London,* **265** (1158), 437–505.

——, D. J. Drewry, and D. T. Meldrum, 1977: International studies of ice sheet and bedrock. *Philosophical Transactions of the Royal Society of London,* **279**, 185–196.

Rodbell, D. T., 2000: The Younger Dryas: Cold, cold everywhere? *Science,* **290**, 285–286.

Rohling, E. J., and G. R. Bigg, 1998: Paleosalinity and δ^{18}O: A critical assessment. *Journal of Geophysical Research,* **103** (C1), 1307–1318.

——, P. A. Mayewski, and P. Challenor, 2003: On the timing and mechanism of millennial-scale climate variability during the last glacial cycle. *Climate Dynamics,* **20**, 257–267.

Rooth, C. G. H., 1990: Meltwater younger Dryas upheld. *Nature,* **343**, 702.

Rostek, F., G. Ruhland, F. C. Bassinot, P. J. Müller, L. D. Labeyrie, Y. Lancelot, and E. Bard, 1993: Reconstructing sea surface temperature and salinity using δ^{18}O and alkenone records. *Nature,* **364**, 319–321.

Röthlisberger, R., M. A. Hutterli, S. Sommer, E. W. Wolff, and R. Mulvaney, 2000: Factors controlling nitrate in ice cores: Evidence from the Dome C deep ice core. *Journal of Geophysical Research,* **105** (D16), 20 565–20 572.

——, R. Mulvaney, E. W. Wolff, M. A. Hutterli, M. Bigler, S. Sommer, and J. Jouzel, 2002a: Dust and sea salt variability in central East Antarctica (Dome C) over the last 45 kyrs and its implications for southern high-latitude climate. *Geophysical Research Letters,* **29** (20), 1963, doi:10.1029/2002GL015186.

——, et al., 2002b: Nitrate in Greenland and Antarctic ice cores: A detailed description of post-depositional processes. *Annals of Glaciology,* **35**, 209–216.

Rozanski, K., C. Sonntag, and K. O. Münnich, 1982: Factors controlling stable isotope composition of European precipitation. *Tellus,* **34**, 142–150.

Ruddiman, W. F., and M. E. Raymo, 2003: A methane-based time scale for Vostok ice. *Quaternary Research,* **22**, 141–155.

Rutford, R. H., C. Craddock, and T. W. Bastien, 1968: Late Tertiary glaciation and sea-leval changes in Antarctica. *Palaeogeography, Palaeoclimatology, Palaeoecology,* **5**, 15–39.

Ruth, U., D. Wagenbach, J. P. Steffensen, and M. Bigler, 2003: Continuous record of mircoparticle concentration and size distribution in the central Greenland NGRIP ice core during the last glacial period. *Journal of Geophysical Research,* **108** (D3), 4098, doi:10.1029/2002JD002376.

Salamatin, A. N., V. Y. Lipenkov, N. I. Barkov, J. Jouzel, J. R. Petit, and D. Raynaud, 1998: Ice core age dating and paleothermometer calibration based on isotope and temperature profiles from deep boreholes at Vostok Station (East Antarctica). *Journal of Geophysical Research,* **103** (D8), 8963–8977.

Sarfati, J., 2004: *Refuting Compromise—A Biblical and Scientific Refutation of "Progressive Creationism" (Billions of years), As Popularized by Astronomer Hugh Ross*. Master Books, 416 pp.

Sarnthein, M., et al., 2000: Exploring Late Pleistocene climate variations. *EOS,* **81** (51), 625, 629, 630.

Saigne, C., and M. Legrand, 1987: Measurements of methanesulphonic acid in Antarctic ice. *Nature,* **330**, 240–242.

Schermerhorn, L. J. G., 1974: Late Precambrian mixtites: Glacial and/or nonglacial? *American Journal of Science,* **274**, 673–824.

Schlosser, E., 1999: Effects of seasonal variability of accumulation on yearly mean $\delta^{18}O$ values in Antarctic snow. *Journal of Glaciology,* **45** (151), 463–468.

Schmidt, G. A., 1998: Oxygen-18 variations in a global ocean model. *Geophysical Research Letters,* **25** (8), 1201–1204.

Schøtt, C., E. D. Waddington, and C. F. Raymond, 1992: Predicted time-scales for GISP2 and GRIP boreholes at Summit, Greenland. *Journal of Glaciology,* **38** (128), 162–168.

Schrag, D. P., 1999: Effects of diagenesis on the isotopic record of late Paleogene tropical sea surface temperatures. *Chemical Geology,* **161**, 215–224.

Schulz, M., 2002: On the 1470-year pacing of Dansgaard-Oeschger warm events. *Paleoceanography,* **17** (4), 1–10.

Schwander, J., 1989: The transformation of snow to ice and the occlusion of gases. *The Environmental Record in Glaciers and Ice Sheets,* H. Oeschger and C. C. Langway, Jr., Eds., John Wiley & Sons, 53–67.

——, B. Stauffer, and A. Sigg, 1988: Air mixing in firn and the age of the air at pore close-off. *Annals of Glaciology,* **10**, 141–145.

——, T. Sowers, J. M. Barnola, T. Blunier, A. Fuchs, and B. Malaizé, 1997: Age scale of the air in the summit ice: Implication for glacial-interglacial temperature change. *Journal of Geophysical Research,* **102** (D16), 19 483–19 493.

——, J. Jouzel, C. U. Hammer, J. R. Petit, R. Udisti, and E. Wolff, 2001: A tentative chronology for the EPICA Dome Concordia ice core. *Geophysical Research Letters,* **28** (22), 4243–4246.

Schwerdtfeger, W., 1969: Ice crystal precipitation on the Antarctic plateau. *Antarctic Journal of the United States,* **4**, 221–222.

Seely, P. H., 2003: The GISP2 ice core: Ultimate proof that Noah's Flood was not global. *Perspectives on Science and Christian Faith,* **55** (4), 252–260.

Severinghaus, J. P., T. Sowers, E. J. Brook, R. B. Alley, and M. L. Bender, 1998: Timing of abrupt climate change at the end of the Younger Dryas interval from thermally fractionated gases in polar ice. *Nature,* **391**, 141–146.

Shackleton, N. J., and J. P. Kennett, 1974: Paleotemperature history of the Cenozoic and the initiation of Antarctic glaciation: Oxygen and carbon isotope analyses in DSDP sites 277, 279, and 281. *Initial Reports of the Deep Sea Drilling Project,* Vol. 29, J. P. Kennett, and R. E. Houtz, et. al., Eds., U. S. Government Printing Office, 743-755.

Shackleton, N. J., 1975: The stratigraphic record of deep-sea cores and its implications for the assessment of glacials, interglacials, stadials, and interstadials in the Mid-Pleistocene. *After the Australopithecines*, K. W. Butzer and G. L. Isaac, Eds., Mouton Publishers, 1–24 .

——, and N. D. Opdyke, 1973: Oxygen isotope and palaeomagnetic stratigraphy of equatorial Pacific core V28-238: Oxygen isotope temperature and ice volume on a 10^5 year and 10^6 year scale. *Quaternary Research*, **3**, 39–55.

Shaw, G. E., 1989: Aerosol transport from sources to ice sheets. *The Environmental Record in Glaciers and Ice Sheets*, H. Oeschger and C. C. Langway, Jr., Eds., John Wiley & Sons, 13–27.

Shaw, J., 1996: A meltwater model for Laurentide subglacial landscapes. *Geomorphology Sans Frontières*, S. B. McCann, Ed., John Wiley & Sons, 181–236.

——, 2002: The meltwater hypothesis for subglacial bedforms. *Quaternary International*, **90**, 5–22.

Shilts, W. W., 1980: Flow patterns in the central North American Ice Sheet. *Nature*, **286** 213–218.

——, C. J. Cunningham, and C. A. Kaszycki, 1979: Keewatin Ice Sheet—re-evaluation of the traditional concept of the Laurentide Ice Sheet. *Geology*, **7**, 537–541.

Shoji, H., and C. C. Langway, Jr., 1982: Air hydrate inclusions in fresh ice core. *Nature*, **298**, 548–550.

——, and C. C. Langway, Jr., 1987: Flow velocity profiles and accumulation rates from mechanical tests on ice core samples. *The Physical Basis of Ice Sheet Modelling*, IAHS Publication 170, 67–77.

——, and C. C. Langway, Jr., 1989: Physical property reference horizons. *The Environmental Record in Glaciers and Ice Sheets*, H. Oeschger and C. C. Langway, Jr., Eds., John Wiley & Sons, 161–175.

Shuman, C. A., and R. B. Alley, 1993: Spatial and temporal characterization of hoar formation in central Greenland using SSM/I brightness temperatures. *Geophysical Research Letters*, **20** (23), 2643–2646.

——, R. B. Alley, and S.Anandakrishnan, 1993: Characterization of a hoar-development episode using SSM/I brightness temperatures in the vicinity of the GISP2 site, Greenland. *Annals of Glaciology*, **17**, 183–188.

——, R. B. Alley, S.Anandakrishnan, J. W. C. White, P. M. Grootes, and C. R. Stearns, 1995: Temperature and accumulation at the Greenland summit: Comparison of high-resolution isotope profiles and satellite passive microwave brightness temperature trends. *Journal of Geophysical Research*, **100** (D5), 9165–9177.

——, R. B. Alley, M. A. Fahnestock, P. J. Fawcett, R. A. Bindschadler, J. W. C. White, P. M. Grootes, S. Anandakrishnan, and C. R. Stearns, 1997: Detection and monitoring of stratigraphic markers and temperature trends at the Greenland Ice Sheet Project 2 using passive-microwave remote-sensing data. *Journal of Geophysical Research*, **102** (C12), 26 877–26 886.

——, R. B. Alley, M. A. Fahnestock, R. A. Bindschadler, J. W. C. White, J. Winterle, and J. R. McConnell, 1998: Temperature history and accumulation timing for the snowpack at GISP2, central Greenland. *Journal of Glaciology*, **44** (146), 21–30.

Siegenthaler, U., and H. Oeschger, 1980: Correlation of ^{18}O in precipitation with temperature and altitude. *Nature*, **285**, 314–316.

Siegert, M. J., R. C. A. Hindmarsh, and G. S. Hamilton, 2003: Evidence for a large surface ablation zone in central East Antarctica during the last ice age. *Quaternary Research*, **59**, 114–121.

Sigman, D. M., and E. A. Boyle, 2000: Glacial/interglacial variations in atmospheric carbon dioxide. *Nature*, **407**, 859–869.

Sirocko, F., 2003: What drove past teleconnections? *Science*, **301**, 1336–1337.

Smith, J. E., M. J. Risk, H. P. Schwarcz, and T. A. McConnaughey, 1997: Rapid climate change in the North Atlantic during the Younger Dryas recorded by deep-sea cores. *Nature*, **386**, 818–820.

Sommerfeld, R. A., C. Judy, and I. Friedman, 1991: Isotopic changes during the formation of depth hoar in experimental snowpacks. *Stable Isotope Geochemistry: A Tribute to Samuel Epstein*, H. P. Taylor, Jr., J.

R. O'Neil, and I. R. Kaplan, Eds., Geochemical Society Special Publication 3, 205–209.

Sonett, C. P., G. E. Morfill, and J. Jokipii, 1987: Interstellar shock waves and [10]Be from ice cores. *Nature,* **330**, 458–460.

Souchez, R., 1997: The buildup of the ice sheet in central Greenland. *Journal of Geophysical Research,* **102** (C12), 26 317–26 323.

——, J. -L.Tison, R. Lorrain, M. Lemmens, L. Janssens, M. Stievenard, J. Jouzel, and S. J. Johnsen, 1994: Stable isotopes in the basal silty ice preserved in the Greenland Ice Sheet at Summit: Environmental implications. *Geophysical Research Letters,* **21** (8), 693–696.

——, L. Janssens, M. Lemmens, and B. Stauffer, 1995: Very low oxygen concentration in basal ice from Summit Central Greenland. *Geophysical Research Letters,* **22** (15), 2001–2004.

——, M. Lemmens, and J. Chappellaz, 1995: Flow-induced mixing in the GRIP basal ice deduced from the CO_2 and CH_4 records. *Geophysical Research Letters,* **22** (1), 41–44.

Sowers, T., M. Bender, and D. Raynaud, 1989: Elemental and isotopic composition of occluded O_2 and N_2 in polar ice. *Journal of Geophysical Research,* **94** (D4), 5137–5150.

——, M. Bender, D. Raynaud, Y. S. Korotkevich, and J. Orchardo, 1991: The $\delta^{18}O$ of atmospheric O_2 from air inclusions in the Vostok ice core: Timing of CO_2 and ice volume changes during the penultimate deglaciation. *Paleoceanography,* **6** (6), 679–696.

——, M. Bender, D. Raynaud, and Y. S. Korotkevich, 1992: $\delta^{15}N$ of N_2 in air trapped in polar ice: A tracer of gas transport in the firn and a possible constraint on ice age-gas age differences. *Journal of Geophysical Research,* **97** (D14), 15 683–15 697.

——, et al., 1997: An interlaboratory comparison of techniques for extracting and analyzing trapped gases in ice cores. *Journal of Geophysical Research,* **102** (C12), 26 527–26 538.

Staffelbach, T., B. Stauffer, and H. Oeschger, 1988: A detailed analysis of the rapid changes in ice-core parameters during the last ice age. *Annals of Glaciology,* **10**, 167–170.

Stauffer, B., 1989: Dating of ice by radioactive isotopes. *The Environmental Record in Glaciers and Ice Sheets*, H. Oeschger and C. C. Langway, Jr., Eds., John Wiley & Sons, 123–139.

——, et al., 1998: Atmospheric CO_2 concentration and millennial-scale climate change during the last glacial period. *Nature,* **392**, 59–62.

Steffensen, J. P., H. B. Clausen, and J. M. Christensen, 1996: On the spatial variability of impurity content and stable isotopic composition in recent Summit snow. *Chemical Exchange Between the Atmosphere and Polar Snow*, E. W. Wolff and R. C. Bales, Eds. NATO ASI Series 1, Global Environmental Change, Vol. 43, Springer-Verlag, 607–615.

Steig, E., M. Stuiver, and P. Polissar, 1995: Cosmogenic isotope concentrations at Taylor Dome, Antarctica. *Antarctic Journal,* **30**, 95–97.

Steig, E. J., P. M. Grootes, and M. Stuiver, 1994: Seasonal precipitation timing and ice core records. *Science,* **266**, 1885–1886.

——, P. J. Polissar, M. Stuiver, P. M. Grootes, and R. C. Finkel, 1996: Large amplitude solar modulation cycles of [10]Be in Antarctica: Implications for atmospheric mixing processes and interpretation of the ice core record. *Geophysical Research Letters,* **23** (5), 523–526.

Steinhage, D., U. Nixdorf, U. Meyer, and H. Miller, 1999: New maps of the ice thickness and subglacial topography in Dronning Maud Land, Antarctica, determined by means of airborne radio-echo sounding. *Annals of Glaciology,* **29**, 267–272.

Stenni, B., V. Masson-Delmotte, S. Johnsen, J. Jouzel, A. Longinelli, E. Monnin, R. Röthlisberger, and E. Selmo, 2001: An oceanic cold reversal during the last deglaciation. *Science,* **293**, 2074–2077.

Steward, M. K., 1975: Stable isotope fractionation due to evaporation and isotopic exchange of falling waterdrops: Applications to atmospheric processes and evaporation of lakes. *Journal of Geophysical Research,* **80** (9), 1133–1146.

Strain, P. M., and F. C. Tan, 1993: Seasonal evolution of oxygen isotope-salinity relationships in high-latitude surface waters. *Journal of Geophysical Research,* **98** (C8), 14 589–14 598.

Stuiver, M., P. M. Grootes, and T. F. Braziunas, 1995: The GISP2 $\delta^{18}O$ climate record of the past 16,500 years and the role of the sun, ocean, and volcanoes. *Quaternary Research,* **44**, 341–354.

Sturm, M., and C. S. Benson, 1997: Vapor transport, grain growth and depth-hoar development in the subarctic snow. *Journal of Glaciology,* **43** (143), 42–59.

Sugden, D., 1992: Antarctic ice sheets at risk? *Nature,* **359**, 775–776.

Sugden, D. E., and B. S. John, 1976: *Glaciers and Landscape: A Geomorphological Approach.* Edward Arnold, 376 pp.

Svensson, A., P. E. Biscaye, and F. E. Grousset, 2000: Characterization of late glacial continental dust in the Greenland Ice Core Project ice core. *Journal of Geophysical Research,* **105** (D4), 4637–4656.

Taylor, K., 1995: Electrical measurements on the Taylor Dome ice core. *Antarctic Journal,* **30**, 94–95.

——, 1999: Rapid climate change. *American Scientist,* **87**, 320–327.

——, R. Alley, J. Fiacco, P. Grootes, G. Lamorey, P. Mayewski, and M. J. Spencer, 1992: Ice-core dating and chemistry by direct-current electrical conductivity. *Journal of Glaciology,* **38** (130), 325–332.

Taylor, K. C., C. U. Hammer, R. B. Alley, H. B. Clausen, D. Dahl-Jensen, A. J. Gow, N. S. Gundestrup, J. Kipfstuhl, J. C. Moore, and E. D. Waddington, 1993: Electrical conductivity measurements from the GISP2 and GRIP Greenland ice cores. *Nature,* **366**, 549–552.

——, R. B. Alley, G. W. Lamorey, and P. Mayewski, 1997a: Electrical measurements on the Greenland Ice Sheet Project 2 core. *Journal of Geophysical Research,* **102** (C12), 26 511–26 517.

——, et al., 1997b: The Holocene-Younger Dryas transition recorded at Summit Greenland. *Science,* **278**, 825–827.

Thomas, R. H., and PARCA Investigators, 2001: Program for Arctic Regional climate Assessment (PARCA): Goals, key finds, and future directions. *Journal of Geophysical Research,* **106** (D24), 33 691–33 705.

Thorsteinsson, T., J. Kipfstuhl, H. Eicken, S. J. Johnsen, and K. Fuhrer, 1995: Crystal size variations in Eemian-age ice from the GRIP ice core, Central Greenland. *Earth and Planetary Science Letters,* **131**, 381–394.

Thorsteinsson, T., J. Kipfstuhl, and H. Miller, 1997: Textures and fabrics in the GRIP ice core. *Journal of Geophysical Research,* **102** (C12), 26 583–26 599.

——, E. D. Waddington, K. C. Taylor, R. B. Alley, and D. D. Blankenship, 1999: Strain-rate enhancement at Dye 3, Greenland. *Journal of Glaciology,* **45** (150), 338–345.

Thouveny N. et al., 1994: Climate variations in Europe over the past 140 kyr deduced from rock magnetism. *Nature,* **371**, 503–506.

Tison, J. -L., T. Thorsteinsson, R. D. Lorrain, and J. Kipfstuhl, 1994: Origin and development of textures and fabrics in basal ice at Summit, Central Greenland. *Earth and Planetary Science Letters,* **125**, 421–437.

Tobacco, I. E., A. Passerini, F. Corbelli, and M. Gorman, 1998: Determination of the surface and bed topography at Dome C, East Antarctica. *Journal of Glaciology,* **44**, 185–191.

Uchida, T., T. Hondoh, S. Mae, P. Duval, and V. Ya. Lipenkov, 1994: Effects of temperature and pressure on the transformation rate from air bubbles to air-hydrate crystals in ice sheets. *Annals of Glaciology,* **20**, 143-147.

Van der Veen, C. J., E. Mosley-Thompson, A. J. Gow, and B. G. Mark, 1999: Accumulation at South Pole: Comparison of two 900-year records. *Journal of Geophysical Research,* **104** (D24), 31 067–31 067.

Van Ommen, T. D., and V. Morgan, 1996: Peroxide concentrations in the Dome Summit South ice core, Law Dome, Antarctica. *Journal of Geophysical Research, 101* (D10), 15 147–15 152.

Vardiman, L., 1993: *Ice Cores and the Age of the Earth.* Institute for Creation Research, 73 pp.

——, 1997: Rapid changes in oxygen isotope content of ice cores caused by fractionation and trajectory dispersion near the edge of an ice shelf. *Creation Ex Nihilo Technical Journal,* **11** (1), 52–60.

——, 2001: *Climates Before and After the Genesis Flood.* Institute for Creation Research, 110 pp.

——, A. A. Snelling, and E. F. Chaffin, Eds., 2000: *Radioisotopes and the Age of the Earth—A Young-Earth Creationist Research Initiative.* Institute for Creation Research and Creation Research Society, 676 pp.

Vaughan, D. G., H. F. J. Corr, C. S. M. Doake, and E. D. Waddington, 1999a: Distortion of isochronous layers in ice revealed by ground-penetrating radar. *Nature,* **398,** 323–326.

——, J. L. Bamber, M. Giovinetto, J. Russell, and A. P. R. Cooper, 1999b: Reassessment of net surface mass balance in Antarctica. *Journal of Climate,* **12,** 933–946.

Verbers, A. L. L. M., and V. Damm, 1994: Morphology and late Cenozoic (<5 Ma) glacial history of the area between David and Mawson Glaciers, Victoria Land, Antarctica. *Annals of Glaciology,* **20,** 55–60.

Vernekar, A. D., 1972: *Long-period Global Variations of Incoming Solar Radiation. Meteorological Monograph,* No. 12 (34), American Meteorological Society, 128 pp.

Vimeux, F., V. Masson, J. Jouzel, M. Stievenard, and J. R. Petit, 1999: Glacial-interglacial changes in ocean surface conditions in the Southern Hemisphere. *Nature,* **398,** 410–413.

——, V. Masson, J. Jouzel, J. R. Petit, E. J. Steig, M. Stievenard, R. Vaikmae, and J. W. C. White, 2001a: Holocene hydrological cycle changes in the Southern Hemisphere documented in East Antarctic deuterium excess records. *Climate Dynamics,* **17,** 503–513.

——, V. Masson, G. Delaygue, J. Jouzel, J. R. Petit, and M. Stievenard, 2001b: A 420,000 year deuterium excess record from East Antarctica: Information on past changes in the origin of precipitation at Vostok. *Journal of Geophysical Research,* **106** (D23), 31 863–31 873.

Vincent, W. F., 1999: Icy life on a hidden lake. *Science,* **286,** 2094–2095.

Wadhwa, M., 2004: Treasure hunting to the ends of the earth. *Science,* **303,** 41–42.

Waelbroeck, C., J. Jouzel, L. Labeyrie, C. Lorius, M. Labracherie, M. Stiévenard, and N. I. Barkov, 1995: A comparison of the Vostok ice deuterium record and series from southern ocean core MD 88-770 over the last two glacial-interglacial cycles. *Climate Dynamics,* **12,** 113–123.

Wagenbach, D., F. Ducroz, R. Mulvaney, L. Keck, A. Minikin, M. Legrand, J. S. Hall, and E. W. Wolff, 1998a: Sea-salt aerosol in coastal Antarctic regions. *Journal of Geophysical Research,* **103** (D9), 10 961–10 964.

——, M. Legrand, H. Fischer, F. Pichlmayer, and E. W. Wolff, 1998b: Atmospheric near-surface nitrate at coastal Antarctic sites. *Journal of Geophysical Research,* **103** (D9), 11 007–11 020.

Wagner, G., J. Beer, C. Laj, C. Kissel, J. Masarik, R. Muscheler, and H. -A. Synal, 2000: Chlorine-36 evidence for the Mono Lake event in the Summit GRIP ice core. *Earth and Planetary Science Letters,* **181,** 1–6.

Wagnon, P., R. J. Delmas, and M. Legrand, 1999: Loss of volatile acid species from upper firn layers at Vostok, Antarctica. *Journal of Geophysical Research,* **104** (D3), 3423–3431.

Watanabe, O., K. Kamiyama, H. Motoyama, Y. Fujii, H. Shoji, and K. Satow, 1999: The paleoclimate record in the ice core at Dome Fuji station, East Antarctica. *Annals of Glaciology,* **29,** 176–178.

——, J. Jouzel, S. Johnsen, F. Parrenin, H. Shoji, and N. Yoshida, 2003: Homogeneous climate variability across East Antarctica over the past three glacial cycles. *Nature,* **422,** 509–512.

Weart, S., 2003: The discovery of rapid climate change. *Physics Today,* **56** (8), 30–36.

Weaver, A. J., and T. M. C. Hughes, 1994: Rapid interglacial climate fluctuations driven by North Atlantic ocean circulation. *Nature, 367*, 447–450.

Webb, P. N., D. M. Harwood, B. C. McKelvey, J. H. Mercer, and L. D. Stott, 1983: Late Neogene and older Cenozoic microfossils in high elevation deposits of the Transantarctic Mountains: Evidence for marine sedimentation and ice volume variation on the East Antarctic craton. *Antarctic Journal of the United States, 18* (5), 96–97.

——, ——, ——, ——, and ——, 1984: Cenozoic marine sedimentation and ice-volume variation on the East Antarctic craton. *Geology, 12*, 287–291.

Welch, K. A., P. A. Mayewski, and S. I. Whitlow, 1993: Methanesulfonic acid in coastal Antarctic snow related to sea-ice extent. *Geophysical Research Letters, 20* (6), 443–446.

Werner, M., U. Mikolajewicz, M. Heimann, and G. Hoffmann, 2000a: Borehole versus isotope temperatures on Greenland: Seasonality does matter. *Geophysical Research Letters, 27* (5), 723–726.

——, U. Mikolajewicz, G. Hoffman, and M. Heimann, 2000b: Possible changes of $\delta^{18}O$ in precipitation caused by a meltwater event in the North Atlantic. *Journal of Geophysical Research, 105* (D8), 10 161–10 167.

——, M. Heimann, and G. Hoffmann, 2001: Isotopic composition and origin of polar precipitation in present and glacial climate simulations. *Tellus, 53B*, 53–71.

Weertman, J., 1968: Comparison between measured and theoretical temperature profiles of the Camp Century, Greenland, borehole. *Journal of Geophysical Research, 73* (8), 2691–2700.

Whillans, I. M., and P. M. Grootes, 1985: Isotopic diffusion in cold snow and firn. *Journal of Geophysical Research, 90* (D2), 3910–3918.

White, J. W. C., et al., 1989: Group report—how do glaciers record environmental processes and preserve information? *The Environmental Record in Glaciers and Ice Sheets*, H. Oeschger and C. C. Langway, Jr., Eds., John Wiley & Sons, 85–98.

Whitlow, S., P. A. Mayewski, and J. E. Dibb, 1992: A comparison of major chemical species seasonal concentration and accumulation at the South Pole and Summit, Greenland. *Atmospheric Environment, 26A* (11), 2045–2054.

Whung, P. -Y., E. S. Saltzman, M. J. Spencer, P. A. Mayewski, and N. Gundestrup, 1994: Two-hundred-year record of biogenic sulfur in a south Greenland ice core (20D). *Journal of Geophysical Research, 99* (D1), 1147–1156.

Wilch, T. I., D. R. Lux, G. H. Denton, and W. C. McIntosh, 1993: Minimal Pliocene-Pleistocene uplift of the dry valleys sector of the Transantarctic Mountains: A key parameter in ice-sheet reconstructions. *Geology, 21*, 841–844.

Wilhelms, F., J. Kipfstuhl, H. Miller, K. Heinloth, and J. Firestone, 1998: Precise dielectric profiling of ice cores: A new device with improved guarding and its theory. *Journal of Glaciology, 44* (146), 171–174.

Williams, L. D., 1979: An energy balance model of potential glacierization of Northern Canada. *Arctic and Alpine Research, 11* (4), 443–456.

Wilson, A. T., and A. Long, 1997: New approaches to CO_2 analysis in polar ice cores. *Journal of Geophysical Research, 102* (C12), 26 601–26 606.

Wise, Jr., S. W., J. R. Breza, D. M. Harwood, and W. Wei, 1991: Paleogene glacial history of Antarctica. *Controversies in Modern Geology: Evolution of Geological Theories in Sedimentology, Earth History and Tectonics*, D. W. Müller, J. A. McKenzie, and H. Weissert, Eds., Academic Press, 133–171.

Wolff, E., I. Basile, J. R. Petit, and J. Schwander, 1999: Comparison of Holocene electrical records from Dome C and Vostok, Antarctica. *Annals of Glaciology, 29*, 89–93.

Wolff, E. W., 1995: Nitrate in polar ice. *Ice Core Studies of Global Biogeochemical Cycles*, R. J. Delmas, Ed., Springer, 195–224.

——, 1996: The record of aerosol deposited species in ice cores, and problems of interpretation. *Chemical Exchange Between the Atmosphere and Polar Snow*, E. W. Wolff and R. C. Bales, Eds. NATO ASI Series 1, Global Environmental Change, Vol. 43, Springer-Verlag, 1–17.

——, J. C. Moore, H. B. Clausen, C. U. Hammer, J. Kipfstuhl, and K. Fuhrer, 1995: Long-term changes in the acid and salt concentrations of the Greenland Ice Core Project ice core form electrical stratigraphy. *Journal of Geophysical Research,* **100** (D8), 16 249–16 263.

——, J. C. Moore, H. B. Clausen, C. U. Hammer, 1997: Climatic implications of background acidity and other chemistry derived from electrical studies of the Greenland Ice Core Project ice core. *Journal of Geophysical Research,* **102** (C12), 26 325–26 332.

——, J. S. Hall, R. Mulvaney, E. C. Pasteur, D. Wagenbach, and M. Legrand, 1998: Relationship between chemistry of air, fresh snow and firn cores for aerosols in coastal Antarctica. *Journal of Geophysical Research,* **103** (D9), 11 057–11 070.

——, M. R. Legrand, and D. Wagenbach, 1998: Coastal Antarctic aerosol and snowfall chemistry. *Journal of Geophysical Research,* **103** (D9), 10 927–10 934.

——, A. E. Jones, T. J. Martin, and T. C. Grenfell, 2002: Modelling photochemical NO_x production and nitrate loss in the upper snowpack of Antarctica. *Geophysical Research Letters,* **29** (20), 1944, doi:10.1029/2002GL015823.

Woodmorappe, J., 1999: *The Mythology of Modern Dating Methods.* Institute for Creation Research, 118 pp.

Wunsch, C., 2003: Greenland—Antarctic phase relations and millennial time-scale climate fluctuations in the Greenland ice-cores. *Quaternary Science Reviews,* **22**, 1631–1646.

Yang, Q., P. A. Mayewski, G. A. Zielenski, M. Twickler, and K. C. Taylor, 1996: Depletion of atmospheric nitrate and chloride as a consequence of the Toba volcanic eruption. *Geophysical Research Letters,* **23** (18), 2513–2516.

Yiou, F., and G. M. Raisback, 1972: Half-life of ^{10}Be. *Physical Review Letters,* **29** (6), 372–375.

——, G. M. Raisback, D. Bourles, C. Lorius, and N. I. Barkov, 1985: ^{10}Be in ice at Vostok Antarctica during the last climatic cycle. *Nature,* **316**, 617–618.

——, et al., 1997a: Beryllium 10 in the Greenland Ice Core Project ice core at Summit, Greenland. *Journal of Geophysical Research,* **102** (C12), 26 783–26 794.

——, K. Fuhrer, L. D. Meeker, J. Jouzel, S. Johnsen, and P. A. Mayewski, 1997b: Paleoclimatic variability inferred from the spectral analysis of Greenland and Antarctic ice-core data. *Journal of Geophysical Research,* **102** (C12), 26 441–26 454.

——, F. Vimeux, and J. Jouzel, 2001: Ice-age variability from the Vostok deuterium and deuterium excess records. *Journal of Geophysical Research,* **106** (D23), 31 875–31 884.

Young, N. W., M. Pourchet, V. M. Kotlyakov, P. A. Korolev, and M. B. Dyugerov, 1982: Accumulation distribution in the IAGP area, Antarctica: 90° E-150° E. *Annals of Glaciology,* **3**, 333–338.

Zielinski, G. A., P. A. Mayewski, L.D. Meeker, S. Whitlow, M. S. Twickler, M. Morrison, D. A. Meese, A. J. Gow, and R. B. Alley, 1994: Record of volcanism since 7000 B.C. from the GISP2 Greenland ice core and implications for the volcano-climate system. *Science,* **264**, 948–952.

——, P. A. Mayewski, L.D. Meeker, S. Whitlow, and M. S. Twickler, 1996: A 111,000-Yr record of explosive volcanism from the Gisp2 (Greenland) ice core. *Quaternary Research,* **45**, 109–118.